CW00801908

The Imp
Polaris

The origins of Britain's seaborne nuclear deterrent

Edited by
Captain J. E. Moore R.N.

with ready help from
Rear Admiral P. G. La Niece CB CBE

Richard Netherwood Limited

First Published in 1999
by
Richard Netherwood Limited
539 Manchester Road
Linthwaite Huddersfield
HD7 5QX

ISBN 1 872955 24 X

Printed and bound in the UK

Acknowledgements

Many thanks are due to the contributors for all their hard work and memory searching, to my daughter Fay Lambert for tidying-up some of the less tidy essays, to the Royal Navy Submarine Museum for their help and provision of Photographs, to Bonny Tall for her tremendous help in converting the mass of typewritten text onto a disc and to my wife Barbara for putting up with piles of paper which so frequently crept out of my study to settle in all manner of places.

Dedication

The successful conclusion of the British Polaris project resulted from the unstinted advice and assistance from the United States Navy and their contractors and years of intensive labour by the various British Teams involved, both naval and civilian. Four men of outstanding ability were responsible for the co-ordination and direction of all this effort and to them this book is dedicated:

the late Sir Rowland Baker K.C.B. O.B.E.

Admiral I. J. Galantin USN

the late Vice Admiral Levering Smith K.B.E. USN

the late Vice Admiral Sir Hugh Mackenzie K.C.B. D.S.O. D.S.C.

Introduction

This is an account of the creation in the 1960's of the UK Polaris Force as recalled by people from all levels who were involved.

With 29 contributors there is inevitably some duplication in the narrative since, in many cases, the same events are being recorded from different viewpoints.

There were numerous aspects which were at that time unique. Headquarters still operated in a world of staff papers and Admiralty dockets. In 1963, in the UK at least, there was nothing like a FAX or a PC; Information Technology, as we know it today, was non existent. Many people found themselves teamed with others who had a markedly different experience and different ways of doing business - Submariners with non- Submariners, Technicians with non- Technicians, Naval Officers with Civil Servants and, above all, the British with Americans. No one could avoid being infected by the spirit of the Project. Fortunately there was still time for touches of humour.

The Polaris Sales Agreement specified that both the UK and US Governments should designate Project Officers charged with the task of carrying out the terms of the Agreement. Rear Admiral Mackenzie occupied the post for the UK over the first 5 years. Until 1964 Rear Admiral Galantin was his US counterpart and contributed much wise counsel in getting things off the ground. From 1964 until his retirement in 1977 Rear Admiral Levering Smith, who had already been the US Technical Director since 1957, replaced Admiral Galantin. Over the years, with his prodigious knowledge and experience he gave unstinted advice and support to his UK colleagues. In recognition of this he was awarded an Honorary KBE in 1972.

He had accepted the offer to write a foreword to this book but sadly, later, had to decline because of the illness which led to his death.

Within the UK Project there were some powerful personalities with the consequent potential for conflict and disagreement. However with persuasion and guidance from Admiral Mackenzie their energies were successfully channelled towards building up momentum leading finally to the successful achievement of the project.

CONTRIBUTORS

Admiral Sir Simon Cassels KCB CBE	Navigation Staff Officer to CPE 1963-66
R J Daniel Esq OBE	Head Submarine Design Team 1963-66
Captain K J Dunlop	Technical Assistant to CPE
Captain H M Ellis	Manning and Training Staff Officer to CPE1963-66
Chief Petty Officer A J Escreet	Crew Member HMS *Resolution* (Starboard)
Lady Margaret Fieldhouse	Widow of the late Admiral of the Fleet Lord Fieldhouse - second Captain SM 10
The late H C Fitzer Esq CB OBE	Assistant Director Electrical Engineering
Admiral I J Galantin USN (Rtd)	Director US Special Project Office 1962-64
Rear Admiral W J Graham CB	SPRN Washington 1961-63; Weapon Staff Officer to CPE 1963-65
Rear Admiral P G Hammersley CB CBE	Marine Engineering Section of DPT SM
Captain M C Henry	First Commanding Officer HMS *Resolution* (Port)
Captain M R C Howlett	Principal Technical Officer Clyde SM Base 1966-9
Captain Mark Jones	Base Supply Officer, Faslane
Rear Admiral P G La Niece CB CBE	Staff Officer(G) to BJSM 1955-58; SPRN Washington 1963-66; Commodore Clyde 1969-71
Vice Admiral Sir John Lea KBE	Deputy Superintendent Clyde SM Base 1965-68

The late Vice Admiral Sir Hugh Mackenzie KCB DSO DSC	Chief Polaris Executive 1963-68
The Rt Hon John Major MP	Prime Minister 1990-97
The late Admiral Sir Rae McKaig KCB CBE	Deputy Chief Polaris Executive 1963-65
A F McLeod Esq	RNAD Coulport, Superintendent Designate/Superintendent 1963-71
Commander D W Mills CBE DSC	Staff Officer to Flag Officer Submarines for Polaris 1963-70
Captain J E Moore	Plans Division, Admiralty 1960-63
The late Professor P Nailor	Deputy Chief Administrative Officer/ Chief Administrative Officer to CPE 1963-67
B A Page Esq ISO	Staff Material Support Rep to SPRN Washington 1963-66; SNSO Clyde SM
Professor S J Palmer CB OBE	Deputy Director Naval Construction 1963-67
A A Pritchard Esq CB	Finance Officer, Polaris Executive 1963-64
The late Rear Admiral C W H Shepherd	1963-68; Technical Director 1969-71; Deputy Controller Polaris 1971-73
Commander H M Simeon	SPRN Washington 1958-61; Weapon Staff Officer to CPE 1963
Rear Admiral M La T Wemyss CB	Plans Division Admiralty 1963-65; Captain SM 3 1970-72

CONTENTS

Part 1 - The Twilight Period Prior to Nassau

Part 2 - The Project Unfolds

Part 3 - Building the Submarine

Part 4 - Base Support

Part 5 - The Polaris Force

PART I

THE TWILIGHT PERIOD PRIOR TO NASSAU

CHAPTER I

The Awakening
John Moore

The first hint of what was to become Polaris was passed to Admiral Mountbatten in October 1955 by Admiral Arleigh Burke. The former had recently become Britain's First Sea Lord, the latter was his American opposite number, the Chief of Naval Operations. This news came to Mountbatten when he knew that the first generation of the V-bombers of the Royal Air Force was to become operational in the following year. Despite his aversion to the idea of a British independent nuclear deterrent the First Sea Lord was well aware that the V-bombers, with their free-fall nuclear weapons, were but a stop-gap before long-range guided missiles could replace them. The American naval plans were a great attraction but their launch platforms had to operate covertly and the best means of achieving this aim was to place them in submarines. The only submersible craft capable of remaining undetected was the nuclear-propelled submarine and it was with two parallel and compatible aims that Mountbatten determined to provide the Royal Navy with such boats. The first aim was to increase the capability of his navy in underwater operations; the second was to prepare an adequate platform for the submarine launched ballistic missile which he was convinced was the right answer for Britain's nuclear deterrent.

Mountbatten's agreement with Admiral Rickover, head of the USN's nuclear propulsion programme, in late 1957 gave the Royal Navy its great advance into this new field of naval warfare, some two to three years ahead of the plans laid on the basis of a British designed reactor.

While these negotiations were in progress and the *Dreadnought* design team was finalising its plans for Britain's first nuclear-propelled submarine, a new contender in the field of long range missiles was at hand. This was the British land-launched Blue Streak, a liquid-fuel design with a range of 2,000 miles. This weapon was to be in the care of the Royal Air Force but, in 1960, the project was cancelled. Overtaken by the advancing technology of solid-fuel propulsion and increased navigational accuracy Blue Streak's demise brought forward the need for a new missile. This was to be the American Skybolt, an air-launched missile which would, if successful and if it could be paired to the V-bombers, provide an interim solution in the face of the rapid improvement of surface-to-air defences. The attraction of a sea-launched deterrent was becoming increasingly apparent but the Skybolt solution remained the British preference. There was much discussion in the Naval Staff about the long-term reliability of the V-bombers and their vulnerability in the modern air-defence environment. Alongside these concerns and very much in a small and closed community the advantages of Polaris were being discussed. Mountbatten had been kept apprised of developments in the USA by RN Staff Officers, firstly attached to the British Naval Staff in Washington and, from 1958, serving as part of the USN Special Project team.

There was much to report. USS *Nautilus*, commissioned on 30 September 1954, had proved the effectiveness of nuclear propulsion in submarines. In February 1958 a supplement to the Fiscal year 1958 new construction programme provided for the construction of the first three American nuclear submarines armed with ballistic missiles - Polaris. It was the culmination of an astounding US programme - in less than two and a half years since Admiral Burke had told Mountbatten of the inception of the missile programme the first boat, USS *George Washington*. was under construction at Groton, Connecticut. Two years and two months later, on 30 December 1959, she was commissioned. On 20 July 1960 she carried out a successful launch of two Polaris A1 missiles off Cape Canaveral.

By that time the Soviet Navy had had submarine launched ballistic missiles at sea in their "Golf" and "Hotel" classes since 1958 and Britain had nothing to show for a lengthy period of design effort and was now committed to an American airborne system which Admiral Arleigh Burke described as "technically feasible provided enough research and development is done on it but a very expensive and vulnerable system".

However, if Skybolt worked the cost was going to be far less, it was hoped, than the production of a new class of submarine designed specifically to carry Polaris. And if Polaris were adopted at some future date who was to pay the huge sums needed to provide the submarines, the missiles, the infrastructure to support them? What effect would this have on the fleet as a whole? While these questions and many other allied problems were studied by a small coterie of senior naval officers and civil servants the remainder of the Admiralty continued their normal duties. Some commentators have criticised the Royal Navy for failing to press the case for Polaris. But the Skybolt decision was made at a time when the American Polaris system was unproven from the point of view of its continuous availability on patrol. Mountbatten as First Sea Lord until April 1959 and subsequently as Chairman of the Chiefs of Staff was convinced that, if Britain were to have a nuclear deterrent, it would eventually have to be a naval responsibility. He was advised that Skybolt could turn out to be a non-starter and that the V-bombers had only a finite life. If the former were the case Polaris was the only alternative. If it were not the case then Polaris would become the successor to the V-bombers.

The Skybolt decision had stemmed from a Governmental review of its strategic needs. In the wake of this review the Board of Admiralty instructed Rear Admiral Michael Le Fanu to investigate possible courses of action should the navy adopt the Polaris system. This was completed in July 1960 and provided a clear statement of the organisational changes which would be required.

Against this background of prudent planning Skybolt remained the chosen instrument. However a crisis was reached in late 1962. Skybolt's cost was rising dramatically, its in-service date was slipping fast to the right and all five flight tests so far had failed. The USA already had Polaris at sea and the land based long-range missile Minuteman was operational - it was decided to cancel the Skybolt programme. The US Secretary of Defense, Mr McNamara, told the British Ambassador of this situation on 8 November, offering three alternatives - Britain would continue alone with Skybolt; the USA would provide Britain with Hound Dog missiles, a less effective system; or that the USA would provide Minuteman or Polaris. Of the third alternative the British would have preferred Polaris, a system which removed the deterrent from the narrow land target of the British Isles and which both the Commons and the Lords had been told in March 1960 was being considered by the Admiralty.

The crisis of November-December 1962 caused acute tension in Whitehall. Mr McNamara met the British Minister of Defence, Mr Peter Thorneycroft, on 11 December; President Kennedy was in frequent touch with the Prime Minister, Mr Harold Macmillan; and from 16-19 December the two leaders met at Nassau in the Bahamas. On the Prime Minister's team were Mr Thorneycroft, Sir Solly Zuckerman, the Chief Scientific Advisor and Admiral Sir Michael Le Fanu who was now Controller of the Navy, in which appointment he was in charge of the provision of the navy's hardware. The Controller was probably the most knowledgeable about Polaris amongst the senior members and Mr Thorneycroft remained a supporter of Skybolt.

It was at this juncture that I became involved in the unfolding drama. By that time I had been serving in Plans Division for over two years, my daily task being in the Ship section (three of us) charged with projecting the "Shape and Size of the Fleet" over the next ten years and calculating the Long Term Costing for these projections. Submarines were part of my remit but I was in no way concerned with any planning for Polaris and had seen nothing of the 1960 Le Fanu report. However in 1961-62 a number of strange papers appeared in my "In" basket.

Since the first underwater launch of Polaris in July 1960 fecund minds in Washington had been preparing alternative methods of delivering this missile. The first I saw was a scheme to provide modules containing Polaris missiles which could be placed in the holds of merchant ships which would then cruise the Atlantic, apparently on their lawful occasions. This naive and pointless proposition died a well-deserved death, to be succeeded by an equally ill-founded suggestion, the Mixed-Manned Multi-Lateral Force (MLF). This was a plan to arm a couple of dozen NATO warships with Polaris missiles and to man them with ships' companies from all the NATO navies. What strange intellect conceived this ludicrous idea we cannot imagine - whoever it was had clearly never served at sea and been faced with the complex regulations of his own navy, much less those of a dozen other widely differing services. Training systems varied widely, advancement methods were very different and the linguistic problems beggared description. We believed this strange notion had reached the waste paper basket by late 1962 but it was apparently still sufficiently alive in early 1963 to rouse Mountbatten's wrath with the USA. We heard nothing more of it.

Another suggestion which was floated in the Admiralty was for a force of hybrid submarines. These would be armed with eight missiles instead of sixteen and would retain the normal capabilities of an attack submarine. For a time this received some lukewarm support but was finally dropped when the Americans pointed out a number of insuperable engineering problems of such a design.

In December 1962 my own concerns were primarily centred on the arrival of our first three nuclear submarines, Dreadnought, Valiant and Warspite and the completion of the thirteen boats of the non-nuclear "Oberon" class. These studies were disturbed by Captain Lewis, Director of Plans, who came into our office and said "John, the First Lord wants a brief on the possible impact of the introduction of Polaris on the Royal Navy. The Cabinet has to advise the PM in Nassau". My first question was who was to prepare this far-reaching document. The answer was succinct. "You are to do it by 0900 tomorrow. The First Lord has given permission for you to consult anyone necessary over an open line." He left me at 1500 - eighteen hours was all I had. George, my opposite number, offered to help but I felt this had to be a one-man effort. With some evident relief he said he had something better to do somewhere else and I was left to ponder the huge ramifications of the project. It would have helped if I had been made privy to the Palmer Report referred to in a later chapter.

The first need was a list of subjects - design, building capacity, weapon procurement, warheads, manpower, training, base facilities, docking, refits, were just a few first thoughts. Then came the great question of how many boats were required on patrol at any one time and how many would be required to meet this target. Building costs - I hadn't the faintest idea so I took the projected cost of *Valiant* and doubled it. Could these boats operate from a depot ship? We were then planning a new depot ship for non-Polaris boats. Would it be sensible to have a shore base to deal with all types of submarines? The crucial questions which came out of my first hour were very basic. Could we design the boats? I knew we would be able to build them but at what cost? Was my wild guess anywhere near the likely truth? And how many? I constructed a bar chart covering twenty years from the completion of the first boat in, say, five years' time and included a refit cycle similar to that we were using for the new nuclear boats, the SSNs. Their reactors would be similar and re-coring was the main holding factor. By 1800 I had a plan - to ensure that one boat was continuously on patrol a minimum of four would be required. Five would be a sensible number to allow for mishaps and, without mishaps, would allow two on patrol at all times.

It was a relief to have got this far. Fifteen hours to go. And then came the awful realisation that the manpower of the submarine branch as it was in December 1962 could never provide the numbers needed without considerable expansion. The American Polaris boats of the "George Washington" and "Ethan Allen" classes (of which nine were already in commission) required two crews of about 140 men each. To man five British boats we would need something like 120 officers and 1,300 ratings, not counting spare crew and shore support. My spirits began to flag. All the officers and a high proportion of senior ratings would need training in nuclear propulsion and Polaris weapons technology. Could we do all that in time? I was unaware of what support and co-operation we might expect from the USN but it seemed unlikely that the Royal Navy could achieve this level of training in my proposed time-scale without a very detailed and urgent programme being set in motion.

But, even if satisfactorily manned and armed with, I presumed, sixteen missiles, the boats would be of little value without depot ship or shore support. At that time I had no conception of what would be needed eventually but, even then, the prospect was a fearsome one. Another factor of prime importance, if there were to be a large congregation of people in the base area and the attached submarines, was the provision of accommodation for their families with the necessary welfare and recreational facilities.

By about 2100 I was sufficiently organised to begin my calls for advice, help and direction. The first on my list had to be Rear Admiral Rufus Mackenzie, then Flag Officer Submarines, who I felt ought to be warned that something was afoot. Then came the round of experts, first in line being Sir Alfred Sims, Director General of Ships. Luckily I knew him from frequent staff meetings dealing with ship design and he proved a most valiant ally. He advised me about the right people to consult and himself set to work to produce some sort of coherent plan for the design and construction of the submarines. For the next three hours I was continuously on the telephone to an array of experts who were all both courteous and helpful despite, in several cases, being hauled out of bed. The Resident Clerk, a senior civil servant, helped me to find the duty typist who was warned of the impending deluge. By 0300 the much revised first dozen pages were completed, it was quite a relief to leave my chair for the short period needed to walk along the deserted Admiralty corridors to the typist's room. More followed at hourly intervals until, by 0530, it was done and a one page summary put on top. I sat down in our Admiralty issue armchair and promptly went to sleep from which I was called by the dear girl with three copies of my neatly typed paper. I wished that the contents were as professionally produced as the text.

It was just after 0700 and I was scruffy and unshaven. Experience of previous late night sessions had taught me to keep some shaving tackle and other necessities in my desk, so, hoping not to trip over any of the Board Members with whom we shared the white-tiled lavatory area, sternly marked "MEN", I stripped off and freshened myself for the next stage, the interview with the First Lord of the Admiralty, Lord Carrington. Having had nothing to eat for eighteen hours I made a quick dash to Lyons Corner House in the Strand, devoured a hearty breakfast and was back in my office by 0830.

By then some of the earlier members of the Division were getting to their desks but there was little time for pleasantries. As the clock on Horse Guards chimed nine I was outside the First Lord's office, facing a smiling master who led me into his office. I placed the twenty seven pages of typescript on the conference table and he read the abstract. Then, after ten minutes or so inspecting the whole text, he said "There's no time to absorb it all. I think we'd better all get together over this." With my back to the door I sensed others entering the room and they then began to seat themselves round the table. On the First Lord's left was the First Sea Lord and then the Secretary of the Admiralty. I was on the First Lord's right and in a few minutes I was explaining my conclusions to what was, in the absence of the Controller, the whole Board of Admiralty. I was called on to explain what I had written. This took half an hour and at 0945 I stood at the First Lord's window watching him and the First Sea Lord making their way to No 10 Downing Street. Were they to recommend to the Cabinet the adoption of Polaris? Had my paper been of any use? Having not seen it from that day I don't know but, at least, Macmillan was given the go-ahead and the Royal Navy was launched on the Polaris project.

CHAPTER 2

The Birth of Polaris in the USA
Admiral I J Galantin USN (Ret)

In 1965, when I was Director Special Projects Office in charge of our Polaris Ballistic Missile programme I received the following letter from Admiral Lord Louis Mountbatten, Chief of the Defence Staff (CDS).

"I happened to be present on that historic day at Key West when Arleigh Burke was rung up from the Pentagon to say that the US Air Force refused to co-operate with the US Navy in producing an IRBM.

The CNO told me he had just given instructions for the Navy to go ahead and produce a missile with solid fuel which could be fired from submarines.

I was so deeply impressed by the idea that I asked if the Royal Navy could be associated with this in a small way; he agreed, and as you know we had a Commander Royal Navy in the Polaris team almost from the beginning."

The "day" to which he alluded was 4 November 1955. Admiral Arleigh Burke USN had recently assumed office as Chief of Naval Operations (CNO) and, as First Sea Lord, Mountbatten was his opposite number in the Royal Navy.

Just a few months before, *Nautilus*, the world's first nuclear powered submarine, had commenced operation. She was demonstrating such underwater endurance, speed and reliability that it was clear that undersea warfare, in both pro- and anti-submarine aspects would be revolutionised. Ever enamoured by new technology, Mountbatten wanted, above all, to go to sea in *Nautilus* when he visited Burke in 1955. Earlier that year the US and the UK had negotiated a "Military Atomic Co-operation Agreement". It was thought this permitted his access to *Nautilus*. It stated that "...the USA may exchange with the UK such atomic information as the USA considers necessary for the development of the UK's defence plans ...".

Unfortunately, Rear Admiral Rickover had another view. He did not consider a trip in *Nautilus* necessary for the UK's defence plans, and believed it would be a dangerous precedent, leading to rapid erosion of our supremacy in nuclear technology. Exercising his consummate political skills through his influential supporters in the Congress, he succeeded in preventing the trip.

Admiral Burke offered Mountbatten a visit to the next most significant ship in our submarine programme. *Albacore* was our hydrodynamic test vehicle, a highly streamlined, single screw submarine powered underwater by electric storage batteries and capable of speeds up to 30 knots. She was then operating out of Key West, Florida.

I was Head, Submarine Warfare Branch (OP 311) of the CNO's OPNAV staff in the Pentagon, and was one of the small group to fly to Key West with the two distinguished naval leaders. A ride in *Albacore* was, indeed, more exciting than one in *Nautilus*, who had the hull form and twin screws typical of diesel-powered subs.

Admiral Mountbatten never forgot the enthusiasm and conviction with which Commander Jon Boyes, *Albacore*'s skipper, described his ship and put her through her paces, the ship heeling and turning, climbing and diving steeply, in a way no other ship could. In my subsequent meetings with Mountbatten, he would always recall Jon Boyes with pleasure.

In 1955 there was mounting concern over Soviet Russia's advances in ballistic missiles. The heavy-lift rockets she was developing, coupled with the atomic or hydrogen bombs she had already tested, were a serious threat to the US homeland. President Eisenhower's Science Advisory Committee saw the seriousness of the situation and urged priority development of both ICBMs and IRBMs. But, most important for the Navy, the committee also stated that a requirement existed for a sea-based ballistic missile.

At this time the use of solid propellants was limited to forward-firing rockets and to short duration, jet-assisted, take-off thrusters. Only liquid fuels could produce the thrust needed for ballistic missiles able to carry atomic warheads to a meaningful range. The Air Force had under development its Atlas and Titan ICBMs and the Thor IRBM. The Army was seeking approval to develop Jupiter, its version of a shorter range IRBM. The Navy had no ballistic missile programme, but approached the other services as to the possibility of a joint venture to develop a 1500-mile missile that could be launched from fixed sites but could go to sea as well. The Air Force was not interested in such a project, but the Army agreed.

The Navy goal was to have Jupiter deployed in surface ships in 1960, and to have a submarine-launched version ready for operational evaluation by 1965. A submarine could be designed to carry the monster missiles, but even a boat of 8500 tons could carry only four.

What the Navy really wanted was a solid-fuel missile which would not only greatly reduce shipboard hazard, but would give much shorter reaction time, and be suitable for submarine use.

Army was notified that Navy's primary goal was a solid-fuel missile armed with a lighter-weight atomic warhead. Once that was attainable we would go our own way or welcome the Army as a partner. To both Army and Air Force the solid-fuel rocket seemed a long-term prospect, but by mid-1956 Navy contractors had demonstrated its feasibility. In December Navy was authorised to proceed with its own solid-propellant system for both surface ship and submarine use. This was the birth of the Polaris sea-based missile system.

By this time Rear-Admiral W F Raborn, given unprecedented authority and responsibility for the Polaris programme, had assembled his lean management team and established a unique government-industrial partnership. Of great importance was his choice of Captain Levering Smith to be Technical Director and Chairman of a Steering Task Group (STG) whose job it was to establish minimum acceptable performance goals for all major system components. In 1956 and 1957 it was my task to set forth the views of the submarine professionals who would ultimately operate the FBM system.

Two aspects of the system were of particular concern; one was the size of the submarine and the other was the mode of launch; would it be from the surface or submerged?

The volume and length of the ship devoted to propulsion were fixed, based as they were on the proven, nuclear-powered propulsion system used in attack submarines. The determinant of ship size would be the missile compartment.

The size of the missile was not yet fixed: we knew only that it would be about 28 feet long, 4.5 ft in diameter and weigh about 30,000 lbs. With that input preliminary design showed that boats with missile tubes varying from 4 to 48 were feasible. Thirty two tubes appealed to cost analysts because that produced a "cost effective" ship ie one that could deliver more megatons per dollar invested. To those who would operate the ship and be responsible for its constant readiness a lesser number gave greater assurance of a "mission effective" ship. We could not fault the balance sheet logic of numerical analysis, but years of operational experience with ships, weapons and men, all elements individually and collectively imperfect, sent storm warnings to seamen. No submarine of the size and complexity contemplated had ever been built. The largest subs had all been cranky in submerged operation, especially near the surface. I argued that what was essential in the deterrent weapons system was assurance of continuous reliability and readiness. From the operators' viewpoint, a ship sized for 32 missiles would not be likely to meet that requirement. We recommended a ship of 5900 tons carrying sixteen missiles.

In this case, the operators' judgement prevailed. Not only were our 41 Polaris subs built with 16 tubes but the British, French and Russian models followed suit.

The second problem involving operational experience was the question of surface versus submerged launch. Though the initial concept for surface ship installation had given way to the submarine, the interim submarine capability to be ready in 1963 was assumed to require launch from the surface. However, for those who had for years experienced the contrast between the often stormy ocean-air interface and calm beneath the waves, it seemed wise to make every effort to provide the most stable platform possible.

There was no conclusive evidence that a missile as large and heavy as that being designed could be successfully launched underwater. Some persons argued that once a boat fired a missile it disclosed its position and might as well be on the surface.

I could give no scientific data to support the case for submerged launch, but I could give an analogy. "For 35 years we've been doing the reverse - dropping a missile at high speed out of the air flat on to its belly and asking it to run accurately just below the rough surface. That's the torpedo. What's so difficult about going the other way? Why can't we shoot a missile to the surface from a slow, steady platform, pierce the interface vertically in a split-second and be on our way?".

Elaborating on my simplistic example Dr C Stark Draper of the MIT Instrumentation Laboratory led the way to discussions and analyses which resulted in making submerged launch the preferred mode from the very start.

In October 1957 the USSR launched its Sputnik, the world's first earth-orbiting satellite. There was urgent re-evaluation of US missile and space programmes. Progress already made with Polaris showed that if a reduced range, 1200 miles, missile was acceptable, the submarine system could be in operation by November 1960. With that as the new goal, construction lead time of the submarine became critical. To save time, the nuclear attack submarine *Scorpion*, already on the building ways, was cut in two and a 130 foot missile section was inserted in her midsection. The ship was renamed *George Washington*.

Design of the submarine was relatively simple. What was most difficult was the design, test and integration of the host of complex subsystems. Aside from the two-stage missile itself, there were the guidance and launch systems, the re-entry body, the fire control system, the ship's navigation system and numerous others. All had to be "invented and produced on schedule".

In December 1960 when I assumed duty as Director Submarine/ Antisubmarine Warfare (OP 31), *George Washington* was deployed in the North Atlantic on the first deterrent patrol. The ceaseless vigil has been maintained ever since by improved submarines carrying more advanced missiles.

OP 31 was engaged in phasing out the submarine cruise missile programme in which the Regulus air-breathing missile, surface launched by submarines, had been, in effect, our first ICBM. However, in the face of Russia's ominous build-up of her submarine force, OP 31's major effort was the improvement of surface and air ASW, and the integration of nuclear powered submarines as a full partner in that most difficult task. The Navy was being increasingly criticised for its seeming inadequate emphasis on ASW. I was the last OP 31 to have the dual responsibilities for submarine and antisubmarine warfare. In 1961 the two were separated and given equal status.

In February 1962 I relieved Admiral Raborn as Director Special Projects Office. Six SSBNs were operational: 35 remained to be completed on a very compressed schedule.

In May 1962 the first and only complete proof test of a US strategic missile, Polaris A1, was carried out by *Ethan Allen* in operation Frigate Bird. The complete system, from launch signal to detonation of atomic warhead on target in the South Pacific was successfully demonstrated.

Polaris A1 (1200 mile range) was succeeded by A2 (1500 miles range) and development of A3 (2500 mile range) was begun. It was an 85% new missile which became operational in September 1964. With its development followed closely by the Royal Navy liaison officer in the Special Projects Office, it was the missile chosen by the UK for the four nuclear-powered submarines of its own strategic deterrent force.

CHAPTER 3

First Contact with Polaris by the Royal Navy
Peter La Niece

On 1 November 1955, together with my family, I arrived in the USA to take over as Staff Gunnery Officer on the staff of the British Joint Services Mission at Washington, DC. During my turnover week the British Naval Staff received from the USN a copy of their Operational requirement for a 1500 miles ballistic missile to be developed jointly by the US Army and US Navy: it was to be based on the former's Jupiter missile. In view of my later career I have always felt that the timing was somewhat prophetic. My predecessor and I duly sent the requirement back to the Naval Staff in London who found it a little difficult to believe. We subsequently learned that some of the technical departments in Bath who were still oriented in an era of old fashioned Gunnery regarded it as rather akin to science fiction.

On 17 November the USN created the Special Projects Office to handle the problems associated with the ship-launched weapon system. The US Army would continue to develop the missile.

It is relevant to realise that the Jupiter missile was 56 feet long and about 9 feet in diameter weighing about 80,000 lbs, or some 40 tons. It would require about 30,000 lbs of liquid oxygen to propel it, fuel which had to be kept stored at temperatures of nearly absolute zero to prevent it from evaporating. It would take about two hours to transfer the fuel to the missile and ready the weapon for launching. The huge missile was to be stowed in the central area of a submarine with its base resting on the keel and the remainder occupying the full height of a huge sail, or fin in RN parlance. The development, for which a target date of an operational ship-based system had been set, was fraught with problems.

By the end of November the USN stated a long range objective to develop a solid propellant ballistic missile for use in submarines. This was within an overall plan for development of Jupiter. They stated that development should be initiated immediately "to alleviate the serious hazards and difficult logistic, handling, storage and design problems associated with liquid fuels".

On 5 December 1955 when Rear Admiral W "Red" Raborn, a former naval aviator, was appointed as Director Special Projects Office, he was told that he could pick any forty officers from the entire

USN. He also picked a small group of high grade civil servants. He was to be responsible directly to the Secretary of the Navy.

On 19 December 1955 a formal Navy Fleet Ballistic Missile Requirement was issued. This document was also passed to the British Navy staff for onward transmission and was received in some circles in the UK with even greater incredulity than had the preceding requirement, It was only many years later that I learned that Admiral Mountbatten, who was then the First Sea Lord, and had recently visited Washington, was also aware of these developments but his debriefing obviously never reached the working level in the Admiralty until much later on.

During the first half of 1956, in parallel with the Jupiter project, work proceeded into the feasibility of a suitable solid propelled missile. A request was received in our office for any information we might have on the problems the RN might have envisaged in handling liquid propellants in a shipboard environment in connection with early liquid fuel developments of the UK Seaslug missile. Information was also sought on details of the Clausen Rolling Platform installed at Aberporth for Seaslug trials. We duly directed these enquires to the appropriate UK authorities. (A rolling platform was subsequently installed at Cape Canaveral.)

In December 1956 studies into a solid propellant missile solution had advanced sufficiently for the USN to obtain formal approval for its development under the code name Polaris. Participation in the Jupiter programme was terminated. The Polaris project was given the highest possible priority.

During these early months, our Staff Submarine Officer, Commander John Coote, who had an excellent rapport with USN submariners in general, had established contact with submarine officers within the Special Projects Offices. Early in 1957 CBNS, Vice Admiral Geoffrey Barnard, John Coote and myself were invited to a briefing on Polaris in the Special Projects Office. Thus began my long personal connection with Polaris. Right from that day, the Americans always had an open door for us, despite the fact that they were all working under great pressure.

In addition to Admiral Raborn, we also met his Technical Director, Captain Levering Smith and others with whom I had previous dealings in the Bureau of Naval Ordnance. I had first met Levering Smith at White Sands Proving Ground in December 1955 just before he was uprooted to direct the solid propellant feasibility study; at a later stage he was appointed Director and attained the rank of Vice Admiral; he and his wife also became long time friends of my family.

The presentation we were given covered the whole spectrum of the project. A fundamental feature of their work was that they had right from the start recognised the need to extend research and technical know-how beyond the then current state-of-the-art; this was particularly as regards inertial guidance, solid rocket motors and ship navigation, not to mention the problem of developing a missile and discharging it from submerged. Moreover they were planning to incorporate solutions to problems in these areas before details had been resolved or fully tested. We also learned that they were following the same philosophy as recently adopted in US Naval Aircraft development of considering the whole package of submarine, missiles and associated equipment as a complete weapon system. They were pioneering novel managerial techniques such as Program Evaluation and Review techniques (PERT) and Critical Path Analysis. The focus of their management control was always directed to those fields of development that needed increased attention and resources; areas progressing according to programme received a minimum of attention. This was loosely described as "Management by exception". Finally, they had established extremely close ties with their contractors and, despite contractual formalities, regarding their association very much as a partnership.

In July 1957 the USN revised the target to provide an FBM submarine weapon system with a 1500 nautical mile range missile ready for operational evaluation not later than 1 January 1965. By October 1957 the AEC estimated that Polaris warhead development could attain Polaris requirements in 1960.

For their part Special Projects established that the FBM programme should be accelerated to provide a Polaris submarine system with a 1200 mile missile by October 1960 and generally speaking at the same dollar cost. The 1500 mile missile would follow later. In December 1957 they received approval to complete the first Polaris submarine by 1960.

Meanwhile various development activities had been pressing ahead. A specially fitted Navigation Test Ship USS *Compass Island* had been at sea for a year. I had visited an experimental launcher known as "Peashooter" which had been erected on a pierhead at San Francisco Naval Shipyard and had satisfactorily operated using compressed air. Subsequently a much more sophisticated submerged launch facility

("Pop Up") was installed at San Clemente Island off the Californian coast.

In early 1958, the First Lord of the Admiralty, the Earl of Selkirk, visited Washington accompanied by the Secretary of the Admiralty, Sir John Lang, and the Naval Secretary, Rear Admiral Alistair Ewing. At CBNS's reception on the Friday night the First Lord was introduced to Admiral Raborn. The conversation immediately turned to the Polaris project in which the First Lord expressed only superficial knowledge. The offer of a briefing was made and immediately accepted. I was instructed to process the customary security clearances. The paperwork presented a slight problem since the relevant form did not have a box for "Sirs" and "Earls"; furthermore I was ignorant of either the First Lord's Christian name or his family name. So he went in as "Earl" Selkirk'; the officer processing the clearance pronounced it as "Oil". Bureaucracy satisfied we were booked in for a Sunday morning briefing at the holy of holies, the Special Projects Office Management Centre.

This was a fascinating meeting. Firstly, because Admiral Raborn conducted it entirely by himself supported by a whole range of charts and vugraphs and a variety of props; a masterly presentation in the best US style. He covered just about everything - technical, managerial and financial. This latter clearly puzzled the Secretary of the Admiralty whose high office had, ever since the days of Samuel Pepys, successfully kept the hands of naval officers out of financial matters. He simply could not understand how Admiral Raborn had full financial responsibility direct to the Secretary of the Navy and indeed to Congress. The First Lord and his team departed with much food for thought.

At working level in some USN circles there was some enthusiasm for the UK to become involved in the Polaris project. Moreover, in May 1957, Senator Jackson of Washington State had made a speech extolling the virtues of Polaris, and particularly to an island nation such as the UK. We had this speech run off and were in the habit of presenting a copy of it to all departing visitors, especially VIPs, for quiet reading on the journey home.

At that time the UK was still developing Blue Streak. This was a land based ICBM to be manned by the RAF. A Joint US/UK Ballistic Missile Advisory Committee had been formed and it was suggested that, on their forthcoming visit to the USA, they should take in Polaris. Together with my Ordnance Engineering colleague, I was attached to this mission. Once again there was a Special Projects Office briefing and we then went to the West Coast to the plants of the Polaris Prime Contractor, Lockheed Missile and Space Company at Sunnyvale , and Aerojet General at Sacramento where the first stage rocket motor was to be manufactured. The general attitude of the joint Ministry of Supply/RAF team was a mixture of suspicion and disbelief.

We then set off for Cape Canaveral and a Caribbean trip to view the US Atlantic Missile Range facilities. We flew, courtesy of the US Air Force, to Puerto Rico, Antigua and the Bahamas. At Antigua, after visiting a radar station, for some reason there was a delay before our on-going flight and I suggested to the RAF officers and the scientists that a visit to Nelson's Dockyard at English Harbour might be a pleasant diversion. There was no enthusiasm for this and we sat for a long time in a hut which passed as an airport lounge, drinking warm Coca Cola minus rum, whilst I quietly ruminated that I was accompanying a pretty Philistine bunch. When we finally returned to Cape Canaveral a Wing Commander also from the Washington staff and myself were astounded to be asked to produce our passports. Since the whole trip had been a guided tour in a US Air Force plane it had never occurred to us to take our passports. We were detained as potential illegal immigrants. It was a Sunday afternoon and it took some time to arouse the British Embassy at Washington and inform them of our predicament. Eventually all was well and we were allowed to return to our families in Washington.

By the time my appointment came to an end in May 1958 there had been considerable further progress in the project including a successful firing of "Pop Up". Also the USN increased the number of FBM submarines to be fitted with 1200 miles A1 Polaris missiles from three to five; they had also started planning for operational command and logistic support.

Although there had been no change in policy in the UK of the RAF providing the deterrent nevertheless Admiral Mountbatten felt the need for maintaining a close liaison with Polaris and, with the consent of the Chief of Naval Operations, Admiral Arleigh Burke, it was decided that my part-time liaison duties with the project were to be undertaken by an officer in a full-time appointment located in the Special Projects Offices.. He was Commander Mike Simeon and I briefed him on my return to the UK. He was to witness further rapid advances leading to the establishment of the Polaris A3 programme.

CHAPTER 4

The UK Strategic Deterrent 1958-62
Alan Pritchard

Early Days with RN Polaris

At the beginning of 1958, the Admiralty decided that the Military Branch of the Secretariat, which worked hand in glove with the Naval staff would be extended to match a growing workload. I was appointed as the first head of a new section to provide support for the Deputy Chief of Naval Staff. This meant deep involvement in weapon system and equipment planning, a tangled jungle harbouring some formidable characters such as Captain Peter Hill-Norton and Rowland Baker. One major preoccupation was the looming decision about the succession to the nuclear deterrent force then provided by the V bombers of the RAF.

The Naval Staff had firms views about the most effective and economical successor system; by underwater deployment of solid fuelled ballistic missiles of the kind under development by the US Navy - Polaris. But there were mixed feelings about the consequences of moving in that direction. The RAF had suffered through over commitment of resources to the strategic deterrent force and there were fears that the necessary money and men needed for a Polaris type system would weaken the surface and underwater fleets and degrade their all round capability. Admiral Mountbatten, then First Sea Lord, was reluctant to press the case for naval deployment without a guarantee that the necessary extra resources would be provided as an addition to Navy votes. He was also concerned that RN nuclear submarine development would not be sufficiently advanced to meet the necessary timescale. And there was no certainty that the US Government would be prepared to provide the necessary information and material for a completely new system despite Navy to Navy links which made this seem possible.

Lord Mountbatten first determined to overcome at least one of these disadvantages - the relatively slow progress of the nuclear propulsion programme. To that end he fostered his relationship with Admiral Rickover who had done so much to father the US Navy's nuclear submarine capability. This was no easy task. Rickover had dedicated his naval career to develop and build a highly effective arm of the service. In so doing he had not been afraid to cross swords with others, especially those with less technical skill, who had crossed his path. However, Lord Mountbatten, with his Royal connections, was able to exercise considerable influence and charm. This was well demonstrated at private meetings at which I was present as note taker during the course of a Rickover visit to London in 1958.

The outcome was that the Admiral agreed to support proposals about to be made that classified nuclear submarine information and a nuclear propulsion reactor and main machinery should be made available to the United Kingdom under the umbrella of an Anglo-American Nuclear Exchange Agreement which was being negotiated. But typical of the man was his insistence that major changes needed to be made in the organisation of the UK nuclear propulsion programme. In particular he advised that more intense management should be instituted within the Admiralty; and that the contractual support should be led by Rolls Royce for whose ability he had great respect. Sir John Lang, then Secretary of the Admiralty, took personal charge of the difficult negotiations within and outside the Department to achieve these changes. They resulted in the formation of a *Dreadnought* Project Team under Rowland Baker of which I was a founder member; and the setting up of Rolls Royce and Associates, including Vickers and Foster Wheeler, as manufacturers of RN submarine propulsion plants. Eric Hedger (Director of Contracts) and I were fully involved in these discussion and in the negotiation of the subsequent contract to buy a S5W reactor and machinery from the Westinghouse Electric Corporation of America. This was signed in Washington in 1959 in the presence of Admiral Rickover who gave us, as mementoes, complimentary Arrow ball point pens which he happened to have available.

A consequence of these developments was that the date of ordering the first RN submarine - HMS *Dreadnought* - to accommodate the American power plant was brought forward and work on the UK prototype system ashore at Dounreay was speeded up to permit early ordering of a second submarine - HMS *Valiant* One of the impediments in the way of timely participation in a Polaris type programme using nuclear submarine platforms was being overcome.

Meanwhile the UK Government had decided to discontinue the development of the Blue Streak ballistic missile. In its place plans were laid for the acquisition of Skybolt missiles which were under development in the United States. These were designed to be fired from airborne platforms, a system which was heavily supported by the air forces who saw in it their hope for continued involvement in the deployment of the strategic deterrent. The Government was undoubtedly influenced by the possibility that this system would amortise over a longer period the heavy investment which had been made in the V bombers.

The Admiralty had not mounted any sustained argument against Skybolt. However the doubts which existed in many quarters about the viability of that system encouraged the RN to maintain and strengthen its links with the US Navy through which information about the progress and implications of Polaris were regularly received in London. An RN officer had been, in fact, appointed to a liaison post in the Special Projects Office in Washington so that the Admiralty was kept fully informed about missile and platform developments and proposed deployment. This Navy to Navy rapport was reinforced by arrangements which were made to provide shore facilities for the intended US Polaris force at Holy Loch.

By 1962 it became apparent that misgivings about Skybolt had been well founded. Development was not going smoothly. More importantly the Kennedy administration was questioning the necessity for continuation with a missile whose performance objectives triplicated those of ground and seaborne systems which were making surer progress. Warnings about the possibility that the US might cancel Skybolt were passed to UK Defence Ministers who found themselves in an embarrassing situation. They had pinned their hopes of maintaining a contribution to the strategic deterrent force on a weapon which seemed unlikely to go into production. The Government had suffered a number of political setbacks and removal of the lynch pin of UK defence planning through the decision of an allied Government could have brought it down. It is relevant that the US Government was preoccupied at the time with events leading up to the Cuba Missile Crisis and it did not appear to be fully alive to the importance attached by the British to the maintenance of their deterrent contribution. The intended cancellation of the Skybolt programme was publicly announced by the US with remarkably little prior consultation. At the same time they suggested that Skybolt could proceed to production in America as an RAF programme with Britain bearing the cost of further expenditure. The delicacy of the situation was not improved by a well publicised quote from Dean Acheson, the former US Secretary of State, to the effect that Britain had lost an empire and had not yet found a role.

The official UK reaction to all this was muted but it was realised that the forthcoming meeting between the President and the Prime Minister at Nassau would provide the best chance of sorting out what otherwise seemed likely to be an international embarrassment. Intensive staff work was undertaken by London to re-evaluate the merits and de-merits of seeking to acquire Polaris in place of Skybolt and the Prime Minister's support team was accordingly strengthened. In the event Mr Macmillan's advocacy carried the day and the Nassau communiqué announced that the UK strategic deterrent would be maintained through the acquisition of Polaris from the US.

CHAPTER 5

Watching Brief 1958-60
Michael Simeon

On a day in August 1958, I was summoned to the Admiralty to be told that I was to go to the United States to act as the Royal Navy's liaison with the US Navy's Polaris programme. My memory of that day is hazy but there was a series of interviews with increasingly august persons: DGD's staff, DGD (Director of Gunnery Division) himself, the Controller, a Deputy Secretary, and others I think. Each time I asked what I was to do in Washington. Each time I was told that the post had been arranged by the First Sea Lord, Lord Louis Mountbatten and that he would brief me later.

In mid-afternoon I was taken in to the First Sea Lord. He explained that he had personally arranged with Admiral Arleigh Burke, the Chief of Naval Operations, for the Royal Navy to have a liaison officer with the Polaris programme and I was to be him. He clearly thought that his deal with Admiral Burke was something of a coup. He said that there was no actual or impending intention for the Royal Navy to take the deterrent role from the RAF's V Bomber Force and to have its own Polaris submarines. No one was even suggesting that. He went on at some length. Finally I was able to put my question. His answer was disappointingly brief. I was to fit in, keep my eyes and ears open - just do the right thing - and to keep the Admiralty up-to-date on what was going on.

The day ended with a de-briefing in DGD. I recall that my conclusion at the time was that my stay in Washington was unlikely to be long. It did not seem possible that the reason for my being there - a private arrangement between the two Naval Operating Chiefs - could long survive in the atmosphere of expenditure cuts which then prevailed and the reality that my reports were to be fed into a policy vacuum. It was only after I had been in Washington for some six months that I got used to the idea that permanence could come, perhaps only come, from such a casual personal arrangement. Anyway I decided not to fight the idea any more, and went out and bought myself a new Ford sedan.

But back to the beginning. In mid 1958 I was a Lieutenant Commander (G*) and a bachelor. I had taken the Long Gunnery Course in 1950 and the Advanced Course in Greenwich two years later. I spent the winter of 1953-54 at the Naval Air Test Center at Point Mugu, California observing trials of the Sparrow I air-to-air missile. On return I was the Senior Naval Officer in two Joint Service Trial Units for air-to-air weapons: No 6 for Blue Sky and, when that project was halted, No 12 for Blue Jay. Following that I was the Squadron Gunnery Officer for the 1st Destroyer Squadron in the Mediterranean, where we did time on the Cyprus blockade and participated in the Suez incursion. From mid 1957 I stood by as Gunnery Officer of HMS *Victorious* then completing a major modernisation in Portsmouth Dockyard. Thus in 1958 I had some qualifications for the job I was sent to do in Washington; I was readily moveable, had a background in missile technology and could speak American.

The Job of SPRN

I sailed in the *Queen Mary* and arrived in Washington in October 1958. There, wearing my new Commander's uniform, I was quickly inducted into the British Navy Staff in the old Main Navy Building and then was installed a short distance away in the Special Projects Office(SP) as SPRN. There I shared an office with a USAF Major (SPAF) and our mentor, Lieutenant Commander Charles D Allen Jr USN. In those days SP was a small group of remarkable people who supervised and urged the efforts of a number of contractors, both industrial companies and services establishments. It had the responsibility for delivering all of the missile systems, other hardware and the base facilities and infrastructure for the Polaris submarine fleet.

As SPRN I was well received by everyone in SP. It was an organisation with a strong sense of mission - to provide as survivable a deterrent force as could then be devised and to beat the US Air Force at it. I think my presence was seen as an independent validation of what they were trying to do. I gained great respect for the strength of their dedication and the quality of their efforts. While the whole activity was very well oiled with money the results were always good and sometimes exceptional. The money was not the key factor.

In SP I attended Admiral Raborn's Monday morning meetings, where the progress of the programme was reported and shared and the efforts of the office were given point and urgency. I followed up on matters of interest and by the end of my stay had witnessed missile trials and visited most of the contractors and the principal facilities involved in the development and the deployment of the missile system.

In addition, I wrote reports. In truth all of this was not really a full time job. I sometimes felt there was too much time for other things.

British Policy Developments

In the 1950s the UK deterrent was provided by the RAF's V Bomber Force. At the end of the decade the developing effectiveness of Soviet air defences created concern over the vulnerability of the ageing V bombers. Their ability to deter would be negated if they could not either penetrate the Soviet defences themselves or stand off and release weapons which could.

In early 1960 this led to a flurry of activity in Whitehall. I was called to London in May and spent a week briefing officers in the Admiralty in London and Bath on the current state of the Polaris programme. I found that there was almost no interest in an RN Polaris programme in either place. The cutting of expenditures is part of the normal backdrop for all discussions of defence policy in peacetime. At the time Naval policy makers were more concerned with defending their current requirements than trying to take on new ones. Many of them thought that the cost of a Polaris force would come out of the Navy votes elsewhere, at least in part, and did not want to risk that at all. As a result Polaris was submitted as an alternative for consideration by the Defence Committee but was not promoted.

At the end of May the decision was announced to extend the life of the V Bomber Force by adopting the Skybolt missile then being developed by the US Air Force. The missile was intended to be launched from the wing of an aircraft and was intended to deliver a thermonuclear warhead at a stand off range of some 600 miles. Since it used existing infrastructure, its costs looked very attractive to the defence analysts that the Kennedy administration was bringing into the Pentagon. Unfortunately its specification far exceeded the technology of the time. The weapon would have been very inaccurate if it had ever worked.

Shortly after this announcement I was included in the entourage of the then Minister of Defence, the Rt Hon Harold Watkinson for his trip from Washington to visit the Strategic Air Command Headquarters in Omaha, the prime contractor for the Skybolt missile, McDonnell Douglas, in Los Angeles, and the prime contractor for the Polaris missile, Lockheed Missile and Space Division, in Sunnyvale, California. At some point in the flight west, I was interviewed by the Minister. I told him that Skybolt was only being developed in case Polaris failed. There was no need, or money, for both in service. Polaris was going to work well. Thus Skybolt would never become operational. This obviously annoyed him and he responded rather shortly that he had the assurance to the contrary by the Secretary of Defense, Robert McNamara. himself. The interview was over and I retired to the back of the plane.

Back in the UK

My successor, Commander (now Rear Admiral) W J Graham and his family arrived in Washington in mid-January 1961. An extended turn-over had been mandated and I believe we were both glad to part when I left for UK in mid-March. During my latter days in Washington I applied to resign from the Navy. As a result my next appointment was changed and I went to the current weapons desk of DGD. This was a job which had its compensations and gave me an education in the workings of the Admiralty. However, I was glad to be offered the opportunity to join Chief Polaris Executive (CPE) when it was formed in January 1963.

My main recollection of CPE at its inception is that it was imbued with a similar spirit to that I had seen in SP, making due allowance for national differences. We might not know how to do it (initially this was frequently the case) but we were sure it could be done. As an organisation it started with nothing except a little space, a few good people and this determination to perform.

CPE grew well. In large part because the rest of the Admiralty not only allowed it to do so but actively supported and helped it in many ways. This was true of the civil service officers as much as, and sometimes more than, the serving officers. The only friction I can recall was partially induced by own error. This was a struggle over the principle that the integrity of the Polaris weapon system should not be risked by introducing some UK components into it (apart from the warhead which had to be British). The offending item in this instance was the SINS navigation system being developed by Admiralty Compass Observatory (ACO) and Sperry (UK) and the final outcome was that the principle was maintained.

My resignation was delayed a few weeks by mutual agreement but finally became effective in August 1963. I left the Navy to get on with other things.

CHAPTER 6

Watching Brief 1961-63
Wid Graham

The story goes that Admiral Arleigh Burke sent a signal to Mountbatten saying "For God's sake Dickie stop pestering me, put one of your men in our Special Projects Office and he can tell you all you need to know".

This resulted in Commander Michael Simeon being appointed as the first Royal Navy officer in the Special Projects Office, short title SPRN.

He was due to be relieved at the very beginning of 1961 and I was the lucky chap to get the job.

I had spent 1960 at sea as First Lieutenant of a destroyer and managed to end the year by being promoted Commander, so my first job as Commander was going to be married accompanied in the USA.

We arrived in Washington DC in the middle of January 1961, just in time for the Inauguration of President John F Kennedy. My wife and eldest son saw the parade, in feet of snow, as it passed down Pennsylvania Avenue while I looked after the younger members of the family and watched the parade on TV in the warmth and comfort of our apartment.

As the job of SPRN had already been established by Michael Simeon there was nothing for me to do but to carry on the good work.

I was on the staff of Commander British Naval Staff Washington as well as a fully accepted member of the US Navy's Special Projects Office. This meant that I attended the SP daily briefings and was able to visit nearly all their offices on an informal basis and ask as many questions as I liked. The only part of the proceedings to which I was not privy was anything to do with the missile warhead. I actually had an office in among the US Navy offices and worked there every day. I also had a desk in the British Navy Staff offices which were happily right next door, the one in Munitions Building, and the other in the Main Navy Building, both on Constitution Avenue. Both buildings have now been demolished.

The Special Projects Office was organised into divisions, each of which was responsible for a particular part of the weapon system. Amongst the divisions were the Missile, the Launcher, the Fire Control, the Navigation, the Ship, and then various support functions which embraced supply, storage, spares and so on. I tried to keep tabs on each part of the system, with the exception of the Ship which was covered by others on the staff of CBNS. I submitted a monthly report to CBNS which was duly sent back to Their Lordships, to keep everyone reasonably au fait with progress.

At this stage the US Navy had just deployed its first SSBN, the USS *George Washington*, to the Holy Loch on the Firth of Clyde where the submarine depot ship was the USS *Proteus*. The business of the Special Projects Office was therefore concerned not only with the development and improvement of the weapon system, but with the support of the operational boats and with the production of more and more SSBNs and missiles. Eventually there were 41 SSBNs with five depot ships to give them support.

One of the most remarkable things about this whole project was the timescale. The concept of a submarine launched ballistic missile had only been considered seriously in the mid-50s and here we were in 1961 and the system was actually operational.

During 1961 and the early part of 1962 I gradually acquired more knowledge of the Polaris system. I visited some of the facilities where the hardware was produced and I became an accepted figure around the Special Projects Office.

The original head of the Special Projects Office was Vice Admiral "Red" Raborn, an aviator who had made his name as a carrier Captain. He had enormous drive and energy and was held in considerable awe by all the civilian contractors who were given hell if they failed to meet their dates, and then might easily lose their contract. I happened to be visiting Lockheeds in Sunnyvale, California at the same time as Admiral Raborn was paying a flying visit to give a "pep" talk. I stood in the crowd at what was a "clear lower deck" type of operation, and listened to a real old fashioned type of harangue on the subject of patriotism, loyalty, hard work, discipline and so on; they all lapped it up and I have no doubt returned to their work determined not to let the side down.

During 1962 Admiral Raborn was relieved by Rear Admiral Pete Galantin, a submariner and a completely different character; much more intellectual, not nearly so extrovert but just as effective in his own way. I found it very interesting, as a dispassionate outsider, to see the two quite distinct styles of leadership.

There were a number of very high grade US Navy officers in the Special Projects Office and a number of them went to on to greater things, but none was more remarkable than Captain Levering Smith.

Anyone who had anything to do with Polaris was bound to be impressed with this quiet, brilliant and effective officer who had been with the project since its earliest days and who stayed with it to the end.

In the second half of 1962 a number of high level meetings were being held concerning the future of Skybolt. Up to this point the interest of the Royal Navy in Polaris had been largely academic, and there were a good many key figures in the Navy who wanted it to stay that way.

At about that time I happened to pay a routine visit to Lockheed at Sunnyvale California, but was surprised to meet the President of Lockheed himself and to be made rather a fuss of. I was bewildered by this performance and reported the incident, if you could call it that, to Vice Admiral Sir William Crawford, who at that time was CBNS Washington. I also represented to him, at about the same time, that I felt that my role as an observer in the SP Office was somewhat bogus as Britain had no intention of ever adopting Polaris as a weapon system for the RN. I suggested therefore that may be when my time was up I should go without relief.

However quite suddenly it all changed. The US announced that Skybolt had run into severe technical problems and the whole project was cancelled. This really put the cat among the pigeons in the UK. Before long it was announced that the British Prime Minister was to have a meeting with the US President at Nassau in the Bahamas. I remember that I was sent for by the British Ambassador, Sir David Ormsby-Gore to be quizzed about Polaris before he went off to have a meeting with the President.

On February 19 1963 the official British delegation was due to arrive to negotiate the Polaris Sales Agreement with the US Navy. The delegation was led by Rear Admiral Rufus MacKenzie and James McKay, the Deputy Secretary (G) in the Admiralty and about half a dozen other VIPs. They had to be met at the airport and escorted to their hotel. Earlier that morning I had taken my wife to the Bethesda Naval Hospital and during the day our fourth child arrived safely. I found myself shuttling between the airport, the hotel and the hospital and eventually had a glimpse of my third son rather late in the evening.

In March 1963 Captain Peter LaNiece was appointed to lead a new and enlarged team in the US Navy's Special Project Office. He did not have his family with him to start with so used my wife as his hostess for the first few months.

The next four months were fairly hectic getting Peter LaNiece and his team of a dozen or so staff officers settled into the Polaris office, supporting the various teams that were working on the Polaris agreement, and preparing to move the family back to the UK. We eventually returned on board the old *Queen Elizabeth* in early July just as the Pope died and the Profumo scandal broke.

CHAPTER 7

Technical Evaluation 1961
Sidney John Palmer

In 1960 I was in charge of all submarine design in the Ship
Department in Bath. At that time our design effort was relatively
modest and it bore no comparison with the enormous design and
research programme underway in America. Naturally we were keen
to find out as much as we could about what they were doing, but their
formidable Admiral Rickover made this extremely difficult for us by
keeping a tight rein on all the data we were allowed to see, even though
we were then buying a complete set of the USN *Skipjack* propulsion
plant, including the reactor, for our *Dreadnought* project.

Late in 1960 the American attitude softened and they agreed to an
IEP (Information Exchange Project) on submarine design but excluding
all the nuclear plant, and in November I led a team to the USA and had
several weeks of very useful discussion on the methods and standards
both navies were adopting for structural design, stability, system design
and related subjects. I mention this because it led to both navies
coming closer together in design detail, as also of course did the
Dreadnought project.

It was at this time that we started hearing about the US Polaris
project. A small working party in London was set up, with Sir Alfred
Sims, Director General Ships, as Chairman with the object of keeping
as closely in touch as we were able with this extraordinary and exciting
venture. This working party soon gathered the main facts about the
USN programme and then the big question arose - should we advocate
a Polaris programme for the Royal Navy? This point was settled almost
immediately when the working party asked Rowland Baker, then the
Director of the *Dreadnought* Project Team, his opinion. His reply, I well
remember, was short and explicit - we all knew the difficulties and the
risk of failure in making even moderate alterations to the design of
cramped and complicated warships, so that to contemplate such
tremendous changes as the Polaris missile system would require would
be completely beyond our capabilities - "completely bloody daft" I
think he said. If the British Government wanted Polaris submarines,
he went on, it should either buy the completed submarines from
America or buy all the American components, including the reactor,
all machinery and all conventional weapons, and assemble them over

here. Sir Alfred Sims, who had had years of experience with submarines, agreed with Baker, and I did too, though not so whole-heartedly perhaps.

In January 1961 the USN, in response to a request from Lord Mountbatten, invited us to send a small team of professional officers to America for three weeks to see exactly what they were doing in their SSBN programme. In due course the team was announced: I was to lead it and the other members were Herbert Fitzer, an outstanding electrical engineer, Charles Shepherd, a weapons engineer recently promoted to Captain, and Geoffrey Perks, a Captain (L) in the Dockyard Department. In the preparation for the visit I was told by my boss, Sir Alfred Sims, that I must stick to gathering facts and not raise hares about the RN having SSBNs!

We set off in February 1961 on what turned out to be the most exciting time in my whole career. We were immediately struck by the open and friendly attitude of the US Special Projects team, which was guiding their Polaris programme, so different from the secretive, almost hostile attitude of Admiral Rickover and his nuclear engineers. The first thing I did was to have a good discussion with Admiral 'Red' Raborn, who was in charge of their project. We liked each other immediately and he promised that we would be told about everything except the missile warhead and the nuclear reactor, both of which were protected by their security rules. We did not talk about an RN Polaris programme because we both knew that the British were already committed to the Skybolt deterrent.

While we were going around shipyards and factories digging out details of their truly incredible Polaris programme we heard that two of the early Skybolt firings had gone badly astray, and our American friends were not slow to point out that difficulties in determining accurately the position in space and the velocity of the aircraft at launch would always make Skybolt an inaccurate and unreliable missile.

As we went from one meeting to the next I was beginning to realise that the incorporation of a Polaris missile section in the RN *Valiant* design (leaving about 90% of the submarine British) would not be as difficult as Sims and Baker had feared. Every discussion with the Americans showed that they were designing a hull of similar shape, with similar standards for stability and blowing tank capacity, with similar fluid systems at similar pressures and similar electrical systems. It seemed too good to be true but I realised it was due to the long collaboration between our two navies, including the visit I had made a year earlier, which had lined up so many of these concepts.

These thoughts were weighing so much on my mind that at the end of the second week I decided to take two days off on my own to think the problems through and I gladly accepted an invitation from Constructor Commander Geoffrey Fuller, our man in Washington, and his wife Pam, to spend the weekend with them, provided I could have a quiet corner with a table and chair where I could be left alone to work things out. In those two days I wrote the summary to our mission's report, the Palmer Report, which proposed that we should build five (yes five) SSBNs based on HMS *Valiant* with a Polaris missile section inserted in the parallel body. In writing this I had both technical problems and political problems to solve.

On the technical side I had to convince myself that it would be practical to open up the Valiant design and insert the missile section. The *Valiant* was one foot greater in diameter than the American *George Washington*, and had a reactor and main machinery designed for 20,000 SHP compared with the 15,000 in the American boat. The hull was of different steel and the shape and spacing in the frames was different.

As Baker had said, it would be disastrous if we started making changes in the American missile compartment, which meant that the scores of pipes and electrical circuits coming into that compartment from the reactor compartment would have to be positioned exactly as they were in the *George Washington*. But our reactor compartment was quite different from the American, and none of the pipes and cables was in a similar position. Eventually I decided that they could be aligned if we inserted a small section, perhaps twenty feet long, between the reactor and missile compartments, and used this to twist the services as required. This would also give us extra space for some special pieces of equipment we would have to add.

Having worked my way through the technical problems I then had to address the political problem. I soon realised that there was only one thing I could do - in defiance of my instruction I must come right out with the proposal that we should drop the Skybolt deterrent for Polaris. The advantages were now obvious - Polaris was more reliable, more accurate, cheaper, safer from attack and, into the bargain, would be about 90% British.

The next morning I called the team together and read them the summary I was proposing for our report. To a man they were enthusiastically in agreement, and for our remaining days in America we all worked hard to flesh out these proposals, which were, in brief, that we should design an SSBN based on *Valiant* with a missile section inserted, and that we should build five of these submarines and base them on Devonport Dockyard (to be near deep water), the Armament Depot at Ernesettle being modified to service the new missiles. The report included our estimate of the cost and time required (which a few years later proved to be remarkably accurate) and an immense amount of detailed information.

When I returned to the Ship Department I reported at once to Sir Alfred Sims and he immediately called a meeting of the Ship Department Board. As he read slowly and carefully through the summary of our report there were several disapproving grunts and some outright criticism that I had gone right outside my brief. Later I briefed Lord Carrington, the First Lord, and the Admiralty Board, and met no opposition anywhere. There was no doubt that the Navy accepted the idea and so, it eventually appeared, did the Cabinet. When Skybolt was cancelled, the Prime Minister, Mr Macmillan, flew to Nassau for a crucial meeting with President Kennedy. Admiral Le Fanu accompanied him and before he left he said to me "You can trust me not to put my foot in it - I shall have your report under my arm all the time".

CHAPTER 8

Setting up the UK Project
Sir Hugh Mackenzie

Skybolt was formally abandoned by the United States in December 1962. Things moved dramatically thereafter. The Prime Minister, Harold Macmillan, met President Kennedy at Nassau in the Bahamas before Christmas, ostensibly to determine how best to bring up-to-date and continue Britain's contribution to the West's nuclear deterrence forces. In actual fact, the Prime Minister had already decided he wanted Polaris and, after a flurry of intense activity over 24 hours, the Cabinet approved his approach. Success was achieved and the resulting "Nassau Agreement " of 20-21 December laid down, in very broad terms, the conditions governing such provision. In short, these were that the United States would provide, on a continuing basis, Polaris missiles and their associated systems and equipment, plus spares but NOT warheads; whilst the United Kingdom would provide the submarines and warheads. It was a simply stated communiqué, but its implementation heralded vast, unknown problems, only solved by the creation of new ventures in the management and control of the production and procurement.

The Third Sea Lord and Controller of the Navy (Vice Admiral Michael Le Fanu) was part of the team supporting the Prime Minister; thus the Admiralty Board were fully alive to the discussions and the final decision, which landed a new role, and additional responsibilities of awe-inspiring significance, on the Royal Navy. On the party's return from Nassau, just before Christmas 1962, the Board started the ball rolling, to meet the immense task to provide the country's future nuclear deterrent. Public announcements went no further than the bare terms of the Nassau Agreement, but behind the scenes much went on, though all wrapped in the veils of secrecy.

I received the surprise of my life on Friday 28 December 1962; that morning in my capacity as Flag Officer Submarines (FOS/M) I had attended a meeting in the Admiralty, not directly concerned with Polaris; later, returning to Gosport on my way home, I was informed that the First Sea Lord (Admiral Sir Caspar John) wanted to speak to me on the telephone, on the "scrambler"; repairing to my office I was connected, whereupon a conversation on the lines of the following took place:-

1SL   *"You're fully in the picture about Polaris: well, I want you to head the organisation we are setting up at the Admiralty to run the thing through."*

FOS/M (doubtfully) *"Yes, Sir."*

1SL   *"Come and have lunch with me on Monday at one o'clock, at White's in St James's and give me your answer then: you can have the weekend to think it over."*

FOS/M   *"Yes, thank you, Sir."*

1SL   *"I tell you here and now that if you say "no", I'll twist your arm until you b.....y well scream."*

FOS/M (after a pause) *"Right, Sir, I'll see you on Monday."*

End of conversation.

Come the Monday (31 December) the answer given was "Yes"; but only after a weekend of much heart-searching: acceptance would give rise to many personal and family problems and sacrifice, to which was added the disappointment of prematurely relinquishing the enjoyably inspiring and rewarding appointment of FOS/M. But the challenge, however daunting, proved over-riding and the die was cast; to be reinforced by a meeting with the First Lord of the Admiralty (Lord Carrington) that forenoon, before the fateful lunch. At this meeting the First Lord emphasised the importance and urgency of getting Polaris into service within five years; and the powers that would be given to whoever headed the special organisation to be set up within the Admiralty, an essential factor to achieving the aim. Thus came into being the appointment of Chief Polaris Executive (CPE).

The next day, New Year's Day, 1963, I found myself in an empty room on the ground floor of North Block of the Admiralty building; empty, that is, except for a chair and a large desk, on which sat a telephone not yet connected; no staff, no paper-work; it was, to say the least, an unusual and perplexing situation.

The provisional terms of this new job indicated that I was responsible to the Controller of the Navy for the Polaris programme as a whole, but that I had direct and immediate access, at any time, to any member of the Board of Admiralty if I needed assistance in overcoming difficulties or problems arising in that particular member's field. Admiral Le Fanu's three year old report, with its proposals and recommendations for the organisation required to bring Polaris swiftly into service in the Royal Navy, was brought out of its pigeon-hole, dusted down, and promptly landed on my desk, to become my bible for the immediate future. It was also fortunate that as FOS/M I, during a routine visit to Washington the previous summer, had been given a very comprehensive briefing by the Director, Special Projects (SPO), (Rear Admiral I J Galantin, USN) on all the methods and procedures used in SPO to keep, so successfully, the strictest control, on a very tight timescale, of the United States Navy's Polaris programme.

Armed with all this background information, matters quickly clarified and the task began to take on a more definable shape. The Le Fanu report was invaluable as a starting point for a race against all the odds, a race in which it was already clear that many obstacles would arise in the years ahead; not the least of these could be summed up by the phase "We don't know how much we don't know." In fact, we were at the very bottom of a steep and formidably high learning curve.

Immediate action was needed to put flesh on the bare skeleton of the organisation outlined in the Le Fanu report; the Admiralty Board accepted in principle that some such measure would be necessary if the programme was to be driven through on time, but it was left largely to CPE to devise its exact shape and size; I was told I would have a free choice in filling the key posts, naval and civilian. In a matter of days these were selected and appointed. Having personally experienced the proverbial "pier head jump" in taking up my new appointment I had no qualms about forcing the pace; the Secretary of the Admiralty (Clifford Jarrett) and the Controller gave full support, and much helpful advice, on how the team should be set up, and who should fill the top billets.

There was one area where things did not run so smoothly. The Admiralty had no responsibilities (or experience) for the design and production of nuclear weapons nor, Polaris being a true ballistic missile, for the related Re-entry System (RES); these lay with the Atomic Weapons Research Establishment and the Ministry of Aviation. Indeed, this Ministry also claimed it had statutory responsibility for all "missiles" and therefore it should have overall charge of the Polaris programme; the Minister of Aviation was adamant that it was his Ministry's job. Only much work and tactful handling by the First

Lord prevented a damaging head-on clash. The all-important argument that the submarines, with their navigation, control and launching equipment, were an integral and inseparable part of the whole Polaris weapon system, won the day. The issue was, after several weeks, resolved by setting up within the Ministry of Aviation, the Polaris Project Office, headed by a naval officer, Rear Admiral F Dossor (PPO); he would have dual responsibility, to his Minister and to CPE, for the design and production of the Re-entry System and the warheads, to the timescale required. The Admiralty remained responsible for the procurement, fitting and servicing of the actual missiles and associated control systems.

By the end of the first week, the main form of CPE's organisation within the Admiralty was agreed, and already some key members were in post; but much detail had still to be settled, and there were, mounting daily as the enormity of the project emerged from the fog of ignorance, innumerable problems of every kind and variety; security, liaison with the SPO, co-ordination with Admiralty departments and between Government Ministries (eg Treasury, Foreign Office, Ministry of Public Buildings and Works), the actual location (Admiralty, London, or Admiralty, Bath) of the growing team, office space to accommodate it, funding of the programme, handling of contracts with industry in general and the ship-builders in particular, selection of the latter: all these, and many others, were of paramount importance, problems to be resolved quickly and correctly before a coherent programme could be drawn up.

Above all, more information from the American end was desperately needed. On 8 January, a mission flew from London to Washington; it was headed by the Chief Scientific Advisor to the Ministry of Defence (Sir Solly Zuckerman) and the Vice-Chief of the Naval Staff (then Vice Admiral Varyl Begg), and included a Deputy Secretary and myself from the Admiralty and the Chief Scientist and other representatives from the Ministry of Aviation. I was able to renew personal contact with Admiral Galantin (Director, Special Projects) and his Special Projects Office; the foundations were laid for the closest of future co-operation, including the early setting up of a Joint Steering Task Group (JSTG), to ensure that the British Polaris Programme was kept fully integrated with its US counterpart, and that it received adequate priority throughout. With Admiral Galantin's vigorous backing, a bond was struck between both organisations, which grew and strengthened as the years went by; without this support the British programme would never have even got off the ground.

Other issues discussed during the hectic three day visit were the number of missiles to be carried by each British submarine (whose number was not yet resolved) and whether those supplied were to be the A2 or A3 version; these issues were absolutely critical to further consideration and planning of the UK programme. The Americans, within the terms of the Nassau Agreement, gave uninhibited information and strongly expressed their views, all immensely helpful to the urgent decisions yet to be taken at Government level.

Back in the Admiralty on 14 January, I found my own organisation growing strongly according to plan; the most important step was the transfer to the Polaris Executive of the *Dreadnought* Project Team under the immensely able, dynamic and forthright leader, Mr Rowland Baker, of the Royal Corps of Naval Constructors. This team had been set up, under the Director-General, Ships (Sir Alfred Sims) to design and oversee the building, by Vickers of Barrow-in-Furness, of HMS *Dreadnought*, Britain's first nuclear powered submarine, albeit with a nuclear reactor provided by the United States. With first hand experience in this sensitive field of contractual relationships with American authorities they were the leading source of knowledge in the United Kingdom on nuclear propulsion, and clearly would have a very great deal to contribute to the Polaris Executive. That Director-General, Ships, was prepared to release them to CPE was a tremendous step forward, and this readily given agreement paved the way for gradual acceptance, in time, of the Polaris Executive by other Admiralty departments, whose first response to the new organisation tended to be grudging, if not plainly hostile.

Effective progress was, however, still stultified by prolonged arguments on the design of the submarines, on the eight or sixteen missile issue and on whether these latter should be A2 or A3. American advice on the submarine design was wholly in favour of sixteen; they warned that any departure from this would require a complete re-design of the entire weapon system, at vast cost in time and money: as regards the missiles themselves, they stated unequivocally that the A2 production line was to be closed down, so confident were they that the A3, still actually under trial, would be a complete success. A time-wasting distraction to these arguments was introduced by a proposal, emanating from Washington, that the Western Alliance should have its deterrent strength increased by equipping it with a multi-national force of surface vessels armed with Polaris missiles (the MLF). CPE was drawn into the discussions of this wild scheme, totally irrelevant to the task of the Polaris Executive, because, by now, Whitehall regarded him as the "expert" whenever and wherever the word "Polaris" cropped up. The very idea of putting such a highly technical, nuclear armed, weapon system into the hands of multi-national mixed crews on board merchant-type ships just did not bear serious examination and so, fortunately, the MLF fantasy was eventually killed off.

But before it had even arisen I had to deal with two other pressing problems; one, easy and pleasant to solve; the other more contentious. The first was Admiral Galantin's arrival in London on 17 January, a return visit to that of the high-powered team to Washington the previous week. Loose ends between CPE and SP were tied up, and the need confirmed for a further formal agreement between the two Governments, more explicit than the one produced in Nassau. It would have to include the exact terms governing the supply and maintenance of Polaris missiles and all associated equipment, the provision in detail of all relevant technical information - essential to successful incorporation of the complete weapon system in the British design of submarine - measures for co-ordinating mutual progress and priorities of the US and UK programmes, and finally, how and when it was all to be paid for. A broad outline plan was evolved of how these mammoth problems should be resolved.

The other, the worrying, problem was closer to home; since the very start I had been working under a strictly enforced cloak of secrecy: there had been no official release of my appointment. The submarine command only knew that FOS/M in person, had suddenly vanished from his headquarters at Blockhouse , and that Captain S/M 5 (Captain E J D Turner), as he then was, was "holding the fort" in his place; my Rear Admiral's flag still flew in HMS *Dolphin*. Likewise, within the Admiralty, a similar obscure situation obtained, with no formal promulgation of the decision to set up a new organisation, with its aims and terms of reference; intense speculation in the Press fuelled the uncertainty and confusion which steadily gained ground afloat and ashore.

I appealed directly to the First Lord and the Controller, stating that it was intolerable that both the submarine command and the Admiralty Departments were being kept in the dark in this way; and that it was utterly wrong that, to the outside world, I personally was apparently still head of the submarine command; to precipitate matters, I intended to order my flag to be struck. It transpired, as I had surmised, that continuing argument with the Minister of Aviation as to who should run the Polaris programme was at the root of the delay: the First Lord forced the issue, the Government gave its blessing to the Admiralty being in charge. Whereupon my appointment was publicly issued, Captain S/M was confirmed as Commodore S/Ms, and all concerned within Whitehall were informed of the existence, aims and broad terms of reference of the Polaris Executive. At last, in the third week of January, my position was openly established and I had a clear target: Polaris to be operational in 1968, five years ahead.

PART 2

THE PROJECT UNFOLDS

CHAPTER 9

Launching the Project
Sir Hugh Mackenzie

The Government required Polaris to be operational in 1968; the Admiralty laid responsibility for this firmly and squarely on me and my organisation, the Polaris Executive.

Formal recognition of the Polaris Executive was a major step forward: no longer an "unknown quantity working in a vacuum" it could now develop sensibly a long term plan directly related to the target date of 1968 for operational deployment of Polaris. Although a projected programme to meet this was still in its infancy, with many vital factors yet to be resolved, eg size and number of submarines, the main structure of the organisation needed to suit the task was now firmly established and ripe for expansion.

I had set up my headquarters within the Admiralty in London; there, from the earliest days, I had superb support from my Chief Administrative Officer (Mr R N P Lewin) and from my "Assistant", or Chief of Staff as I preferred to regard him (Captain J R McKaig) later to be designated Deputy CPE. Bob Lewin, an Assistant Secretary from the Admiralty, had vast experience in the workings of Whitehall - of which I had virtually none, having never served in the Admiralty; his unstinting loyalty and invaluable, wise advice did much to ensure that the new organisation would be, to the greatest extent possible, autonomous, but yet fully integrated into existing Admiralty and Government machinery: in this he had an able assistant in Mr P Nailor, who later succeeded him in 1966, and years afterwards, as Professor Nailor, wrote "The Nassau Connection", published by HM Stationery Office, in 1988, a highly authoritative and well-referenced account of the crucial years of bringing Polaris into service.

Rae McKaig had been the Commander of HMS Ganges, the Boys' Training Establishment in Suffolk, in 1958 when I had been its Captain. On the "dry list" he had, despite this, been appointed, as a junior Captain, to take command of HMS Manxman, a minelayer brought out of Reserve for service in Singapore. His qualities, however, were so outstanding and had made such an impression on me, that I insisted he be "hi-jacked", at the briefest of notice, to take up yet another chairbound job. It says everything for his sense of duty and loyalty that, in spite of a very real disappointment at being suddenly wrenched from the quite exceptional chance of his getting to sea, he threw himself so whole heartedly and energetically into this new, very onerous post, demanding all of his talents, and more. His input into planning the programme was the major factor in its eventual success.

I was also fortunate in being able to retain the services of my Secretary (Commander J R Grimwood) whom I had had when FOS/M at Blockhouse; and an immediate essential addition to the Team was a Security Officer (Commander P Shaw), whose overall writ covered Admiralty, London and Admiralty, Bath, together with, as the organisation grew, all out-stations. Others were soon drawn in - Jimmy Launders, Ken Dunlop, Henry Ellis, et al. Backing them all was a small and efficient typing staff.

This initial nucleus, so hurriedly assembled in London, was the corner-stone on which the whole project ultimately depended: for supervision and direction, for ensuring financial support and, when or where necessary, for fighting the battles with higher authority and gaining political approval. In times of major difficulty or crisis - which were many in the early years and never finally disappeared - it was where "the buck stopped".

Simultaneously, a much larger, complicated, and more technically weighted organisation was growing within Admiralty, Bath. As already described, the *Dreadnought* Project Team (DPT) under its charismatic and dynamic leader, Rowley Baker, had been made over, en bloc, to the Polaris Executive. His title of DPT was retained, as Director, Polaris, Technical. Under him a Technical Directorate was rapidly established, consisting of Mr S J Palmer RCNC, Captain C W H Shepherd, Captain L D Dymoke and Mr H C Fitzer, respectively responsible for submarine design and construction, the procurement, installation and proving of the Polaris weapon system, and the Marine Engineering and Electrical Engineering aspects of the submarine's nuclear propulsion plant. They were all experts in their own fields, and their closest cooperation and co-ordination as a team was vital to the immense task of designing, building, equipping, testing and tuning, and finally completing as 100% ready for operational service, the largest, most technically advanced and complicated submarine and associated weapon system ever built in this country: only someone of Rowley Baker's calibre could have pulled them all together so successfully.

A great load of responsibility rested on their shoulders, much of it in unknown or scarcely explored territory. Charles Shepherd had to master the intricacies of a weapon system new to him: submarine,

missile, launching, control, navigation; and, in particular, all the requirements for training of personnel, naval and civilian, for installation and
testing and tuning of equipment. His was the most daunting task of all;
accomplished with the assistance of a very able and dedicated team
which he conjured up from the widest sources remarkably quickly.

For the others: overall submarine design, how to incorporate an
entire American weapon system, and the nuclear propulsion field, all
three presented special problems. The widely acclaimed, newly
launched, first British nuclear submarine *Dreadnought* was fitting out at
Barrow-in-Furness. She had an American nuclear reactor, supplied
under very special and strict terms, and so was not suitable as a
prototype for design work. A British reactor was still under trial at
Dounreay and had yet to be installed in *Valiant*, presently also building
at Barrow; so no British nuclear propulsion plant had yet been tried at
sea. Further down the line, also in the hands of Vickers at Barrow, was
Warspite, on whom work had only just started.

As day followed day and the scope of the task became clearer, so
grew the problems facing the Technical Directorate; these were not
only professional, there were administrative ones as well: recruitment
of suitably qualified staff; accommodation for these, requiring new
buildings and drawing offices; security clearance of personnel and
physical security of buildings; all pressing for early solution; all with
their effect on the long-term plan for the overall programme, and
therefore involving, to some degree, myself and my London staff.

I had recognised from the very start that modern management
techniques would be essential to the strict control of the programme.
I had been well briefed by SPO on how these had contributed to the
success of the American programme, and I was determined to
introduce such methods as Critical Path Analysis, Programme Evaluation Review Technique (PERT) and Programme Management Plans
(PMPs), suitably adapted for British use. The Secretary of the
Admiralty gave his full backing, and CPE's staff was augmented
accordingly: not an easy job to fulfil, for these new ideas were by no
means accepted readily and universally. In the initial months of the
programme much time and effort had to be devoted by myself and my
staff to persuade Admiralty Departments, and industry, where directly
concerned, of the necessity and of the purpose of the new methods.
It was an uphill struggle, but we won through in the end.

Pressure and uncertainties were relieved momentarily when it was
finally decided, around the end of January, that the submarines would

each carry sixteen missiles. This enabled serious design work to start on an area which, it was already clearly seen, would be critical to the eventual success of the programme. Until design criteria for the submarine were established, no action could be taken to get the, as yet, potential shipbuilders properly committed, nor could "long lead" items be ordered.

The number of missiles per submarine having been determined, it was comparatively easy to decide that, initially, the programme would cater for building four submarines; the Government decreed that they would be completed at six-monthly intervals, and that the option for building a fifth would be kept open. Much disputatious argument, and lobbying for custom, then took place on who should be the shipbuilders. Vickers, at Barrow-in-Furness, was the obvious front-runner, being the only yard with experience of building nuclear-powered submarines; naturally, they offered to take on all four, but it was abundantly clear that they had neither the resources nor capacity to meet the tight timescale to which the programme was tied. Another yard, or yards, had to be found. Cammell Lairds at Birkenhead and Scotts at Greenock, both with great experience of building conventional submarines, were the only contestants; the choice fell on Cammell Lairds, who were judged better able to modernise and enlarge their facilities, and especially slipways, essential work if the requirement was to be met. It thus emerged that Vickers and Cammell Lairds would each build two, respectively the first and third and second and fourth. Vickers was to be "lead-yard" with responsibility for supplying Cammell Lairds with all necessary drawings and information, a difficult contract to fulfil, posing endless problems induced principally by shortages of suitably qualified staff, and leading to constant recriminations between the two rival firms. All this required never ending attention from DPT to smooth matters over.

With the major question of the number of missiles per submarine settled and the Polaris Executive thus able to devote more of its energies to devising a valid long-term plan for the overall programme, I - with an easier mind than I had had for some time - left for Washington on 19 February, as part of a strong Admiralty team, plus Ministry of Aviation representation. Led by Deputy Secretary (G) of the Admiralty (Mr J M Mackay), its object was to negotiate in detail the terms - financial, material, security - governing the timely supply of Polaris missiles and equipment as envisaged in the Nassau Agreement. After weeks of intense argument and discussion, for which the British delegation had well prepared itself in advance of going to Washington, there emerged a draft Polaris Sales Agreement, which it was hoped would be acceptable to both Governments. That it achieved remarkably favourable terms for the United Kingdom was due to Jim Mackay; a big man in every way, mentally and physically, he was an extremely patient but forceful negotiator who, when he thought it justified, pursued matters inexorably until he had achieved a successful conclusion. The skill with which he tackled each issue, some highly technical and complicated, was an eye-opener, and earned respect and admiration from both sides. In the event, without demur or further amendment, the Agreement was signed by both Governments on 6 April 1963. Its terms were clear (see Appendix I to "*The Nassau Connection*") and it formally opened the door to the closest co-operation, at all levels, between the Polaris Executive and the Special Projects Office; co-operation which was steadily, though not so easily, extended into wider fields, between the main British and American contractors, eg Vickers and Electric Boat. It was noteworthy that the Agreement specifically excluded the field of nuclear propulsion. Thus I was never drawn into direct contact with Admiral Rickover and his dominant empire; if problems arose in this area they were pursued via separate channels.

I returned to London on 2 March, some weeks before the negotiations were concluded; I had sensed that these were going satisfactorily, and that I could better serve the needs of the British Polaris Programme by being back in my headquarters in London to progress the vital issues continually coming to a head. Leading them was getting the two shipbuilders with Rolls Royce and Associates (RR&A) into the act; the latter were responsible for the nuclear reactors for the propulsion systems of all the submarines, projected or building, and there were "long lead" items required by all three organisations, the time for ordering which was already critical. Decision was needed on the A2 or A3 version of the missile; the Ministry of Aviation was dragging its feet, a better organisation was required within it, and better relationships must be mutually established. The Polaris Executive, and particularly the Technical Directorate, must be expanded to take account of the vast logistic effort required to ensure the provision of a Polaris base with suitable maintenance facilities for submarines and missiles. A "public relations" exercise must be mounted, to improve the public image of Polaris, and counter much ill-informed propaganda that was still rife. The problems never grew less:

they constantly expanded as knowledge of the task grew day by day.

Despite this apparent turmoil of never-ending new problems, there were, indeed, encouraging signs to greet me on my return. By superhuman efforts Bob Lewin and Rae McKaig, between them, had produced a "Longcast" for the whole Polaris programme, giving a date for the operational deployment of the first submarine in June 1968, with the remainder following at six-monthly intervals. It was a monumental work, showing all major critical dates as then known, and was backed by solid cost estimates, a sound basis for the inevitable further arguments with the Treasury; and it contained realistic targets for the construction, fitting out and trials of four submarines, plus full base supporting facilities, as supplied by Rowley Baker and his Technical Directorate in Bath.

Naturally, as time progressed Longcast 63 was refined as knowledge was acquired; but in essence it became firmly established as the basis for all planning of the programme, and to it was geared all the management techniques in use, such as PERT and PMPs. The Admiralty Board accepted it, without any significant amendment, in April and thereafter it was promulgated to all directly involved in the programme, which eased, immeasurably, the task of the Polaris Executive. There was now an officially approved document showing projected expenditure and target dates. It proved to be, in great degree, a true forecast and was an absolutely invaluable tool of management; it set the parameters for keeping costs within the original estimates and for the timely completion of the programme.

Coincidental with Longcast 63, I introduced regular Progress Meetings; once established these became fortnightly reviews of how the Polaris Programme was faring, embracing its whole wide scope. The various members of the Polaris Executive reported in detail on whether satisfactory progress was, or was not, being made in their particular sections or part of the programme for which they were individually responsible. Attended by the Management Committee, consisting of CPE, PPO, DPT, CAO and Deputy CPE*, they were designed to illuminate problems and difficulties, little time being spent on things that were going well. The Management Committee could thus concentrate their efforts on action to keep the programme on course. Preparation for the meetings undoubtedly consumed much time and effort from all concerned, but, provided reports were

* CPE. Chief Polaris Executive. PPO Polaris Project Officer (Ministry of Aviation). DPT Director Polaris Technical. CAO Chief Administrative Officer. Deputy CPE. Deputy Chief Polaris Executive.

truthfully based and not over-optimistic, on which I insisted, they presented regular and frequently recurring opportunities for remedial measures to be quickly instituted, whenever and wherever it appeared that target dates, or costs, were in danger of slipping, or over-running. They also required that those reporting had a real knowledge in depth of all that was involved in meeting their own target dates: any light or superficial approach was unacceptable.

With the formulation of Longcast 63, it became clear that "full supporting facilities" for Polaris when in service would require the design and construction of a completely new shore base for nuclear-powered submarines, including the provision of a floating dock large enough to take Polaris submarines, SSBNs as they were now commonly referred to. Also needed was an appropriate armament depot for the storage of the Polaris missiles and their nuclear warheads, combined with storing conventional torpedoes and warheads. The new task of maintaining and servicing the missiles presented new technical problems, to which the existing armament supply organisation had to be adjusted; the nuclear warheads would have to be serviced by the Atomic Weapons Research Establishment (AWRE) which meant that special arrangements had to be made for their transport to and fro. This logistic part of the programme, on its own, was a vast undertaking spread across an enormously wide spectrum; not only Admiralty departments hitherto unaffected, but involving, inter alia, the Ministry of Public Buildings and Works (MPBW), local authorities, Health and Safety Executive, Scottish Department, Ministry of Transport, and a host of Civil Engineering interests. Special measures were urgently needed within the Polaris Executive to grapple with this many-headed monster, which could only be brought successfully under control if its management was kept under strictest surveillance and given the full treatment of the new techniques such as PERT and PMPs.

The Technical Directorate under DPT was accordingly expanded to include a new division responsible for all such logistic matters, headed by the Polaris Logistics Officer (PLO); it took some time to select the right man, with arguments on whether he be a naval officer or a civilian, but by early May Captain L Bomford, newly retired from the Navy, was in post, ready and willing to shoulder an immensely complicated and involved assignment. Without his determination and ability to drive the right path through a tangled web of many diverse and self-centred interests, the programme would have fallen into complete disarray.

Although these requirements for a special base were clear to me, the Government was slow to give its go-ahead. The Admiralty accepted that Faslane on the Clyde, already approved as the base for "hunter-killer" nuclear powered submarines, was the most suitable place; but the Treasury and Ministries of Defence and of Transport disagreed, because of possible financial savings if the base were at Rosyth, and if at Faslane because of potential dangers to the "Emergency Oil Depot" located in the Gareloch.

With the support of FOS/M, I fought the case on the grounds that, operationally, Rosyth was unacceptable and that Faslane should be developed to cater for both "hunter-killer" and Polaris submarines. With the backing of the Admiralty Board final approval was obtained for an entirely new shore base - jetties, maintenance and training facilities, accommodation, married quarters etc - to be built at Faslane on the Gareloch, supported by an Armament Depot at Coulport on the shores of the adjoining Loch Long. From the overall "military" point of view it was the only sensible conclusion, but it gave rise to much opposition locally, from sincerely held views on potential nuclear threats to health and safety and because of general disturbance to the environment. Much time and effort had to be expended on assuaging local authorities and persuading the people concerned that their fears and doubts were groundless. The Base would never be a "happy ship" if the local inhabitants were determinedly against it; I felt every measure to circumvent this was fully justified and accordingly this received full attention from the highest political level.

In April a proposal from the Secretary of State for Defence (Mr P Thorneycroft) threw my very existence into the melting pot: it suggested that I personally be replaced by Dr Beeching, who had recently acquired fame, or infamy, for his reorganisation of British Rail. Fortunately, the First Lord, First Sea Lord and Controller all believed the Navy could "run the show" and rose to my defence; the proposal, which could only have been totally disruptive of all the effort so far expended by the Navy on building up the Polaris Executive, was hurriedly dropped. It did, however, give rise to thoughts on the advisability of enlisting, from business or industry, such experience of modern "project management" as was then available (not very much!). In consequence, Sir Frederic Hooper, lately retired as a very distinguished Chairman of Schweppes Ltd, a then current "market-leader" in successful business practices, was invited by the Controller to act as an "Honorary Consultant" to CPE. It was a helpful and useful move, through which I gained much from informal meetings and discussion with Sir Frederic: these talks confirmed that planning and programme were generally on the right lines and that no fundamental changes were required. They also reinforced a compelling need for contracts with industry to include rigid terms and penalty clauses governing timely completion, and that negotiations over such contracts, which tended to be long drawn out, must be swiftly concluded. Sadly, the talks came to an end before the year (1963) was out, through Sir Frederic's unexpected and untimely death. But his input into the Polaris programme's successful conclusion should not go unrecorded.

As earlier described, in January 1963, the Director, Special Projects (SPO) had suggested to me that an essential factor in the smooth running of their joint enterprise would be the setting up of some manner of working party, which would meet regularly to review the British programme, its aims being to ensure that there was no clash of priorities with the American programme, to identify any possible causes of delay to the former arising from conflict with the latter, and, if necessary, to put in train remedial measures. This matter was then steadily developed in further discussion, was subsequently covered in the Polaris Sales Agreement, and finally implemented with the first meeting of the Joint Steering Task Group (JSTG) held in June 1963, in Washington under the Chairmanship of the Director, Special Projects. Henceforth the JSTG meetings were to become a regular feature of the Polaris programme, held alternately in Washington and in either London or Bath, quarterly initially, and then at four monthly intervals.

Formal business of the JSTG was customarily confined to matters relating to and arising from implementation, including interpretation, of the Polaris Sales Agreement. Comprehensive though the latter was, it laid down only the main principles governing the supply of Polaris to the UK: guidelines, extending in much greater depth, were plainly required to define in detail what, how, and when supply was to take place of material, technical information, documentation, drawings, training and instruction, even down to resolving differences in language: there thus came into being the Technical Arrangements, ancillary to the Polaris Sales Agreement, but a very essential part of it; the formulation and execution of these arrangements formed much of the work of the JSTG meetings, and involved those concerned in mastering detailed knowledge of Polaris in regard to their respective spheres.

It is interesting to note that, in 1993, JSTG meetings, basically still in the same form, were part of the joint Trident programme. There is no doubt in my mind that Admiral Galantin's original suggestion was a key factor in the success of the British Polaris programme.

The Polaris Sales Agreement, the JSTG, the Technical Arrangements, taken together, were all a logical outcome, and an acknowledgement, of the Nassau Agreement. They provided the formalities for bringing to fruition the vital issues contained in the latter; but yet more was required to ensure that things ran smoothly, especially to overcome the geographical separation of the two organisations directly responsible. Happily the two "Project Officers", as established by the Polaris Sales Agreement, saw eye to eye over the need for closest co-operation, and were quick to appoint Liaison Officers to each other's headquarters. A Captain RN (SPRN), although under the titular authority of CBNS in Washington, served on the staff of SPO and provided a direct link between Special Projects and the Polaris Executive; similarly a Captain USN (SPUK) was on CPE's staff in London. By April Captain P G La Niece was in post in Washington and Captain P Rollings in London; ill-heath unfortunately forced the latter's retirement within a few months; after his temporary replacement by Captain Hamilton, he was finally succeeded by Captain W P Murphy. The two Liaison Officers were indeed the oil which kept the many intricate and closely inter-meshed wheels of the British and American organisations revolving smoothly. The burden of the work fell mostly in Washington, and hence on Peter La Niece's shoulders; his previous experience in Washington was a fortunate bonus. In essence, both officers were very vital cogs in the machinery of bringing Polaris into Royal Naval service.

Whilst much time and effort was, properly, devoted in those early months to obtaining a sound foundation for the closest transatlantic co-operation with SPO, at all levels, it was also clear that there was simultaneously, an imperative need to make known, nearer at home, the full meaning of Polaris and what would be entailed in the vast programme about to be embarked on; neither its scope, nor urgency, had percolated through Whitehall beyond a few highly placed officials. A unique degree of collaboration between Ministries contributing to the Polaris programme, and the co-ordination of effort within them, would be necessary if the required head of steam was to be raised, and maintained. Chaired by the Secretary of the Admiralty, the Polaris Interdepartmental Policy Steering Committee (PIPSC) was, in spite of its horrific title, a useful adjunct to spreading the gospel and, if problems arose with Ministries which I was unable to resolve by direct negotiation, it helped to find a solution in keeping with the importance and priorities of the programme. Similarly, within the Admiralty, the Polaris Committee (later known as the Polaris Policy Committee), chaired by the Assistant Chief of Naval Staff (ACNS), Rear Admiral P Hill-Norton, was a considerable help to me in keeping the Naval Staff Divisions, and the Second Sea Lord's departments dealing with (uniformed) manning requirements, alive to the ever-mounting needs of Polaris. To advise on ways and means of countering ill-informed and adverse publicity still carried by sections of the media, a small Publicity Committee was formed under the chairmanship of the Civil Lord of the Admiralty (Mr Ian Orr-Ewing); it served its purpose effectively and by the late autumn of 1963 had overcome what had tended to be a running sore adversely affecting the cohesion and efficiency of the Polaris Executive.

By May 1963, as the full implications of the SSBN building pro-gramme became clearer, its dependence on the successful installation and proving of the first British designed nuclear propulsion plant in *Valiant* (the first entirely British SSN), under construction at Vickers at Barrow-in-Furness, was seen to be absolutely crucial. It was thus an anomaly that, while I had overall responsibility for the SSBN pro-gramme and, under me, DPT and his team possessed virtually all the expertise in nuclear submarine design and building, Director General Ships (DGS), under the old-established Admiralty organisation, re-tained all responsibility for the two SSNs, *Valiant* and *Warspite*, then authorised. To avoid conflicts of interest it seemed logical they should come under CPE's wing, their building programmes receive his management treatment, and their priorities be judged in relation to Longcast 63. I proposed accordingly. To thus deprive DGS of his professional responsibilies was a sensitive matter requiring delicate handling; happily, DGS, in person, accepted the arguments for such a change, which not only paved the way for Admiralty Board approval of the proposal, but avoided an open and destructive clash between DPT's Naval Constructors and those working for DGS.

Warspite at this time was still barely beyond the drawing board stage, although the contract for her construction had been placed: notwithstanding, the Treasury, when considering the contracts for building SSNs, re-opened her case with strong pressure that her construction be deferred until after the whole Polaris programme had been completed. I, actively briefed by DPT, argued otherwise: the inclusion of *Warspite* in Vickers' planned load of work, and the avoidance of a hiatus between *Valiant* and the first SSBN, was seen as an absolutely essential step in the firm's build-up to taking on the full weight of their SSBN building programme. After much fierce argument common sense prevailed, and so by August I had added to my responsibility the timely completion of *Valiant* and *Warspite*.

By mid-summer of 1963, ie within six months of the Nassau Agreement, the "sketch design" for the SSBNs had been completed, and it had received Board approval: basically it took *Valiant*'s design, cut it into two and between two halves inserted the complete Polaris weapon system of sixteen missile launching tubes and all related control equipment.

It was a stupendous, mammoth task, dependent on much close collaboration with SPO and their "lead" shipyard, the Electric Boat Company, and on the receipt from them of much detailed technical information, all requiring the resolution of innumerable and complicated "interfaces" between what was of British and what was of American origin. At this time, there was an added local distraction caused by the imposition of special new measures for security, which demanded that DPT and all his staff be housed in a self-contained, and still under erection, complex of offices and drawing offices, separate from the rest of the Admiralty, Bath. It was a measure of Rowley Baker's forceful leadership, complete command of the situation, and determination that the programme as agreed in Longcast 63 was capable of fulfilment, despite continued protestations from outside sources that it was "crying for the moon".

The design, having been approved, was "frozen". DPT, backed fully by CPE, was adamant that there be no alterations or additions at the whim of Tom, Dick of Harry, no changes other than those dictated by safety or from the trials of *Valiant*, and that all four Polaris submarines be exactly the same. This was a vital factor in their timely completion, though the edict suffered one or two bruising attacks: the first one of them came early on, from a strongly argued plea from the Director of the Compass Division, within the Admiralty, that a British designed Ships Inertial Navigation System (SINS) replace the American supplied equipment fulfilling this function, a very essential part of the Polaris weapon control outfit. The proposal was fiercely supported by the Director-General Weapons (DGW); but to replace in this way one component of the whole carefully balanced system was anathema to me, as ably advised by Charles Shepherd. It took prolonged argument over many months before the battle was won, and much longer before friendly relations were restored with DGW. The other case came much later in the programme, about late 1966 or early 1967, when it suddenly came to light that the length, between bulkheads, of the torpedo stowage compartment in *Renown* (the first of Cammell Lairds' two boats) differed by one inch from that of her prototype *Resolution* at Vickers: consternation erupted all round, but fortunately there were no major consequences. Laxity in adherence to, or in interpretation of, documents and drawings, somewhere along the line between the lead yard and follow-up yard, was deemed the cause. It was a horrifying discovery at the time, but it gave little more than a ripple of disturbance to the overall programme.

Though occasions inevitably arose from time to time when Rowley Baker and I had differences, mainly over details of relative priorities, the initial and determining support which he gave to the whole conception of strict control of the Polaris programme never wavered. In particular his dedication to meeting dates and to detailed planning, with timely completion of contracts and, just as importantly, sub-contracts, was absolutely vital in dragging the ship builders, both Vickers and Cammell Lairds, into the modern age of submarine construction by persuading them that they must adopt new measures and techniques of management; without these they could not hope to meet the targets set. Expert they may have been in steel working and the actual construction and fitting out of conventional ships' hulls but in 1963 they had no conception of what they were taking on in building, fitting out, and testing and tuning of an SSBN. It was something far more complicated than anything they had dealt with before, involving the assembly, installation and rigorous testing of thousands and thousands of items of equipment, many highly technical, to be supplied by several hundred sub-contractors, some in the United Kingdom, some in America, all to be achieved to a strict timescale. It took months and months of argument and persuasion by DPT, and myself, before they committed the resources necessary for detailed planning, which was absolutely essential if the SSBNs were to be built on time.

Perhaps the argument was finally won at some point during the winter of 1964/65. There were weaknesses in the programme and an emergency meeting was arranged at Barrow, attended by myself with the strong support of DPT and the leaders of his team at Bath. Dates were slipping; Vickers, represented by the Managing Director of the shipyard (Mr L Redshaw) and many more members of his staff than I could muster on mine, were being urged to mend their ways and devote more effort to planning the programme. Affairs grew heated, to the extent that the Managing Director furiously accused me personally across the table of "being only a bloody amateur who knew nothing of shipbuilding". It was, of course, true as far as actual shipbuilding went, but not so in regard to modern management techniques, which were the subject under discussion and in the use of which Vickers were sorely lacking. Despite the anger on both sides, the meeting continued and ended relatively peacefully. I felt some points had been gained. Next morning, in my office in London, I was rung up by Charles Shepherd from Bath, he having been at the previous day's stormy meeting. "Had I seen in today's papers that a horse called Polaris Missile had won the 4.30 (or some such) race at Newcastle yesterday, owned, trained and ridden by an amateur?". No, I had not seen it, but I took the point, and was very grateful for having my attention drawn to it in the light of the previous day's meeting. I promptly sent the following telegram addressed personally to the Managing Director at Barrow: "Please note that the 4.30 at Newcastle yesterday was won by Polaris Missile, owned trained and ridden by a bloody amateur". The message was received in the same spirit as it was sent, and from then on there was no cause for rancour or enmity between myself and Len Redshaw: friendly relations prevailed, without which the many problems that continued to arise would never have been successfully resolved. It was a happy outcome to what had threatened to become a critical row.

The pressure on myself and my staff continued throughout the summer of 1963; the initial essential elements of the overall programme had been defined - the design of the submarines, the locality of the base, the milestones to be achieved - but as knowledge expanded so did the problems. How, where and from where were the resources to be found to meet the new and ever-growing requirements, and how could their costs be contained within the budget? On all sides, particularly from the Polaris weapon sector, there were strident but well-founded cries for more staff, highly qualified technically: information should have been flooding in from America, but wasn't; how could it be speeded up, but could it be digested usefully when it came? How were the submarines to be manned, one or two crews per boat, and how and where were these to be trained? What training facilities would be needed in the new base? Wherever one looked there was a new question to be answered.

I was also much concerned at the ignorance that existed on Polaris generally within the Admiralty, and beyond: more specifically, on the lack of understanding of the organisation that had been specially set up to bring into operational use within a very pressing timescale the new national deterrent. Lack of knowledge, wherever it occurred, was a stumbling block to steady progress. Accordingly, a series of courses and lectures on "Polaris and its Management" was given to audiences drawn from Admiralty Departments and other Government bodies involved with the programme; additional formal "Presentations" were prepared to be given as necessary to the Admiralty Board, to the Ministry of Defence (as yet not the power in Whitehall or the land as it was to become in 1964), to Ministers, and to Members of Parliament. Time and effort spent on these endeavours reaped a worthwhile reward by helping to speed up decisions and by removing much innate opposition.

Throughout the second half of 1963, my London staff and I became more and more involved with factors affecting the operational deployment of Polaris, particularly as it was to be the country's sole deterrent force from 1970 onwards. With four SSBNs as planned the minimum requirement of one submarine always at sea on deterrent patrol could just be met, whilst yet accommodating the obligatory periods in harbour for routine maintenance, long refits and nuclear refuelling. On paper it appeared feasible, but the plan made no allowance for possible accident or major breakdown in any of the submarines. Because of the over-riding importance of maintaining at all times the absolute credibility of the deterrent, I was convinced that the plan was basically unsound. Equally important, I believed that it would impose, in peace time, an unnecessarily high degree of stress and strain on sea-going crews and base staff alike; I sensed a lack of appreciation of the fact that to ensure a submarine-borne deterrent remained truly credible at all times, it required that, for week upon week when at sea, the crew were in all respects equivalent to being on patrol under conditions of war. Likewise, to keep the submarines at sea on a schedule permitting not the slightest variation, required a similar approach from all those who worked ashore. For these reasons I maintained that the Polaris force should consist of five SSBNs instead of four; only in this way could the constant credibility of the deterrent be totally guaranteed, and the inevitable pressures on all concerned that this demand be reduced to tolerable levels.

The argument continued for months and was not finally resolved until 1964. Meanwhile, on the assumption that a fifth SSBN would eventually be authorised, it was imperative to place orders for its "long lead" items in order to avoid foreseeable delays to its construction; to circumvent inevitable objections from those holding the purse-strings, these were referred to as being a "contingency reserve" or as essential "spares"; in this guise they passed muster, and timely provision was made for building the additional submarine.

Two further important issues required resolution before the end of 1963. The first was the scope and function of the Royal Navy Polaris School (RNPS), which was to be incorporated in the shore base at Faslane; its early completion a year ahead of the operational deployment of the first SSBN was a critical milestone; with no exact prototype in the United States to emulate, it had to be designed from scratch, with a decision taken on whether it was to be for training and instructional purposes only, or its use expanded to include "Test Instrumentation". After prolonged transatlantic discussion, the latter was rejected as an unnecessary complication. Coincidental with this problem was that of the initial training of the Polaris weapon systems crews who would be manning the RNPS and the first of the SSBNs: until the former was completed, facilities in the United Kingdom were non-existent. Accordingly, an instructional programme, covered by the Polaris Sales Agreement, was arranged with SPO, whereby the first of the officers and ratings selected for this highly specialised training would carry out an intensive course of six months or so at the US Navy's Polaris School at Dam Neck in Virginia. To find suitable officers and ratings of the necessary high qualifications presented some difficulties; the submarine service on its own could not provide them, and there had to be a call on those in General Service; the response was satisfactory, but it was a drain on the rest of the Navy. I later had to join in battle with the Treasury, over the payment of adequate allowances for the trainees at Dam Neck, to compensate for their increased "cost of living" whilst on such extended courses. It was a protracted fight, but eventually it was won.

The second major issue concerned the design and construction of a floating dock capable of lifting an SSBN which had to be in place at Faslane and ready for use by mid-1967, in under four years. The skids had to be placed under all work on its design, and once this had been speedily completed its construction was given to Portsmouth Dockyard who, to everyone's surprise, delivered satisfactorily without constant prodding; it was a major achievement.

CHAPTER 10

Negotiating the Sales Agreement
Alan Pritchard

The reaction in the Admiralty to the Nassau communiqué was traumatic. It had already been agreed that a Special Projects type organisation would be needed which would weld together experts from every department involved in the programme. Although the Admiralty would take the lead, other agencies responsible for warhead manufacture, missile procurement, and support such as base construction would be heavily involved. Key personnel, headed by Rear Admiral Mackenzie, Chief Polaris Executive (CPE), were appointed and accommodated and high quality supporting staff made available. As a first step the Vice Chief of Naval Staff led a team of those likely to be immediately involved across to Washington to engage in discussions with the US Defense Department and to make contact with their opposite numbers in the Special Projects Office (SPO).

This visit, early in January 1963, was the only occasion in my experience when there were any hints of coolness about the ensuing joint programme. For a start we stayed in a hotel which also accommodated Skybolt experts on their way home to Britain. Some of these obviously blamed us for moving into an area of defence which they had regarded as their prerogative. Then we came across officials from the US Defense Department who did not seem to have favoured the decision to involve Britain in the Polaris programme. One in particular went to some lengths to spell out the limitations and controls which would apply to the working of any agreement. It was stressed that there was to be no access to nuclear warhead or propulsion information other than through the special provisions of the 1958 Agreement. The novel idea of charging the UK for a share of Polaris development cost was mentioned, this being later resolved after a Prime Minister/President exchange which settled on a 5% surcharge on equipment procurement. Another new concept was a proposal to average out the cost of missiles and equipment purchased for both countries so that lower priced tail end orders would bear their share of early learning costs. This led to some complexity in the repayment arrangements and involved the setting up of a Trust Fund into which the UK paid quarterly in advance pending final cost adjustment. Overhead charges were also mentioned to pay for the cost of SPO assistance for the UK programme.

In contrast the relationships with the SPO itself were friendly and businesslike. The timing of British entry to the programme proved to be convenient to them with the A3 missile trials nearing a successful conclusion and a further programme of submarines - as it happened the last batch - of the 616 class about to be ordered. We were welcomed by Admiral Raborn who introduced his successor as Head of SP, Rear Admiral Galantin, As PE Finance Officer designate, I met George Bergquist, Bernie Kahn and Tom Aitkin who provided detailed cost information and gave full details of their financial control systems. Similarly, helpful exchanges took place between naval and other professional experts from both sides. The broad scope of the future Polaris Sales Agreement (PSA) was discussed and remitted for further development.

The first draft of the Agreement reached the UK over a weekend soon after our return. Immediately a Sunday afternoon meeting of the Bath contingent took place in Rowland Baker's drawing room. Subsequent meetings were called in London by CPE and his staff. It was agreed that a negotiating team to be led by the Deputy Secretary (Navy) James McKay would visit Washington without delay. It comprised Rear Admiral Rufus MacKenzie, Rowland Baker, Bob Lewin, Captain Charles Shepherd, Eric Hedger and myself as well as representatives of the Ministries of Defence and of Aviation Supply and the Foreign Office. The American team was led by Admiral Mott from the Judge Advocate General's Office with top level SPO representatives and officials from the Defense and State Departments. Thanks to the groundwork which had been done by the British Naval Staff in Washington, there were no insuperable problems. However we were surprised at the extent to which the development programme and system engineering were undertaken by the contractors within broad limits set by SPO. Large sums were estimated to be required for contract technical services and there was little opportunity of exercising technical oversight of the kind customarily applied by Admiralty Design Departments. On the other hand production estimates were largely based on practical experience backed by cost incentive contracts with penalty clauses for shortfalls in performance and delivery and cost overruns. In certain areas fixed price competitive tendering applied. All in all it was felt that cost control of a largely developed and in service system would be more effective than might be obtained by the Royal Navy, with its smaller programme, working in isolation with

American contractors.

Discussions in full session alternated with meetings between those expert in particular fields. The latter concentrated on codifying detailed procedures for executing the joint programme in a series of "technical arrangements". These eventually ran into a considerable number but the thought then given to downstream contingencies and such areas of outfitting and spares support undoubtedly saved future headaches and money. The value of joint discussions between SPO and CPE was recognised by the intention to hold quarterly meetings - Joint Steering Task Group (JSTG) - alternately in London and Washington to review progress and resolve problems.

The PSA was signed and ratified by Governments by April 1963 and thereafter work went ahead on both sides of the Atlantic in developing the UK programme of British built submarines, equipped with Polaris as an integral extension of the US Naval System. In CPE financial control was exercised by myself (P36) with a small staff drawing on Navy material and other votes as necessary to meet the overall programme defined in the computerised planning and control document - PEPLAN.

Estimates, commitments and expenditures were summarised quarterly when a special financial presentation formed part of CPE's progress meeting. A total Project Budget was prepared forecasting expenditure of £350m over the capital programme lasting six years. Contract and Finance Officers were outposted in the RN section with SPO in Washington and they maintained a constant watch with SP staff over procurement in the United States. The ready availability of computerised financial and progress information made their task relatively straightforward. The TWX system of teleprinter transmission between London and Washington was invaluable.

A number of crucial decisions with major implications had to be taken in the first half of 1963. For example, there was the choice of the A3 missile rather than the earlier A2; the fit of 16 missile per boat rather than a lesser number; the choice of a second shipbuilder to follow Vickers as the lead building yard; and the location of Faslane/Coulport as the chosen operational base. There was also considerable debate about the need for a fleet of five SSBNs, for a fully equipped Polaris School under Royal Navy management and for a complete weapons system held ashore in the UK as an insurance against any catastrophe occurring after the contractors had terminated production. The first two were approved but the third was not. There was pressure from those interested in using British equipment in some areas such as the navigation system where this could be developed within the construction timescale. It was decided that the dangers of such a course were too great and that the US weapon system design should be followed wherever possible.

The importance attached by the British Government to the timely introduction of Polaris into the Royal Navy ensured that the programme had the highest priority and there were no difficulties about obtaining financial approval for whatever was needed. There was no "shadow cutting" to allow for programme delay. However early in 1964 a forthcoming General Election was announced and the Opposition Party committed themselves to the renegotiation of the Polaris Sales Agreement should they win. Mr Wilson's Labour Government was duly elected and a study was immediately launched into the possibilities and implications of cancelling the UK programme. Although orders for equipment to a considerable value had by then been placed, much of the shipbuilding material would have been diverted to the hunter-killer submarine programme and the total loss in terms of cancellation charges for weapons equipment would have amounted to less than 1% of the estimated programme total. However, the new Minister of Defence, Mr Healey took a robust view of the merits of the programme. The fifth SSBN was deleted from the programme which otherwise was permitted to continue without interference.

My own direct involvement in the CPE organisation ceased in mid-1964 when I took over as Head of the Material Division with financial responsibility for all areas of naval shipbuilding and weapons and equipment production. As expenditure on Polaris formed a major component, Peter Swain, who had returned from Washington to take over as P36, kept me fully informed about progress with the naval material aspects of the programme, much of whose expenditure I was able to authorise. It was not until the end of 1967 when I was moved elsewhere that I severed my links with CPE and through him with SP.

Looking back over the ten year period when Polaris figured largely in my working life, I can truly say that it was the most satisfying time of my career in the Government service. In part it was due to its high priority which overcame all frustrations and stop/go usually experienced in other areas: but there was a sense of purpose and of comradeship with colleagues in Britain and in America which ensured high quality performance and maintained momentum. The programme completed its capital phase on time and also exactly in conformity with its 1963 cost estimate. It has subsequently served its purpose in helping to maintain the peace with remarkably little in the way of incident or difficulty. The PSA with its inbuilt clause covering "developing systems" has served well as the springboard for the UK Trident programme. When I was recently in Washington the Naval Attaché and the SPRN told me that the Technical Arrangements were still being used as the guidelines for this latest programme over thirty years after they were first written.

In the early 1970s the Chairman of the Public Accounts Committee, which analyses and often criticises Government expenditure, suggested that the UK Polaris programme should be investigated by the Comptroller and Auditor General to confirm his belief that the report would serve as a model of a really effective, well managed major project. This idea was not followed up. It seems unfortunate that such a way of publicising a success story was not undertaken. It may be that this compendium of personal recollections now underway will help to remedy the omission.

CHAPTER 11

Initial Tasks
Sir Rae McKaig

In the bitter January of 1963, I was in command of the *Manxman* at Chatham carrying out sea trials following her conversion to an MCM support ship, and prior to taking her out to Singapore to relieve the even more elderly HMS *Woodbridge Haven* which I would then bring home. My thoughts were with the programme and such things as Standing Orders, and planning for sea-training at Portland.

One evening FO Medway, Admiral "Bill" Beloe, sent for me unexpectedly. "Your former captain, Admiral Mackenzie (at *Ganges* 58/59) has sent for you", he said "to help him in the Polaris Programme. You are to report to him in London with despatch. Good luck".

Forty-eight hours later, having turned over *Manxman* to my First Lieutenant, and with scarcely an opportunity to work out what possible contribution I, as a signalman, could make to a project seemingly exclusively the province of submariners, nuclear and weapons engineers, I was in the scruffiest suite of rooms in the Old Admiralty Building. Admiral Mackenzie, sitting behind one of the only two desks in the place told me calmly that he wanted me to be his naval Assistant, with the special duties of liaison on Naval Staff and Personnel matters, and as Chief Planning Officer, in executing the British submarine deterrent programme. Stemming from the political decision taken by President Kennedy and Prime Minister Macmillan at Nassau in December 1962 the aim was for the Royal Navy to take over deterrent responsibilities from the Royal Air Force by mid-1968.

As, stunned by this message, I reeled into the outer office, other figures were apparent in the dusty gloom, calling variously for chairs, desks, telephones and tea.

Admiral Mackenzie had brought with him from Fort Blockhouse, his Secretary, Commander John Grimwood, Commander Henry Ellis to be in charge of crewing the submarines and Commander Ken Dunlop for engineering liaison. There were also Mike Simeon, lately in charge, as he put it, "of sword-frogs and cutlasses" in the Gunnery Division; but formerly, and more significantly, as soon became apparent, in Washington; Bob Lewin Assistant Secretary and Peter Nailor Senior Principal; and for want of a better home at present Captain Charles Shepherd, a messmate from HMS *Crispin* in 1949, who was to be the

Project's Weapon Director. And lastly, a lady of uncertain age sent by
the Civil Establishments Department to prop up this upstart organisation who was concerned whether we wanted China or Indian tea.
When we voted for Indian she declared us no gentlemen. All these
people, less the typist were to be close colleagues in the coming
months and years.

Faced with the task, it was quickly agreed that the first order of
business was to establish, without delay, the place, and special nature
of the Chief Polaris Executive (CPE) in the Admiralty and Whitehall
hierarchy. For within days it was clear that his welcome in both was
at the best patchy. There was an understandable policy vacuum on
deterrent matters on the Naval Staff whose minds were concentrated
on such problems as the future of the carrier force and the imminent
absorption of the Admiralty into the Mountbatten-style Ministry of
Defence. The introduction of the SSN dominated the minds of the
submarine staff, as it did the submarine design people in DG Ships at
Bath. While DG Weapons and the Ministry of Aviation (MOA),
responsible respectively for the design and acquisition of ship missile
systems and missiles, were only too obviously suspicious about the
impact of a vast, politically imposed "non-naval" programme on their
existing priorities, responsibilities and finance.

Some factors were, however, decisively in CPE's favour. Against
the contingency that the Royal Navy might adopt Polaris, a Senior Ship/
Weapons team from Bath had visited the USA in 1961 to study the
technical implications of a UK programme. In addition in 1960 Admiral
Le Fanu, when DG Weapons, had reported on a possible Admiralty
organisation for introducing Polaris He was now Controller. And not
least, following private agreement between Lord Mountbatten as First
Sea Lord and Admiral Arleigh Burke as CNO, since 1958 a Royal Navy
Commander had been serving in the Polaris Special Projects (SP)
Office in Washington, the incumbent until recently being Commander
Simeon.

Finally the Admiralty Secretariat leapt to our aid. Here, we were
not dealing with the departmental journeymen, whom, in previous
Admiralty appointments, one had tended to regard as obstructionists,
if not, most unfairly, as enemies, but with the intellects at the top,
enthusiastic that their Department should not be found wanting on a
national task. In a 45 minute meeting between CPE and the two
Deputy Secretaries, Jim Mackay and Piers Synnott, amid clouds of the
latter's snuff, the priority of the project was settled - not overriding as

many in the Admiralty feared - but "sufficient to meet programme objectives"; CPE established under the Controller but with direct access to each individual Board Member in the event of objectives being threatened; and subtle, but simply expressed principles laid down for the allocation of staff to the project. The resulting Admiralty Office Memorandum issued on 6 February 1963 established, in a masterly blend, the CPE's direct authority over central aspects of the programme, essentially the submarines and Polaris Weapon System, with project management powers to co-ordinate its achievement elsewhere. It was to stand us in good stead over the coming years within the Admiralty and Ministry of Defence: but, as is the way in Whitehall, with less effect on the MOA and other Ministries.

Emboldened by this new legitimacy, CPE issued on the same day his first Longcast - No 1 - and two days later a note circulating the bones of his embryo organisation and intentions. Information to establish milestones was sketchy, but the aim was unequivocal:-

"To deploy on station the first RN Ballistic Missile Submarine with its missiles, and with full support, in July 1968 and thereafter the remainder at six monthly intervals. These dates cannot be allowed to slip."

My only personal contribution was to insist on the words "with full support".

The staff of CPE also agreed privately from the beginning to set the highest standards and example in conducting their business - quick reactions, early issue of minutes and papers, and prompt decisions at all levels. Unencumbered as we were by past history, Admiralty dockets and departmental baggage, this was a fairly easy intention to fulfil at the outset. But with CPE's personal encouragement it became a lasting characteristic of the organisation. And CPE's Secretary designed and had produced a Polaris tie.

Also at the beginning of February 1963 the Controller entered authoritatively into our lives. He held an initial meeting with CPE London staff and those who were to lead the major technical effort in Bath, Rowland Baker of DGS and Captain Charles Shepherd for the Weapons content. With his mixture of charming informality masking iron determination he said he would stay close to the Project until he was satisfied that Polaris Executive could handle it. Seeking reactions to the task round the table, he drew the immediate comment from

Rowland Baker that it was impossible. Those like myself who did not then know Rowland were filled with gloom.

Also discussed was the interaction between the Polaris submarine build and the fledgling British SSN programme with *Valiant* (SSN02) and *Warspite* (SSN03) already under construction or ordered at Vickers, Barrow.

A second building yard would in any event be necessary for Polaris, but even so a break in the SSN build up looked inevitable. The question was, when should it occur? Eventually it was decided to adhere to the existing *Valiant/Warspite* timings, but to put them additionally under CPE's direct supervision. By so doing the build up of nuclear propulsion experience in Bath and Barrow would continue unbroken and to the benefit of the Polaris and later construction programmes; and two additional SSNs would be available to the Fleet at the first opportunity. The SSN building "gap" came later.

After a whirlwind three weeks, I put it rather naively to Admiral Mackenzie that it was time for me to visit the United States to learn about the fabled planning and management techniques by which the USN had achieved their remarkable results with Polaris.

This was firmly vetoed. In fact CPE was off there himself on 16 February - for two weeks as it turned out - to negotiate in company with Jim Mackay the Polaris Sales Agreement which would formalise the political accords reached at Nassau and by a subsequent high level mission. I was to stay put and help get the show on the road in the UK.

There was plenty to do. Two major and related Naval Staff questions called to be settled at once, with several "long lead" secondary decisions to be made.

The first was the nature of the Royal Naval operating philosophy for the SSBNs carrying the UK deterrent. Were they to be operated from a depot ship, and therefore flexible in deployment, as in the USN, or from a fixed shore base. If the latter, where?

The second was should the Royal Navy procure the currently in service Polaris A2 missile (1500 nm range) or the A3 (2500 nm range) then about to start its final proving trials from Cape Canaveral?

On the first point I went to see the Assistant Chief of Naval Staff (the then Rear Admiral Peter Hill-Norton) and explained the critical nature and need for speed in decision if credible and real support for the submarines was to be available when they deployed. Within days the decision came that a UK shore base was preferred and I was to chair a working party to select the location, to report in three weeks.

The working party was not to leave the Admiralty, nor to "consult widely" but to use available charts and lands information "in house". After considering military, navigational, lands and infrastructure criteria, we came up with a short list of Mallaig, Devonport and Faslane on the Gareloch; finally recommending the latter, amongst other reasons because the Admiralty owned 600 acres of heather overlooking Loch Long at nearby Coulport which would accommodate storage, servicing and loading facilities for missiles - and was currently being used by the Weapons Department for rather desultory torpedo trials. Opting for Devonport would among other drawbacks have involved compulsory purchase of much of the incomparable Antony estate near Torpoint for missile storage: a real Cornish problem which I was glad to have avoided as I went as FO Plymouth a few years later.

It was accepted that the SSBN refitting base should be at Rosyth, already designated for SSN refits.

When the decision in favour of Faslane/Coulport was transmitted at a meeting to a rather sulky group from the Weapons Department, the occasion was only memorable for one of their representatives not only threatening dire consequences for the torpedo programme, but declaring himself opposed on moral grounds to the whole policy of a nuclear deterrent. Such declarations, one at least at more senior level, occasionally enlivened the early months of the project.

Almost as an afterthought to the base decision, a day's flying visit to the USN Polaris Depot Ship at Holy Loch with Jack Daniel of DG Ships and Charles Shepherd, brought out the requirement for operational docking of SSBNs between patrols. A submission was made in this sense, recommending a custom designed floating dock for the Faslane Base. There was a flurry of debate in favour of a graving dock, possibly inspired by civil engineers whose life's ambition was to design and construct one. But in the end the floating dock solution prevailed, to be tethered with appropriate power and other supplies to the quayside. The dock was designed and built at Portsmouth, one of the last major constructions in a Royal Dockyard.

The A2/A3 decision, though simple in essence, caused more immediate high-level controversy. On one side there were those, inspired by MOA, Treasury and some general anti-US thinking who argued that if Britain was to suffer the indignity of procuring its deterrent system abroad, it should be proven and in service, with costs fully known. An odd attitude bearing in mind that only months previously, Britain had been committed to the wholly unproved, and as it turned out, infeasible Skybolt. Against this view CPE's Staff, on behalf of the Naval Staff who were mute on the subject, argued firstly for the greater operational flexibility conferred by the A3's greater range together with its ability to carry multiple warheads, and secondly for the US confidence in the A3 expressed by their vast investment in submarines and facilities under construction for the new weapon inspired by SP's previous successful record. Finally, and as it transpired later, most powerfully, CPE maintained that if the Royal Navy fell into step with the USN and the A3 they would be equal if junior beneficiaries of the latter system's design development. If the A2 were chosen, it would be necessary for the USN to be asked to maintain Stateside support for an obsolescent system for which they had diminishing national use; with unknown cost implications for the United Kingdom in the future.

An intense debate raged for some weeks, spearheaded in CPE by Commander Mike Simeon whose powerful intellect and recent knowledge of SP provided ammunition for the A3 case which eventually carried the day at the top.

Subsequently we were to watch the progress of the A3 proving launches, which did not enjoy a trouble-free run, with keen interest. In the end, however, faith in SP was justified. Presumably a very similar discussion ensued in the run-up to the Trident decision.

As an interjection, in these and other major questions, it was not only oral argument that CPE staff had to carry in their case, but in paper submissions in proper and usual Admiralty form to Board and Ministerial level. In this we benefited greatly by having from the outset and throughout the Project fully integrated senior members of the Admiralty Secretariat within PE who knew how to "work the machine" at speed. An introduction by Bob Lewin to the Head of the Military Branch Ken Nash or his Principal Patrick Nairne resulted, after twenty minutes conversation and acute questioning, in a dazzling draft in which every point one had made was accurately and succinctly laid out, and with added value.

Though not so time critical as the Base and missile decisions, the next major Naval Staff issue to be tackled, and one that had to be left open in the early directives was whether the BNBMS (British Nuclear Ballistic Missile System) should be carried in four or five submarines. Instinct was for five but the case had to be made. Later in January 1963 my naval staff at CPE London was increased to its final five by the addition of a navigator, Lieutenant Commander Simon Cassels, who liaised with the Hydrographer, the redoubtable "Egg" Irving, whose ships had much to do in BNBMS Support; and by a distinguished and senior submarine CO, Commander Jimmy Launders, with a strong mathematical and analytical bent. Launders set to work on the operational plans for BNBMS deployment. Accepting the USN two crew system (Port and Starboard as opposed to Blue and Gold), their 56 days out/28 days in operational turn round pattern, and with estimates for refit/refuelling time culled from the minimal experience with *Dreadnought*, he calculated that, to ensure to the Government a constantly available minimum deterrent, at least two boats should be always on patrol, to allow for one aborting unexpectedly. This required a five SSBN force.

Armed with Launder's calculations we set about convincing the Naval Staff that they should support CPE's case. This they eventually did although the question rapidly became a political football at the highest level which took its time to run into touch. The fact that the French Government, entirely independently of course, had also opted for five submarines for their national deterrent, finally assisted our view.

Several other questions to be solved or investigated also surfaced during these early months; some for instance concerned with the operational integrity of the overall system, such as the provision of assured continuous service communications under national control to SSBNs on patrol. But my first memory of this initial period took me well out of the line of duty. National press reaction to the Nassau Agreement had been far from positive: the Labour opposition declared its intention of cancelling it, if elected (a General election loomed in 1964); and as the weeks passed press and public comment seemed increasingly adverse: much was on the lines that if Britain could not devise its own deterrent, it should not expend resources on one from the USA which would be in no sense independent. CND was very active.

These influences, coupled with the generally unenthusiastic attitude at working level in the Admiralty seemed to me to be starting to prey on the resolve of the scarcely weaned CPE Staff. After some agonising, I took it upon myself to telephone an ex-naval friend, now a power in Fleet Street; and within a week was at a corner table in the Ecu de France with a defence correspondent previously regarded by me, as by most Service officers, with a mixture of fear and respect. Clearly very well informed, he proved an alert listener. Whether due to this conversation or through other contacts, one newspaper group at least, not historically pro-Navy, then became and remained a staunch advocate of the British Polaris programme.

Days later with the Polaris Sales Agreement ready to be signed in Washington, to my relief Admiral Mackenzie returned. The way was now clear for our weapons people to do business with SP, to start serious submarine design and begin to "make it happen". But that is another story.

An Incident at Coulport

As the physical work started on the Faslane base, we thought it wise to have someone on the site who could keep an eye on what was going on, and be in touch with the local feeling.

Flag Officer Submarines appointed a young engineer who moved into a semi-derelict lodge by the works and in the intervals of playing the bassoon, well fulfilled this task under the title Resident Officer Polaris Executive (ROPE).

One morning he telephoned me in London and said "I've received a postcard, yes a postcard, this morning from Mr Emrys Hughes saying he intends to visit the base tomorrow morning. Perhaps someone should be here to give support". Emrys Hughes was the MP for Kilmarnock and a well-known left wing Socialist, fervently anti-deterrent.

I went up to Garelochhead on the night train and our visitor arrived promptly at 1100. He reacted with silence to a conducted tour of what was then little more than an earthwork, and refusing an invitation to lunch, retreated to his car and sandwiches. Afterwards we set off in an Admiralty car with seaboots in the back on the mountain road to Coulport where work was yet to start.

Determined not to be accused of concealment I said "To see this site properly we have to climb a little". We donned boots and I led off up a knoll about 900ft above the jetty which gave a spectacular panorama of lower Loch Long. As we climbed Mr Hughes fell further and further behind and was obviously making heavy weather. At the top he collapsed purple faced and seemed oblivious of my tour d' horizon. We returned in silence to his car and waved him goodbye.

That evening the Admiralty driver took me to the station and the train to London. "Our guest did not seem exactly to enjoy himself" I said. He chuckled "I know", he said "I gied him twa left boots".

We heard nothing more from Mr Hughes either in the House or otherwise; but his colleague and our friend the MP for Dumbarton complained bitterly of his breach of etiquette in making an unannounced visit to his constituency.

CHAPTER 12

The "Bull Pen"
Sir Simon Cassells

In January 1963, arctic weather gripped Portsmouth. Ice floes cluttered the harbour. Offshore a frigate was struggling to complete post refit trials when her commanding officer was summoned to the radio telephone. "Sorry to bother you" said a familiar voice, "but your relief will be on the jetty at 0900 tomorrow morning. Can't tell you why because I don't know either, except that you are to report to the Admiralty in person at 0900 the following day".

What a bombshell. What had he done? A massive error in the last CB muster, or the cash account? Had CinCFleet suddenly lost confidence in him? Was his name on the recent promised list for promotion a mistake? With a heavy heart he broke the news to the Ship's Company as the frigate headed for harbour and a final ice-packed alongside.

There was no spring in my step as I entered Ripley Block. I was expected and, dreading the summons, escorted to a small, dingy, ground floor "cubicle" - certainly no office - filled with pipe smoke. "Ah" said a tall, personable, dark haired figure, waving a straight-stemmed pipe, as he rose from his desk "Delighted to see you. Sorry to put you out of your command but we need you here. Besides the Admiral and myself, and a couple of submariners, we have only one other specialist staff officer so far - to get Polaris up and running in the Royal Navy within six years. Ready to start - now?".

So began three stimulating years in the Polaris Executive. The small staff of two were soon put into a large, lofty ceilinged room with an adjoining office for Captain Rae McKaig, Rear Admiral "Rufus" Mac-kenzie's pipe smoking deputy. The first arrival, Commander Mike Simeon, a very bright "dagger" G, was charged with the Weapon system and the overall programme, later known as the PEPLAN. A few days later he came in with an enormous sheet of paper marked out in months and years. With a flourish he set down upon it the first "milestone" - Order Steel; - then looked across and said "Now you will have to work out when the first boat can get out of Barrow". This meant "Droggie" (the Hydrographer) forecasting the tides for the port for the rest of the decade and others explaining the mysteries of the Walney Channel to determine what dredging could be done to what timescale. The "windows of opportunity" (a new phrase at the time) were few. But the huge programme of getting the first boat to sea was conditioned by these two "milestones".

The most immediate task was to decide where the Polaris Base should be. Armed with charts of all the UK ports and the Sailing Directions, and retiring to a stuffy dungeon in the Citadel, the choice was soon whittled down to twenty, then four (possibly five), Rosyth, Faslane, Devonport, Falmouth and Mallaig. At that stage the merits and drawbacks of each were set out in Annexes for a Paper, which Rae McKaig drafted with ease after poring over the mass of material in the dungeon, recommending Faslane. From start to decision this took a fortnight.

Then came the navigation sub-system, on which the accuracy of the weapon delivery crucially depended. This entailed flying to Washington with Lt Cdr Bill Boyton, an "L" officer working on inertial systems at the Admiralty Compass Observatory, Slough, and being briefed on the US competitors, Sperry and Autonetics. The learning curve could hardly have been steeper.

On return much wrangling took place. The US had a proven system in service. ACO was developing SINS Mk2 and claimed this would be superior, more reliable and equally available on time. It was a most uncomfortable few months for the "ham in the sandwich". Finally it was clear that the US system had to be taken on - lock, stock and barrel. Slough was bitterly disappointed. Relations were stiff for some time thereafter.

Other tasks mounted up. Completion of the Staff Requirement. Communications, aerials, telescopic/periscopic masts of greater length. With onboard space at a premium, rigorous vetting of spares, handbooks to be committed to microfiche, review of classified material and its stowage, Design of alongside berths and associated deep pontoons, design of tug bows and bow fenders. Navigational marks for approaches to Faslane. Widening/dredging the Rhu narrows (now demolished for Trident). Particular hydrographic and oceanographic needs.

The Polaris staff room, affectionately known as the "Bull Pen", acquired more members. The hierarchy sprouted US type designators. I was rapidly demoted/converted to P211. US management techniques and applications were adopted. PERT, networking and PMPs were applied to just about everything.

In April 1964, the whole Executive moved to a first floor suite in the unified Ministry of Defence building. The spacious "Bull Pen" shrank in size and ceiling height. The occupants could not avoid being entertained by the strong, sonorous voice of Captain McKaig, now designated P2, dictating in the adjoining room. This usually closed with vigorous blows of pipe upon ashtray, followed by a pause for recharge before the next summons. When it came, discussion would be punctuated with "That's right" if something found favour, or "D'you see", if not. Much was committed to a little black book which, with his pipe, he was rarely without. He drove himself hard, very hard, but he never demanded this of others: his towering example was enough to test their conscience. He was readily approachable, always dignified, courteous and even tempered and seemed to have an inexhaustible energy. Despite the tremendous pressures upon him he took enormous trouble in bringing on his immediate staff.

P211's liaisons and authorities to consult grew apace. DN Plans, DND and DSD in the Admiralty itself; Rear Admiral "Egg" Irving, the Hydrographer (first at Cricklewood and later in the Old War Office building), was exceptionally kind, enthusiastic and helpful in several ways; various sections of DG Ships and DMS at Foxhill, Bath; ACO, Slough, and Admiralty Surface Weapons Establishment, Portsdown, where contacts made while serving in a previous appointment there now happened to be useful; Ministry of Public Buildings and Works, Empress State Building; CBNS Washington and the US Oceanographic Office in Suitland.

One of the more enjoyable tasks was working with the Clyde Lighthouse Trust in devising the navigational marks for the Faslane approaches. It came at a time when the Trust was developing "sealed beam" lights. Those in support of Polaris were the first to be installed. Today they are widely used. The sensitivity of leading marks defied mathematical presentation. The only way to arrive at satisfactory solutions was by trial and error on site, running in on them at a mocked-up height of eye for an SSBN.

Another was tramping over various Hebridean islands with a naval surveyor and an ASWE scientist in search of the best locations for hydrographic surveying two-range DECCA transmitter sites. Plenty of geese and seals seen, not much whisky, except one evening when paying a courtesy call on the then Laird of Colonsay, Lord Strathcona.

When the time came for me to turn over to my successor, two key issues remained. One was to establish the course content for training SSBN navigators. The other was to decide whether to follow the US in installing a new, very bulky navigational aid - short title BRN-3. It was the fore-runner of what every self-respecting ocean-going yachtsman has today - Navstar GPS.

CHAPTER 13

Making the Organisation Work
Peter Nailor

It wasn't easy to get used to the idea of Polaris. In the first place, the programme started up during the worst winter for at least fifteen years. On Boxing Day there had been a foot or so of snow across most of England and Wales, and it was followed by several more heavy falls; the thermometer plummeted way below freezing, and stayed there, night and day, until the end of March. Trains, buses and cars did the best they could, but London was sclerotic, and Bath was like the Alps, but without ski-lifts. It was challenging enough to get to work, let alone to take in something that looked as if it was going to turn the Admiralty inside out. Heaven alone knew what it was going to do to the Navy...

In the second place, I found it difficult to track down anybody who could tell me very much about what the programme was going to involve. I had been working as the First Lord's Representative on the Admiralty Interview Board (AIB) at HMS *Sultan*, and enjoying the job very much. It wasn't the easiest place from which to keep up with office news and gossip, and what I knew about Polaris and Nassau I had learned from the newspapers. My own experience told me that the Nassau communiqué had been cobbled together with rather more of the seams showing than usual, and that the shift from Skybolt to Polaris was going to upset the RAF and the Ministry of Aviation as well as the Navy. I thought that I was well out of all that fuss and bother.

And then, on 29 December 1962, my head of branch, Patrick Nairne, called me at home and told me that the Permanent Secretary wanted to see me on New Year's Day. Jarrett wanted me to work in the organisation that was going to be set up to manage the new programme, and my job on the AIB was going to be unfilled until they could find someone to replace me. When I saw Jarrett - for about ten minutes - I remonstrated with him about that, but in the event it was five or six months before the job was filled. And then I went off to find Bob Lewin, whom I knew only slightly and who was to be my new boss. He wasn't where he was supposed to be, in a small and incommodious suite of broom cupboards, and nobody who was there expected me, or knew what I was supposed to do. Everybody was at meetings: in the organisation itself, in the Secretariat branches that might have helped, and in Plans Division. There was obviously a great to-do going on, so

I went to lunch; and had just about the only two hour lunch break that I was to notch up for the next five and a half years.

John Grimwood, secretary to Rear Admiral Rufus Mackenzie, Chief Polaris Executive (CPE), was in the broom cupboard when I got back, and was a great help. I met Rufus the next day, and was appalled to find that he had not served in the Admiralty before and that he had very fixed views about telling everybody, even the Treasury, exactly what was going on. The only way to get people on our side, he said, and to keep them working with us was to tell them the truth. I thought he was positive and very nice: and I wondered if this idea of his would really work. I had been in the Admiralty long enough to be fairly cynical about Admirals; but when Bob Lewin and I eventually managed - on 4 January - to sit down and talk about what we were supposed to do, we agreed that the novelty of the programme and the support that we were getting from the Board all worked in the same direction as Rufus's ideas about management style. And neither of us ever had cause or impulse to be cynical about Rufus.

I found I was to look after staff, staff support, office accommodation, office administration etc etc. It was these etceteras that worried me, and by 15 January I found I was setting up trans-Atlantic conference calls, flight bookings, visas, clearances on a scale that was, in 1963, still quite unusual: especially if you had no budget allocation, no formal existence (since the setting-up of CPE had still not been announced to the Office), and only the vaguest idea of where most places under discussion were. However, I had got a chair and a waste-paper basket, and the ear of Piers Synnott, the Establishment Officer, so we were up and off. Within another couple of weeks CPE (London) had better offices: three weeks after that the outline plans for the new office-block at Foxhill, Bath had been agreed. The staff in Movements Department were extraordinarily helpful, especially in the early days. They found a way of getting visas from the US Embassy in less than 12 hours; they had heard of Sunnyvale (and Dam Neck!) and they understood much more than I did about the novel world of mass transportation by jet aircraft that had just started. The Comet had been one giant step forward-and-back, but the 707 was as significant to the rest of the world as the Conestoga wagon was to the American pioneers who crossed the prairies.

Unfortunately, the BOAC version did not yet penetrate as far as Washington; you had to change planes at Logan or Idlewild. Dulles Airport was still a sea of mud, and the shuttle trips by Douglas DC4 or Lockheed Electra into Washington National were, I heard and subsequently found, specially timed and sited so as to make connecting and transferring a long and tiring game of chance. I remember Charles Shepherd once knocking his EIIR issue briefcase from the luggage trolley as we struggled in vain to make our connection; the duty-free flagons of gin which had largely filled it broke, and we had to tip the debris down a handy drain. By the time we had waited for the next flight, and got to the Windsor Park Hotel in Washington, most of his luggage and all of his papers smelt of juniper berries; and the stitching of the briefcase had corroded away, leaving him with a sticky mess of soggy leather-faced cardboard. We were all very impressed, for a little while, by this experimental demonstration of cirrhosis, and HMSO simply did not believe my explanation about why he should get a rather more substantial replacement for his bag.

For many months after we had set up the CPE offices there was a major problem about information. So far as the rest of the Admiralty was concerned, we were both novel and odd. A great part of the Office knew nothing about what we were trying to do; but for the Controller's and Fourth Sea Lord's departments in particular we were upsetting their usual arrangements and pinching many of their best people - to what purpose few, in those early days, could be sure. Inside the organisation the position was not much better. It was relatively easy once John Grimwood got going, to find out what FBM submarines looked like and what Special Projects Office (SP) was. SP had excellent handouts and wads of publicity material about their own activities, so we could describe some of the major components that would figure in our own programme to our own staff, contractors' staff, and the rest of the Admiralty. But this was pretty elementary stuff, and we knew it did not give much of a feel for the complexity, the extent - and, above all, the urgency - of what we had been charged to do. It wasn't only the sheer size of the job, but what it meant in new methods, new standards, new concepts that was so difficult to comprehend; and we were stuck with the problem of explaining it to others while trying to understand it for ourselves.

The sort of information that we needed, to set up our own structures and objectives, simply was not there at the beginning. There was no gestation period for the Polaris programme: it happened. Between the middle of November 1962, when it became clear that Skybolt would be dumped, and the middle of December when the basic deal was done at Nassau, the commitment was settled. The details of the international side of the commitment were worked out by April 1963 when the Sales Agreement was signed; but this was really only like signing adoption papers. What this lusty new obligation really meant took a lot longer to work out.

Nevertheless, we had determined by then how many boats there would be (give or take one), what the basic design would be, that we should have a base rather than a support ship, and that we would adopt, broadly speaking, the US model of operating with two crews. But that still left a lot of things to find out about; special communication and navigation kits, the requirements for spares, repairs, maintenance, training, the details of what these huge new hulls would involve for the builders and overseers as well as the designers and planners: not to mention the costs, the methods of paying, the management for fitting our requirements into the American programme (which had been extended from 29 to 41 boats, and much affected by the *Thresher* disaster) and all the complexities of the front end and the SP-Rickover interfaces. The Le Fanu reconnaissance and the early technical investigations done in 1960-61 had given us no more than a glimpse of what we were up against; and it was something of a shock to find that Special Projects, who were so welcoming, were also fundamentally unprepared. They had been thrown into this joint programme as precipitately as we had been; and they had to discover what it meant in terms of extra staff, the copying of plans, diagrams, schedules of information, liaison, supervision, and general support just at the time when we began to hammer on their doors for help.

In the end, this common experience of finding out together what needed to be done was an important source of shared commitment; but in the beginning, it was a bit of a mess. We read the SP handouts, and saw for ourselves how well they were doing their own accustomed jobs. But we got frustrated when they were unable, immediately, to provide for us all that we knew we needed to have. That is to say, to give us all the information we had to understand to be able to ask intelligent questions and make informed decisions. There was so much we did not know: and it was sometimes irritating when SP asked us to tell them what we wanted. We needed their help to find out. It was almost as irritating when they told us, *faute de mieux*, what they thought we ought to have! When we knew them better, we trusted their judgement and opinions and their commitment; but by then we had learned a lot, and knew that we had in fact become a partner in a most unusually capable enterprise. The classical example of our early, joint, dilemma occurred at the time of the signing of the Sales Agreement; I had had to discover how we could procure a bank draft for $1m, to establish the Trust Fund that would be the account from which our purchases could be paid for, but when we had got it, and Peter La Niece had the cheque in his pocket ready to hand over, he found that Bernie Kahn had not yet got the legal authority to receive it. Forty-eight hours later he did find an office in the Pentagon that could accept it into a Government account; and we both dined out for some time, on stories about what we might have done with the interest that could have been earned at the best over-night deposit rates.

Six months later, we were still finding out significant details about the way in which SP worked, and which were so much taken for granted by them that they had not understood how much they needed to explain to us. They had so far decentralised (and, as we would now say, privatised) their management system that a great deal of the information and data that we - and most of the rest of the United States Navy - would regard as available in-house was, in their programme, controlled and managed by the major contractors. The pamphlets told us, indeed, that Lockheed, for example, were the missile system managers; but they did not prepare us for the fact that you had to put money into Lockheed to get any details of the system information out. In our organisation, you rang somebody up in Bath or Barrow, and the schedules or the drawings were sent down to you. But in the SP system, you had to have a contract with the firm, which entitled you then to ask questions, to which they then provided answers, guidance and support and an invoice. It worked pretty well, once you found out what the ground-rules were, and how to frame the questions properly. But initially it seemed very confusing and rather more expensive than we thought it might be - even if we had previously considered that there was so fundamentally different a way of doing such business.

Much later, in 1974, Charles Shepherd asked me to prepare an account of the organisation and achievements of the Polaris pro-gramme. This resulted in The Nassau Connection which was printed as a Navy Department confidential document in 1978, and published in unclassified form by HMSO in 1988. In the interim, it was used as a brief in the Trident negotiations. There was some temptation, when I was writing my notes up, to go beyond what the official record of even the interviews provided. They did not give much opportunity to use some of the best anecdotes, like, for example how Rufus and Rowley Baker managed to organise things so that virtually the whole of Bath and

London staff were able to attend one or other of the submarine launches. It was difficult, just from the record, to describe the excitement and the hard work which made the programme such an influential and unusual experience. But, against that, it was also difficult to work in illustrations about some of the less precise difficulties that we had faced. I interviewed eleven very senior people, who had not been in the programme, about its effects on the Navy and eight of them used precisely the same words about it: "a frightful chore". I told myself they wouldn't have got the new carrier anyway.

What I was looking for, and did not in the end find, was a concise and convincing way of explaining the success of the programme. It was something of a comfort that Harvey Sapolsky (a noted American author of a book on Polaris) who had done a rather broader account of the FBM programme, had felt a similar need, and experienced similar problems.

He told me that, although he had seen all the tricks, as it were, that the SP magicians had had up their sleeves, he had found it very difficult to explain why all the tricks worked as well as they had; the harder you tried, the more it seemed that you were just cataloguing success without fully explaining why it happened. Success is difficult to account for; it seems to be easier to analyse failure, because there is usually some event, or some predicament which, with the advantage of hindsight, appears to have been crucial. When you try to pick out some equivalent factor in success, it sounds like either an insider's coy reminiscence or a contrived attempt to add drama to administrative history. To say that a complicated programme produced a whole that was greater than the sum of its parts still doesn't strike me as a very helpful explanation; but that is what happened.

CHAPTER 14

"The Continuing until it be thoroughly finished" from Drake's Prayer Sir Hugh Mackenzie

With a year gone by, the task of the Polaris Executive in January 1964, appeared manageable, though remaining immensely formidable; the Executive's strength had grown to twenty four in the London headquarters and to two hundred and sixty in Bath; all had acquired a realistic grasp of what was required of them and were imbued with the spirit of Drake's Prayer; none was aware that the years ahead would never be an easy ride. But management plans and regular fortnightly progress meetings were beginning to pay a dividend and my staff and I in London felt we had a firm grip on the situation and were in a position to meet many difficulties and problems, foreseen and unforeseen, that daily arose.

Whitehall had accepted, generally, the existence of a unique organisation in its midst and were prepared to co-operate in the achievement of its aims, though there remained a few pockets of obstruction or resistance which required special action by me. Within the Admiralty the Departments of the Director-General, Weapons, responsible for Navigation and Communications, continued to aspire to run their own show, regardless of the 'interface' problems that would arise should changes be made to the overall design of the Polaris Weapon System. The introduction of regular DGW/CPE Liaison meetings ironed out the problems and ensured that everyone concerned with conventional weaponry and equipment had only one target in mind, the successful completion of the force of submarines and its supporting facilities to the timescale laid down by CPE and to the design parameters established by DPT. Action in the shape of regular meetings also needed to monitor progress at AWRE and the Royal Ordnance Factory, Burghfield, where shortages of staff, compounded by difficulties in deciding design criteria, threatened at times the ultimate aim of the whole programme - the operational deployment of a viable and credible deterrent in 1968 - through failure to meet production dates for the nuclear warheads and associated re-entry systems. Penetration aids to help defeat Russian anti-ballistic missile defences were a critical issue.

Construction of the hulls of the first SSBNs by Vickers and by

Cammell Lairds was well underway by the end of 1963, and both shipyards were steadily expanding the facilities needed to cope with such a demanding programme; the scale of the civil engineering work was colossal, all to be integrated with the actual construction and assembly of the huge hull units of the submarines themselves, and under appalling conditions of the winter's weather; but there were no serious hold-ups, not even over costs, which fortunately had been largely agreed in the earlier discussions on the placing of the submarine building contracts.

There was, however, one critical threat to progress: the supply of the special steel, QT35, needed for the pressure hulls of the submarines; not only were there few suitably equipped and qualified manufacturers within the UK, but the steel-makers themselves had little experience in producing, in quantity, such high quality material: a situation further complicated by an acute shortage of molybdenum, an essential component in this particular brand of steel and, moreover, one that had to be imported from abroad. The United States, a normal source of supply, could not help because of their overriding demands; the world had to be scoured for alternative sources. Some critical weeks passed before DPT informed CPE that the steel-makers were now happy, having secured a sufficient quantity of molybdenum to meet their needs for some time to come: its origin, Russia! Despite this quirky solution, the building of the submarines continued to be threatened by shortages of QT 35 steel; as the shipbuilders' requirements increased under the full weight of the programme They perforce had to fall back on supplies of American HY80 steel, of comparable quality, and which fortunately became available as the US Navy's own SSBN building programme coincidentally eased.

To get a better grasp of these problems, in the first few months of 1964, I embarked on a comprehensive round of visits to the main steel manufacturers and to other heavy engineering firms engaged in the production of 'long lead' items critical to the nuclear propulsion plants of all the submarines building. These visits had a two-way purpose: on the one hand they allowed me to acquaint myself at first hand with major contractors and the difficulties they were experiencing, whilst on the other I used the opportunity to impress on them the urgency of the work they were engaged on, and the need for the most detailed planning and for strictest quality control: only if these two matters received adequate attention could they hope to meet the country's vital requirement of a credible deterrent.

For over a year, the Press, and the media generally, had not lacked copious mention of Polaris, with options pro- and anti-, and imaginative articles of every description. To try and 'keep the record straight' I had had interviews with the Defence Correspondents of the major newspapers, but this had little effect. It was still a matter of surprise to me to find, on my visits away from Whitehall, how little understood were the real issues lying behind the deterrent and all the clamour it aroused. People were largely ignorant of, or ignored or disputed, the fundamental purpose of deterrent forces, whether Polaris, V-Bombers or whatever: namely to preserve peace in the face of an aggressive USSR whose military might and stock of nuclear weapons were second to none, and whose occasional actions and constantly proclaimed intentions were the very antithesis of peaceful co-existence. But the deterrent would only work if the potential aggressor was fully aware that any transgression on his part would bring on him, inevitably, an unacceptable level of damage. CREDIBILITY was the key: the effectiveness of the deterrent all depended on the potential enemy not daring to believe that it would not be used or, if brought into action, would not function properly. Provided the deterrent or the country wielding it, gave no grounds for such belief, it would continue to guarantee that the world's greatest military power would not embark on any aggressive adventure. A sidelight to all this vital factor of credibility: once, when discussing the design of the nuclear warhead for the Polaris missile, Solly Zuckerman remarked light-heartedly to me "If only we could be sure the Russian never knew, and never found out or suspected, we could put a bag of sand instead in the front end - save a lot of money!" And so it would have, but the risk could not be taken.

Polaris, as developed by the United States Navy, fulfilled all the essential criteria for a credible deterrent: tremendous efforts had been successfully expended to ensure the reliability of the whole system, from front end of the missile to its "launching pad", the SSBN. I was determined that the same standards be set and maintained in the British Naval Ballistic Missile System (BNBMS), as the British Polaris force came to be named. To emphasise this aspect it became necessary to include the basic arguments for Britain possessing the deterrent in all my "pep" talks to industry and my presentations and lectures on the make-up and functioning of the Polaris Executive, whenever and to whomever these were given. Inevitably this led to my direct involvement in the political arena - which, personally, went much against the grain - but without such an approach the misguided arguments of CND and kindred "peace marchers", unchallenged, posed a constant source of disruption to the task of the Polaris Executive - gearing everybody up to completing the programme on time: the more active CND, the more the case for Polaris had to be repeated, time and time again.

As 1964 advanced, the prospect of a Labour victory in the forthcoming autumn General Election loomed larger and larger; their widely proclaimed views on defence generally and on Polaris in particular, the latter varying from "re-negotiation of the Nassau Agreement" (whatever that meant - it was never made clear!) to cancellation of the whole programme, were not sources of confidence or comfort to the Polaris Executive. But strong in the belief that our cause was worthwhile and in the genuine interests of the country, myself and my team, in the face of this mounting wave of political propaganda, re-doubled our efforts to keep the programme forging ahead; if enough progress could be achieved and sufficient money firmly committed by the time of the election, the future would be more assured. Notwithstanding this, there is no doubt that the wide publicity given to Labour's views in the run-up to the election gave rise to doubts and fears amongst many, in industry and elsewhere, whose wholehearted co-operation was critical to the Polaris programme. To counter such misgivings a yet heavier burden was laid on the Polaris Executive in their never-ending fight against anything that could cause the programme to falter.

The first concrete evidence of progress was exposed to public view on a bleak, cold day at Vickers' shipyards in Barrow on 26 February 1964 when at a brief ceremony the keel of the first of the SSBNs was formally "laid". In contrast to what was normally involved on such an occasion, in this case a massive 250 ton section of the pressure hull had been moved from the welding bay in the huge construction shed where it had been built, to rest in its final position on the slipway where it would be joined in due course to other sections, and when all complete, finally launched. It was a momentous, even historic, moment as Director General, Ships, declared it in place: it had been achieved on time and was an encouraging augury for the future.

On the same day the Government finally approved the construction of the fifth SSBN. I went happily to bed that night - only to succumb two days later to double pneumonia, which effectively removed me from all work for over a month. In my absence the fort was ably held by Rae McKaig in London and Rowley Baker in Bath, the latter having to lead the team attending the fourth meeting of the Joint Steering Task

Group (JSTG) in Washington in March.

In April 1964, the Government's major reorganisation of the Ministry of Defence and the three hitherto separate Armed Services came into effect; the Admiralty as a distinct organisation disappeared and its function was centralised within a greatly expanded Ministry of Defence. Admiralty Board members, Naval Staff Divisions and senior Civil Service officials and departments, along with the Polaris Executive, suffered the physical upheaval of having to move office into the vast, impersonal, but much newer, main building of the Ministry of Defence, just across Whitehall from their long-established quarters in the old Admiralty building. Fortunately, there had been ample time to plan the move in advance, and it was superbly executed, with virtually no interruption to day-to-day business. Compared to the former conditions - hurriedly improvised, cramped, and where maintenance of proper security had been a nightmare - my London staff and I now were given a suite of offices, conference room etc, adequate for our needs. Furthermore, these were equipped with their own self-contained and specially designed security measures and their own teleprinter network, over and above those provided in the main building: it was an enormously improved set-up. I also gained personally: I now found that I could have an "official" car, from the general pool, to take me to and from work: hitherto public transport had had to suffice for journeys to and from home; this concession had not come easily, but was thanks to the persistent lobbying by my loyal secretary, John Grimwood. The transfer to MOD Main Building had, in certain ways, made life that much easier.

But despite these advantages the transition by no means led to the solution of all our problems; in fact, in some degree it made the path to success more difficult, Under the old Admiralty organisation members of the Board were a power unto themselves and I knew that an appeal to any one of them would produce immediate results. Now there was no longer a First Lord, and appeal to one of the "Sea Lords" or to the Minister of the Navy could always be subject to scrutiny and ruling by the Secretary of State for Defence and/or the Defence Council. The path had become longer and more tortuous, leading the Polaris Executive increasingly to rely on their own efforts and carve their own way; fortunately, there was no change in the objective they had been given.

The keel of the second SSBN was laid on 26 June, in Cammell Laird's shipyard at Birkenhead; it was another significant milestone achieved on time, but giving no grounds for any complacency with the submarine building programme: difficulties abounded for both the Polaris submarines and the hunter-killers (SSNs), A shortage of high grade welders, suitably qualified for the special QT35 steel prescribed for their hulls, was chronic in both shipyards, requiring a nation-wide search to be instituted, which included Devonport and Rosyth Royal dockyards, to see if more could be recruited. This had limited success, but the problem remained lurking until the main construction work on the hulls had been completed.

Strikes, and threats of strikes, by various key sections of the skilled workforce in each shipyard continued to have a generally unsettling effect on the programme by jeopardising many critical dates. In particular, a draughtsmen's strike at Barrow, lasting several months, caused serious disruption to the ordered flow of essential drawings from the drawing office, vital to both Vickers and Cammell Lairds, and also had a downstream, long term effect on the placing of orders with sub-contractors for the multitude of "ship-builder supply" items of equipment required for each submarine.

Progress on *Valiant* was unsatisfactory; she had been launched in December 1963, and was at a critical stage of fitting out; but, in my view as briefed by DPT, insufficient manpower was allocated to the task if she were to be finished on time. Action had to be taken with Vickers, to urge them to provide more resources; but this had to be done without jeopardising progress on their other contracts; in other words, it was no use robbing Peter to pay Paul. There was no easy solution; shortages of skilled work people were endemic to the whole Polaris programme, particularly because of its highly technical content and the demands for stringent quality control. The latter, originating with the nuclear propulsion system, was essential to the Polaris Weapon System and now cast its web throughout the whole submarine, introducing new and much higher standards of workmanship, attention to detail and, for everyone concerned, a vastly higher level of cleanliness in the work, whether submarine or shop, than ever before expected, or achieved. Great efforts had to be expended in the way of recruitment, indoctrination and training in order to master the new criteria.

There were persistent difficulties preventing the satisfactory completion of the primary circuit of *Valiant's* nuclear reactor; as mentioned earlier, this was the first British design of a submarine nuclear propulsion plant and a prototype tested at Dounreay had seemed satisfactory. Doubts now arose about the quality of some of the piping, stemming from a substance called Inconel, which was essential to the make-up of the stainless steel obligatory for the piping system. These doubts were compounded by difficulties arising in the manufacture of some of the main circulating valves, which were failing to meet the rigorous tests demanded. The help of Admiral Rickover in Washington had been sought; this was channelled through Solly Zuckerman and the Chief of Defence Staff, Admiral Mountbatten, the only people with whom Admiral Rickover would have any dealings. Despite his well known antipathy to everything British, he was more than helpful and quickly provided a satisfactory solution to both problems.

Within eight days of the new Labour Government taking power following the General Election of 15 October 1964, my staff and I gave a full-scale illustrated presentation to all the newly appointed Ministers who were in any way connected with the Polaris programme, from the Secretary of State for Defence (Denis Healey) downwards. Much thought, time and effort had gone into the preparation of this, in full recognition of the view that the audience might be somewhat hostile. The theme concentrated on three straightforward and simple aspects; firstly, who were the Polaris Executive and what was their task, secondly, how were they setting about it, and thirdly, how far had they got. The opportunity was also used to emphasise the need for Government decisions, if any were to be taken, being either a "Go" or "No Go" version: wavering permutations would be anathema, saving neither money nor effort. In the event, reception was far from adverse; I was encouraged by a docile but interested reaction and I hoped that to both sides the presentation was illuminating - except, perhaps for one Minister in the front row who remained soundly asleep from within five minutes of the start of proceedings: perhaps it had been a mistake to stage the occasion in the afternoon, so soon after lunch.

There were no immediate results from the presentation, the Government's intentions for Polaris became no clearer, and all the pre-election propaganda of re-negotiating Nassau or doing away with Polaris continued to dominate the scene. By mid-November both Vickers and Cammell Lairds were reporting that political uncertainty was causing key men to drift away from their Polaris organisation. Within Whitehall the wheels were running, however, and I was constantly called upon to give further briefings, to the Secretary of State for Defence, Chief of Defence Staff, First Sea Lord (Admiral Luce) amongst others. With all the many question marks hanging over the

Polaris programme, that autumn was a particularly busy time. In addition to the political uncertainties and the never-ending difficulties in the shipyards there were other pressing problems, all needing action. The build-up of the projected base at Faslane, particularly the married quarters for officers and men, some of which must be ready well within three years; the terms of service for the staff of the new Armament Depot at Coulport, many of whom would be highly qualified technically and for whom there was no precedent, a source of endless argument with the Civil Service, their unions and the Treasury. There would be men under training at the United States Navy's Polaris School at Dam Neck in Virginia from next year and much had to be done to ensure their welfare and to establish appropriate allowances to meet the then high cost of living in the US and the unfavourable dollar rate. Again the Treasury resisted and the help of senior Ministers had to be sought before the matter was settled satisfactorily.

By the end of the year the situation looked brighter politically: a week-end at Chequers given over to Defence matters had at least established that the Government intended to keep Polaris as the national deterrent and that there would be no change in the priority accorded to bringing it into service, though there remained the vital question of how many submarines would be built. The immediate task of the Polaris Executive had been confirmed - the first submarine to be operational by mid-1968, the others to follow at six-monthly intervals, with supporting facilities at the shore base to conform There was no deviation from the original challenge, which was reinforced by the Minister for the Navy early in 1965 when introducing the annual Naval Estimates in the House of Commons: he stated it in plain terms: "... the toughest peace-time task the Navy has ever been given".

In mid-December 1964, at the seventh JSTG meeting in London it was time to say "goodbye" to Admiral Galantin, who was moving on to become Chief of Naval Material of the United States Navy (CNM corresponding to Controller and Third Sea Lord in the RN); he was to be succeeded by Rear Admiral Levering Smith, who had been Technical Director to Special Projects for many years and was, indeed, the architect and expert on all matters concerning Polaris. There were no resulting changes whatsoever in the special relationship between Special Projects and Polaris Executive, except that, if anything, the technical team in the latter gained from the input of personal expertise from Admiral Levering Smith himself. He was just as insistent as his predecessor that the British would get a fair deal in the timely provision of information and material: the log-jam of mountains of documentation began to clear.

The argument over the number of submarines to be built came to a head in January 1965. At a meeting of the full Defence Council considering this, with the Secretary of State in the chair, I was invited to open the batting with my views. I maintained, as I had done with the previous administration, that five were required to assure that in operational service one at least would always be on patrol, thus guaranteeing with as nearly 100% certainty as possible the all-time credibility of the deterrent, yet without risk of too much "over-stretch" and too great stress on those manning and supporting the force. Dwelling in some detail on the operational factors, I laid particular emphasis on the morale angle, knowing full well the strain that would fall on the submarine crews on patrol, and on those ashore on whose support they relied. On ending, I was thanked by the Secretary of State for all I had said but politely told that my arguments were "irrelevant". Only Sir Solly Zuckerman (Chief Scientific Advisor to the MOD) gave any indication of support - neither Chief of Defence Staff nor First Sea Lord said anything - and there was no further discussion. There soon followed a meeting of the Defence and Overseas Policy Committee of the Cabinet which pronounced the final verdict: the Treasury had demanded the force be cut to three submarines, but the Ministry of Defence won the day with a compromise on four, which the Government accepted readily.

The consequences of this decision were not difficult; steps were immediately taken to stop further expenditure on the fifth submarine; where contracts were irrevocable, with material already in the pipeline, or where huge cancellation charges would arise, the order would be completed and the product would serve as "spares"; other orders were cancelled, with minimum cancellation charges. It was a relief to have a firm decision at last: the programme was now back on what had originally been planned in April 1963, and everybody could now concentrate on bringing it to a successful fruition. Any further action in connection with the fifth boat was of secondary importance. "No going back, get on with the authorised programme", was my message to the Polaris Executive.

Nevertheless there remained a lingering doubt: by accepting this reduction from five submarines to four, was I committing men who would man the force to a degree of stress over and above that which was normally acceptable for service in submarines in peace time? The pressure arising from the duty of keeping the nation's deterrent permanently at virtually immediate readiness for action would undoubtedly be very different from anything hitherto experienced - the only similarities were with conditions on patrol in wartime - and with no fifth boat there was no reserve to fall back on. Only time would tell whether the load placed on those in the Polaris force by this decision would prove too much. In the event perhaps it was not so. but in my heart I continued to believe that keeping a fifth submarine in the programme would have been a wiser decision: the additional cost would have been small, and the advantages to all who had to operate and maintain the force would have been immeasurable. I believe the true reason for its cancellation was political, not financial: a sop to the Left Wing of the Labour Party. All that their clamour achieved was to lay an almost intolerable burden on the men, and women, responsible for the efficiency of the deterrent.

CHAPTER 15

Size of the Polaris Force
by Martin Wemyss

I came to Plans Division to relieve John Moore from Perisher teaching, a lovely job with lots of action and minimal paperwork. Fortunately, I was not entirely new to the Admiralty and Whitehall, where paper is paramount, having served for two years as the submariner in the Russian section of the Naval Intelligence Division. But the two jobs were, though logically linked, quite different in style. In the NID we were so secret we were locked away in the Citadel under the Horse Guards, invisible and practically inaudible. A visit to the First Sea Lord's office meant a long hike through the subterranean gloom of the Admiralty's nether regions via a small cavern where a sinister dark person of indeterminate gender served the best draught Guinness outside Ireland. Commanders (two) of the ship shop in Plans were allowed not only free access to the First Sea Lord's office and files, but also to his loo where useful chance encounters could take place not only with Admiral Luce himself but also with Admirals Frewen and Hill-Norton, Vice and Assistant Chief of the Naval Staff (VCNS and ACNS). These formidable gentlemen, essential links in our paperwork chain, were more open to chat in such circumstances than when back behind a desk. The move from the Admiralty to the Ministry of Defence put an end to such quirky nonsense. There, keys to executive loos were closely guarded but this was not, in my view, to the benefit of good staff work.

A principal function of Plans Division was to take a central role in the determination of the shape, size and funding of the Navy over the ten year period of the Long Term Costings. For instance on the day I joined champagne corks were popping to celebrate the approval of the purchase of the long lead items for the building of the first of a new generation of aircraft carriers. One of my first jobs was to collate the arguments for the building of new survey ships for the Hydrographer. Clearly the advent of Polaris would have a significant effect on the Navy as a whole including the Hydrographer. Though the Chief Polaris Executive, Rear Admiral Mackenzie, had greatly delegated powers, and the Controller of the Navy, Admiral Le Fanu, was the Board member most directly concerned with oversight of the project, there were matters which were properly within the responsibility of individual

Board members. My place in all this was to act as desk and leg man for VCNS and ACNS and to be Secretary of the Naval Staff Polaris Planning Committee, a co-ordinated group chaired by ACNS which brought together under VCNS and ACNS the more operational aspects of the projects and which concerned the submariner in being the means by which the boats could be built, equipped, maintained and supported in scientific, engineering and manning terms. The committee dealt with such matters as Command, Control and Communications in normal circumstances and in emergency, security, hydrographic survey, meteorology, weapons and equipment outfits and a host of others.

By the time I arrived at Plans, the Polaris Executive was firmly in place with management plans in operation monitoring every aspect of the project with the full support of all Board members, including those normally jealous of the boundaries separating their several departments. Others are much better placed than I to describe how this quite small but select project team came together and how its modus vivendi was established. Suffice to say as an outsider but one who worked in parallel with it for two years and more that the whole organisation had a wonderfully cheerful and positive atmosphere about it which I have not experienced again in Whitehall. The project was completed within time and budget. The experiment of setting up a management team with such powers across the board was so monstrously successful that it has never been repeated.

Despite all the progress which had been made by the time John Moore left Plans there was one fairly major matter yet to be decided. That was how many submarines were needed to mount and sustain a credible independent deterrent against the USSR, defined as one which would pose an unacceptable level of damage. The level of damage inflicted would depend on which targets must be hit and how many missiles would be needed to ensure their destruction. The experts had calculated that the missile outfit of one submarine on station could provide the basic minimum provided there were no effective defences but that it would be highly desirable that two submarines should be maintained continuously on station, invulnerable to pre-emptive attack. Exhaustive studies were undertaken within CPE of refit, inter-patrol maintenance and crew training and weapon trial requirements and all the factors which would make up the patrol cycle of a force of four submarines, the number so far approved for order by the Tory Government. These were brought together by Commander Jimmy Launders in a monster bar chart which demonstrated to the initiated that a four submarine force could keep only one and two thirds on station in a steady state cycle. The only problem with this remarkable document was that it contained so much information that it was daunting to the point of incomprehensibility to a newcomer, particularly as it was in black and white in order to be compatible with the only reproductive office equipment available.

In the Ministry matters of great moment with long and detailed gestation periods tend to survive or die in a matter of days, if not hours. Thus, in this case, if the fifth submarine were to be ordered, the case would have to be made to the Tory Government with a General Election imminent. Labour in opposition were threatening to cancel the whole project. Deployment being an operational matter as the construction of a fifth submarine would have ramifications Navy-wide, VCNS was given the task of putting forward the case for it. Two points needed to be established. Firstly that to pose a credible independent deterrent in the medium term two submarines would need to be deployed on station. Secondly that to achieve this on a continuous basis would require a fifth submarine. The deterrent level case had been made to the experts and only needed restatement. The key to the size of the force was the Launders' bar chart. The problem was to sell this not only to the other Services in the Chiefs of Staff Committee but to Ministers and the Treasury. Within the Board of Admiralty the case to perm two from five was not difficult to make. Indeed, the old rule of thumb whereby to keep one submarine on station required three; one on, one in the wash; and one on passage; would have required six, and five was a saving. The chances that the Chiefs of Staff would go along with the Navy's recommendation were improved by the agreement of the Government to pay a significant proportion of the cost of establishing the Polaris force from Government contingency funds rather than from the Defence vote. The sticking point was likely to be the Treasury, not notable for knowledge of naval affairs nor normally sympathetic to expenditure on vastly expensive military projects.

The solution to all this lay in a box of crayons. When each element in the life cycle of a submarine which prevented it from being armed and on station had been allocated a colour and the boxes in the bar chart had been filled in for four submarines over many years, the whole chart was a thing of beauty and glory, fit for the Tate. Furthermore, as time on station was white it was glaringly obvious when only one submarine was available. Provided no-one challenged the detail which was behind the coloured blocks the case was made. As far as I am aware, no-one dared to do so when confronted with this glorious multicoloured work of art over a yard long.

It took a weekend in the operations room, fed and watered by the duty Commander, with the bonus of Sunday lunch provided by the Resident Clerk's girlfriend, to colour seven copies of the Launders' bar chart, enough for the Chiefs of Staff for their meeting two days later. I was not present at that meeting but the next thing I knew was a summons to accompany Admiral Luce, the First Sea Lord, to a meeting with Mr Thorneycroft, Minister of Defence, at Storey's Gate. I was to be armed with a copy of the chart and be prepared to explain it if required to do so. I was indeed called up from the bottom of the table. I do not remember having to do much explaining but I do remember that it took two very senior gentlemen to hold the ends of the unfurled chart and that the Minister, not a small man, sat in a chair on blocks which made him even more impressive. The fact that his feet did not reach the floor was revealed only to one standing, as I was, behind his shoulder. For a junior Commander this made an otherwise somewhat overwhelming occasion much more human. Then it was back into the car and on with the Minister, to see the Prime Minister, Sir Alec Douglas-Home. Within some ten minutes the chart had been produced, some sharp and pertinent questions had been posed and we had been dismissed with the promise of an early decision. Some days later permission was granted to order a fifth submarine.

There was then a pause for the Election followed by the heady days of the Healey divide and rule defence reviews. Cancellation of the carrier programme and TSR2. Disbandment and amalgamation of famous regiments. Withdrawal from the Far East, the Middle East and the Mediterranean. Enough to keep the planners of all three services quite busy for quite a time. Early on in the Wilson 100 days the question of the future, if any, of the Polaris programme came up for decision. Having scripted the Naval Staff input I was allowed to attend the main briefing for Ministers, seated in a wastepaper basket at the back of the hall. Whether or not Labour had ever intended cancellation, it was soon decided that the project would continue. The explanation given to the left wing of the party was that the programme was too far advanced, thousands of jobs were at stake and it would be cheaper to go on than to stop. However, the fifth submarine was taken back out of the programme and we were invited to show that it could be done with a force of only three.

Once again it was a simple matter to restate the deterrent level which could be achieved with a force of three submarines. What had to be pointed out, however, was the danger of reliance on a single unit in a political crisis which could lead to threats of nuclear attack. Out came the Launders' bar chart. Even with the fourth submarine folded away it was still a very impressive document which showed clearly those periods when only one submarine would be on station and ready to respond to an order to fire. One lunchtime Captain Rae McKaig, Admiral Mackenzie's deputy, and I had a look at a range of defects or accidents which might occur in a single unit on patrol and what effect this would have on the continuity of the deterrent. By constructing overlays to illustrate each case and applying them to different places on the Launders' masterplan it was possible to demonstrate that in each case sooner or later there would come a time in the cycle when no submarine would be on patrol. It was then a matter of suggesting that Murphy's Law would ensure that such a time would coincide with a period of extreme international tension. Despite later reference to this bit of work as "a careful analysis by the Naval Staff" I do not believe it would have stood up to much rigorous examination. But it was enough. Once again I accompanied the First Sea Lord to meetings with the Secretary of State and the Prime Minister, armed this time with two versions of the Launders' diagram. One with a force of three with overlays, the other with a force of four showing how comfortably one submarine could be kept on patrol and how often a second could be provided. Thus the size of the force was agreed and it is of interest that the four Polaris submarines are being replaced by the same number of Trident ones.

CHAPTER 16

Success in Sight
Sir Hugh Mackenzie

With the major hurdle of Labour's pre-election apparent antagonism to the deterrent and corresponding doubts as to the size or continuance of the Polaris force finally surmounted, the Management Team and Polaris Executive could settle down to what became a largely routine task. The scope and detailed requirements of the overall programme were clearly defined, the major "milestones" established, critical areas identified, lack of progress or unforeseen obstacles accurately and quickly reported, and the earlier opposition to the unusual organisation and its methods having mainly faded away, all that was needed was to maintain, almost on a 24 hour basis, the tightest of grips on an ever-changing situation. As construction progressed in shipyards and the future base, whenever and wherever delays threatened, positive action had to be taken at once to get the programme back on course. It remained over the years a hard and unremitting slog for everyone.

I found that if I had to appeal for help to higher authority, Ministers of the new Government personally gave their support wholeheartedly, and even enthusiastically. The Government, naturally, however, remained sensitive to anything to do with Polaris and were reluctant to encourage much in the way of publicity for the programme and what it was achieving. I ran foul of this later when, at *Resolution*'s commissioning ceremony at Barrow in October 1967, in answer to a question from the press, I gave my views on the by then dead-end issue of the fifth boat: I was sharply told to keep my mouth shut in future.

During 1966 the first concrete results of the programme began to show: the more significant included the completion of the Royal Navy Polaris School (RNPS), with its formal opening, on schedule, on 30 June; the acceptance into service of *Valiant* at the end of July; the launch of *Resolution* on 15 September; and by the end of the year *Warspite* safely through her Contractor's Sea Trials. The RNPS with its conspicuous missile launch tower dominating the surrounding apparent chaos of half completed roadways and buildings, amidst seas of mud, threw down the gauntlet to all engaged in the vast construction work yet to be completed in the Faslane/Coulport complex. Vickers at Barrow had achieved wonders, but many problems still remained in the shipyards: Cammell Lairds were lagging badly with their two Polaris submarines, and there was a "hiccough" in the flow of QT35/ HY80 steel for the hulls of the hunter-killer submarines, SSN 04 and 05, the contracts for which Vickers had secured as a follow-on to their Polaris work; orders were about to be placed for two more, SSN 06 and 07, but all was overshadowed by the discovery of hair-line cracks in the welding of Dreadnought's pressure hull. The possible consequences were frightening and a hugely disruptive schedule of ultrasonic testing of all welds in the hull of all submarines had to be hurriedly ordered; that it was accomplished without completely destroying essential orderly progress was to the enormous credit of all who had to grapple with this devastating problem.

It was time for changes in the Polaris Executive; I had no wish to jeopardise in any way the career prospects of anyone on my staff, fully accepting that naval appointments normally last for around two years, though in exceptional circumstances they could possibly be extended to three: anything longer might prejudice the individual concerned; a similar custom applied to those in the Civil Service. Bob Lewin was succeeded as Chief Administrative Officer in 1966 by Peter Nailor, who in turn was succeeded by Michael Power in 1967; Captain Philip Higham relieved Rae McKaig as Deputy CPE in 1966 and, after undertaking the full Polaris training course at Dam Neck - which he did with flying colours - Captain C H Hammer took Peter La Niece's place in Washington that summer; later that year Pat Murphy, the inimitable and trusted Special Projects (SP) Liaison Officer in London was relieved by Captain J Love USN: further changes at the top included Mr H J Tabb RCNC (Royal Corp of Naval Constructors) succeeding Mr S J Palmer as DPT's Deputy; lower down the echelon similar changes regularly took place; all were accomplished smoothly and caused not a ripple of disturbance to the programme. The one major exception to this orderly exchange of duties was Charles Shepherd, head of the Polaris Weapon Section at Bath and an absolutely key member of DPT's team; he was quite irreplaceable and I took special measures to retain him in post for the full span of getting Polaris into service, receiving assurance from higher up that in no way would his future suffer thereby.

On his relief Peter La Niece produced some figures illustrative of the scope of his appointment in Washington, in which he had been responsible not only for close liaison with SPO but was intimately involved in the placing of orders for all US supplied equipment, and in the training of UK personnel in the US naval establishments or with industry eg Electric Boat Co and Lockheeds. The figures from April 1963, to July 1966, were

Mileage flown (personally)		220,000
Visit clearances submitted		1,525
Purchase orders placed	over	600
UK trainees supervised		520
Measurement tons shipped from		
Charleston		3,300
(Nov 1964 to June 1966)		

The Defence Review ordered by the Government in 1966 had little effect on Polaris, though the "freeze" on recruitment throughout the Government Service of any additional staff gave rise to minor problems. By the beginning of 1967, I was fairly confident that, if pressure was maintained and barring some frightful accident, an initial major aim would be achieved; perhaps it was the most important of all, the operational deployment of *Resolution* mid-1968, with all necessary supporting facilities available at the base on the Clyde. The remaining targets also seemed not beyond reach.

But there were still omens that were not so good: Cammell Lairds, lacking the experience Vickers had gained from building *Dreadnought* and *Valiant*, were dogged by labour troubles and shortages of skilled staff, particularly for the management of their programme. Nevertheless, with things generally shaping up well, I turned my staff's attention increasingly to the problem that would arise when the Polaris force became operational and had to be kept so throughout their lives, which DPT suggested should be regarded as twenty years: this was the criterion his design team had worked to. Just as special arrangements had had to be made to build the force, so there would have to be special arrangements for its refitting, refuelling and general maintenance to standards not yet experienced. Rosyth Dockyard was earmarked for the task of major refits and nuclear refuelling, and a start was made on all the work that would be necessary in preparing the yard to undertake this heavy load; a committee under Vice Admiral Sir Raymond Hawkins was charged with recommending how supervision of the task could best be ensured and what, if any, organisation would be needed to keep Polaris up to the mark once CPE's task of "design and build" had been accomplished.

More milestones were successfully passed in 1967: *Renown* and *Repulse* were launched, the base at Faslane was commissioned as HMS *Neptune*, *Resolution*'s Contractor's Sea Trials (CSTs) proved successful. Despite some subsequent teething troubles, she was accepted into service in October, thereupon embarking on a rigorous period of work-up and trials, with the ultimate aim of carrying out her DASO (Demonstration and Shake-down Operation) involving full scale firing of one missile, in February 1968. Training of submarine crews was in full swing and the earlier difficulties of finding enough men of the right calibre to provide two crews per boat without devastating the manpower of the rest of the Navy, had been satisfactorily overcome.

1968 duly brought the reward of successful DASOs by both crews of *Resolution* and of her being handed over in June to C-in-C, Home Fleet, her operating authority; she was out of my hands and the Polaris Executive now concentrated on completing the remaining three Polaris submarines and the hunter-killers now under our wing. As the year advanced it became clear that progress on *Repulse* at Barrow (the fourth SSBN in the programme) was so good that she would be finished before *Renown* in Birkenhead; the programme was adjusted accordingly.

In August 1968, I handed over my task to Rear Admiral A F Trewby, who became Assistant Controller (Polaris)(ACP) under the revised organisation now set up, with responsibility for completing the original building programme and for ensuring that resources and facilities and the organisation behind them, would guarantee the continued operational efficiency of the Polaris force to the same high standards which had governed the previous five and a half years.

It was sad to leave such a wonderful team which, against all the odds, had accomplished so much; but I felt that, with the first of the submarines operational, it was the right moment to hand over to my successor a "going" concern, full of confidence and with its tail up.

PART 3

BUILDING THE SUBMARINE

CHAPTER 17

Designing the Submarine
Jack Daniel

In the post war era we enjoyed a friendly relationship with the submarine design desk in the US Navy's Bureau of Ships and its associated research establishments, particularly the David Taylor model basin and the underwater sound laboratory. We had exchanged information about our systems and designs and our theoretical and practical research and development in submarine strength and hydrodynamics. It has been acknowledged that British inventions like the angled deck and the slotted tube catapult "kept the US Navy in the aircraft carrier business"; it is equally true that the UK's fundamental work on submarine structures, hydrodynamics, noise reduction and systems safety did much to improve US submarine design at that time.

This exchange of information between naval constructors had continued into the nuclear era, although we were excluded from nuclear propulsion data by Admiral Rickover's Code 1500. This was eased somewhat when the UK was allowed to purchase a S5W nuclear propulsion plant and given access to engineering data to enable Rolls Royce and Associates to manufacture submarine nuclear reactor components in the UK and Vickers Shipbuilders and Engineers to install these in the submarines. In all of this the co-operation of the US companies designated by Code 1500 and the Bureau as the agencies to transfer information, material and assistance to the Royal Navy and its agents was exemplary.

Domestically we had already designed a submarine around the reactor system being developed by the Admiralty, Harwell and industry. With the decision to buy the US reactor, I redesigned the British submarine to incorporate the complete S5W propulsion plant. This was *Dreadnought.*

Design work was resumed on the all-British SSN albeit with substantial changes in the nuclear components to make use of the S5W technology. Particular features of the British design were mounting the main propulsion turbines and gearing on a massive raft, resiliently isolated from the hull and the provision of alternative methods of providing power to the secondary propulsion motor. This was the *Valiant* design.

In the late 1950s we had learned of the proposal to launch strategic ballistic missiles from submerged submarines and had received information about the "submarine" aspects of the system and more general information about the missile and the on-board systems required to locate, discharge and guide the missile to its target. At the beginning of 1958 we learned that some of the *Skipjack* class were to have 130ft added to their hulls to take two rows of eight missile tubes, fire control and navigational equipment. The vessels would initially be armed with the Polaris A1 missile. Such was the urgency that the first ship, USS *George Washington*, was commissioned 26 months after laying down and accomplished the first underwater launch in July 1960. Meanwhile, a new larger *Ethan Allen* design was in preparation with characteristics based loosely on the *Thresher* design.

Within Ship Department, as head of the nuclear submarine design section, I had informally looked at design options for a Royal Navy ballistic missile submarine based on the *Valiant* design. Problems foreseen were the maintenance of constant depth firing readiness when launching 16 missiles weighing 20 tons a piece in rapid succession, guaranteed command signal reception and, a fundamental submarine requirement, the provision of sufficient main ballast tankage to provide an acceptable reserve of buoyancy. And of course maximum silence at all times.

Following the Nassau Agreement, in January 1963 I was deputed to lead the "Deep Technical Mission" to the US Navy in Washington DC "to obtain definitive information on the Polaris missile system to enable the UK to design the British ballistic missile submarine with confidence". In parallel we initiated the necessary reassignment of staff to form design teams in Bath and elsewhere to deal with the submarine, the missile, its payload and the missile associated systems.

In the Special Projects Office in Washington DC we were seen as the special responsibility of the Captain who had the ship sub-system desk and who arranged our programme of lectures and visits to the SP desks responsible for the launcher sub-systems, the fire control sub-system, the navigation sub-system and to those responsible for the overall management methods and procedures for the US programme. We met Admiral Galantin and his deputy Captain Levering Smith, the genius behind the US Navy's strategic missile programme.

At the time of our visit the *Ethan Allan* class had entered service and the first ships of the *Lafeyette* class were about to be commissioned, all deploying the Polaris A2 missile. Design work was already well advanced on the SSBN 640 class, six vessels of which were authorised in the fiscal year 1963 programme. These would deploy the A3 missile having nearly twice the range and a greater payload capacity than its predecessors which would be phased out as stocks were built up and shipyard conversion resources permitted. The US commitment to the successful development of the A3 missile and its associated systems was total and its timescale was compatible with the UK programme; it was clear that the UK should purchase this system, not only because of its superior military qualities and availability from current production, but also to avoid the possibility of early uniqueness of the British deterrent system.

Accordingly we were given full information on the ship-building and ship installation requirements for the 640 class configuration. In each of the relevant sub-systems this represented a step change from earlier technology. The principal design consideration was the manner in which the US missile spaces might best be married to a *Valiant* class machinery, sensor and weapons arrangement, observing the differences in diameter and diving depth. That the "US spaces" should retain the same special geometry was, in our view, mandatory.

It became clear in discussion that whilst the SP desks had information on the missile sub-systems, detailed information on their interface with the submarine was not available in Washington. We obtained permission to visit the Electric Boat Company at Groton. The Electric Boat Company was already under contract to support the UK through the S5W/*Dreadnought* arrangement and they co-operated fully in supplying outline data concerning the 30,000 line items of shipbuilder's supply equipment necessary for the installation and operation of the overall missile system in an SSBN. The major part of these items were being procured by the company for the US SSBNs and it was established informally that, given government approvals, the company would be willing to give design support and procure/supply these items for the UK Polaris programme. We reported accordingly on our return to the UK.

With the *Valiant* class in build the nuclear design team had started studies on the next generation of SSN and had established the major characteristics of what was to become the *Swiftsure* class. This was put to one side (for several years) and work proceeded apace on the British Polaris submarine design. Urgent measures were taken to assemble the substantial team in DPT at Foxhill to deal with the ship and weapons design, logistics, support, armaments and contracts. As the designer I was determined that we should improve on some of the

US ship systems and also take every opportunity to improve on some of the difficult areas that had become evident in construction of *Valiant*. Fields in which we resolved not to adopt US practice were in the hovering system and in the fabrication of pressurised systems. This latter was a carry over from the *Dreadnought* systems, where we had been very concerned at the use of brazing where we would have insisted on welding. As a further safety improvement I decided that all hull valves would be ball valves, capable of rapid closure by a 90 degree movement, the whole being welded integrally in the pressure hull.

This concern for submarine hull and systems integrity was underlined by the tragic loss of the first ship in the US Navy's *Thresher* class in April 1963 and the resulting changes the US Navy eventually made in systems and valve design and fabrication procedure. These "subsafe" changes were introduced in US new construction submarines (with consequent delay) and in submarines in service.

The design of the UK submarines pressure hull, external hull and some internal structure was released to Messrs Vickers in April/May 1963 to enable special steel to be ordered. Deliveries commenced in December and fabrication began.

Design work had started in March and the design received Board approval in December; a remarkable achievement.

In the marriage of *Valiant* and the 640 class missile system it was necessary to make provision for the greater crew size, additional auxiliary systems power and so on. Additional tank spaces were required and also additional main ballast tankage. Within the design philosophy that we had postulated to ensure the most acceptable whole-life hull stress regime, it was not possible to locate sufficient main ballast tankage within the streamlined external hull and outside the pressure hull. Accordingly, an internal MBT was arranged with Kingston valves to shut when deep.

Particular attention was given in DPT and in the development of the detailed design by Vickers to the provision of space for equipment maintenance and removal, observing the high availability required of these ships with their double-crew routine. In parallel, deep study was given to the numerical basis for the provision of spare gear, on board, at the base or elsewhere and the designation of minimum stock levels in each category.

It was evident from manpower considerations that Vickers had insufficient capacity to construct four or five submarines in the time available; another builder would be required. We were also concerned at the prospect of moving these large, deep, vessels through the shallow Walney Channel at Barrow and also at the possible danger of launching and moving such submarines in the busy River Mersey should Cammell Lairds be the second builder. All of these worries led us privately to consider whether it might be better to build the SSBNs in a new facility adjacent to Devonport naval dockyard.

The conclusion was that the work must be placed where the special submarine skills already existed and the cost of extra dredging accepted. Accordingly two ships were ordered from Vickers at Barrow and two from Cammell Laird at Birkenhead., with Vickers taking responsibility for lead yard services to Cammells and for the construction programme in general under Mr Len Redshaw who was appointed Builders' Chief Executive. Six other companies were, in due course, sub-contracted to prepare and fabricate steelworks. Procurement action for machinery and equipment for all the SSBNs was taken at Vickers and a contract entered into with the Electric Boat Company, Groton, for the supply of design information and drawings of the missile associated spaces, equipment schedules and specifications and for the supply of components and materials for the missile associated ship systems which it was judged would be better purchased from companies already supplying the US programme. A special office to handle this procurement was set up at Barrow and a Vickers/MOD office was set up at Groton - outside Electric Boat Company at Rickover's insistence.

The procurement of the missiles, their on-board launching, navigation and fire control systems, together with jigs, test equipment, spares and specialist assistance was handled directly by the CPE organisation and SP. UK companies were introduced into these contracts as the MOD's agents. A separate organisation was set up by the MOD to design and manufacture the missile payloads.

When the decision to acquire four or five SSBNs was taken in February 1963, hull fabrication for *Valiant* was well advanced and that for *Warspite* had started. The decision had to be made whether to stop *Warspite* and reassign the material where possible to the first SSBN or to let work proceed as fast as possible and complete *Warspite* ahead of the first SSBN. For evident reasons the latter was the best militarily and this was also the most efficient use of industry's resources. She was commissioned in April 1967, some months ahead of the first SSBN.

We were allowed to visit the US Navy's submarine tender USS *Hunley* in the Holy Loch to view the depot facilities considered necessary to support operational SSBNs, including the exchange of missiles. In addition to the tender there were two docks and numerous stores vessels and auxiliaries. The US situation operating several thousand miles from their industrial bases was, of course, quite dissimilar from the UK's and the visit confirmed the desirability of supporting the UK force from a shore base. The visit clearly demonstrated the penalty the US Navy was paying for allowing some laxity in the procurement of certain fittings. For example systems components had been procured to performance specifications by different builders from various manufacturers. Differences might exist between successive batches from the same maker. The result to the operators was not only a logistic support nightmare but also potentially a sub-safe threat. By contrast we in DPT rigidly specified standards and identicality on a no-deviation basis; not difficult one might say when dealing with a few vessels and no lobbying Senators.

Our experience with the US authorities, Electric Boat Company, Westinghouse and other US suppliers on the *Dreadnought* contracts had been wholly satisfactory and the experience with SP and US industry on the Polaris project was equally impressive in spirit as well as in contractual law. An example: it was my practice to visit the Electric Boat Company every three months to formally review progress on the supply of design information and equipment purchased from or by Electric Boat Company. For the latter we would wade through vast schedules in which each line item was identified by plan numbers, source, required delivery date, percentage complete and expected date. Well into the programme certain large electrical cabinets of Electric Boat Company manufacture were shown at successive meetings as 60% complete. Exceptionally I asked that our resident should see these items there and then. It was found that they did not yet exist, nor did the electrical gear they were destined to contain. Furthermore the same items meant for US SSBNs building and closer to completion than our ships also did not exist. Ever since the *Dreadnought* days we had chided our friends at Electric Boat Company that they completed their submarines despite their planning system, meaning that in the last few hectic months expediency played its part; but this was more serious, something had fallen right though the system. The Electric Boat Company swept magnificently into action with a crash recovery plan. In the event the effect of these delays on the US SSBN programme was absorbed within the delays consequent upon the introduction of their post-*Thresher* sub-safe measures.

I mention this occurrence to remark that notwithstanding the fact that the US Navy's own programme was threatened with delay at that time, SP as always, insisted that the items for the UK retained their place on the production line.

Whilst design work was proceeding and action was in hand to train and qualify the sub-contractor companies in fabricating and welding the special submarine steel, action was also taken to build additional offices at Foxhill (Bath), Barrow and Birkenhead, notably for the strategic weapons experts and to prepare both shipyards for building the large SSBNs, including enhancing the planning and material control systems and security arrangements appropriate to the nuclear and missile secrets to be preserved.

Physical security at Cammells was a constant worry; for example, the very first delivery of a large quantity of high value bronze castings from the US was made to a secure store in the shipyard on a Friday afternoon. They were found to be missing on the following Monday morning. For their part, US personnel liked visiting Cammell Lairds because it gave access to Liverpool and the Beatles. All seemingly arrived with firm instructions from their offspring to bring back John Lennon, or, failing that, a piece of The Cavern's stage. The latter was big business for the shipwrights at Cammells.

We were extremely fortunate in the US naval officers and contractors' representatives who were seconded to work on the British project in the USA and in the UK. Their encyclopaedic knowledge, unfailing good humour and dedication to the task in hand were a constant inspiration to their British colleagues. We were conscious that this came from the very top where the three monthly JSTG meetings held alternately in the USA and UK provided the exchange of information at the highest level. The most memorable JSTG for me was that held in Bath at the time of the Bath Festival when we all went to a "Roman Orgy" and swam in the Roman Bath.

There was much speculation at the possible outcome of the general election to be held in Britain in 1964. The Labour Party was generally considered by the media to be the likely winner. The Party Executive was opposed to the retention of nuclear weapons and committed to cancellation of the UK Polaris programme, but important personalities in the Shadow Cabinet were thought to be somewhat ambivalent on the issue. Ever mindful of employment, there was talk of turning the Polaris submarines into SSNs.

To satisfy my curiosity I took the Polaris design and removed the

Polaris missile system and rejigged the remainder to produce a balanced SSN design with the minimum of waste of ordered materials and equipment. The resulting design was about 30ft longer than *Valiant*. A profile and plans were drawn and given the title HMS *Harold Wilson*. It was shown to a few friends in the project and put away. Imagine my feelings when the First Sea Lord sent for the *"Harold Wilson"* design.

We pressed on with equipment orders. We committed funds. In some areas where equipment or material was being procured from the US, the US supplier had completed production for the 640 class and would cease production on completion of the UK order. To reopen production would be prohibitively expensive. We had to decide on the "whole-life" spares requirement or, usually where components would be built into the submarine structure, whether to order for four or five SSBNs. Missile tube hull castings were the most important example. These large, expensive, castings in special QT steel were fitted at the intersection of each launcher tube and the hull to handle the complex stress situation at these places arising from the massive sea-pressure forces when dived. Much against advice, I invited British Steel to fill the requirement with forgings or castings and provided some MOD funds for development. Some years earlier at the outset of the nuclear submarine programme we had formulated the requirement for a weldable, notch, tough, high yield strength, quenched and tempered steel similar to that under development in the USA. We invited British Steel to produce the steel for which we suggested a wider commercial demand would emerge once the steel was commercially available. British Steel HQ was not really interested; they could see no commercial use. Their stated interest was to produce mild steel and strip steel for the manufacture of cars for which they said the demand would never cease. After substantial delay we approached Ravenscraig where the splendid MD willingly accepted the challenge and brought in other plants. It is another story that some of the early steel had minor laminations but this never threatened our submarines. As predicted, a substantial demand for this sort of steel arose for other purposes.

With the missile tube castings the same picture emerged. British Steel never put the full weight of its organisation behind the problem; they forged a cylinder but there was no prospect of meeting the shape required or the delivery dates and such large castings in the required quality were quite beyond them, so they withdrew, apparently with great relief. So castings for five SSBNs were ordered from United Steel in St Louis as an addition to the last batch for the USN. United Steel's major contract was the production of main battle tank hulls (in two pieces) and turrets, cast in the sort of steel for which British Steel HQ had seen no demand in the late 1950s. The plant was under US Army inspection. The castings for the UK boats were not shipped on the due date and we learned that the Army had refused to accept the entire US/UK batch. It was reported that this was due to cracks. BuShips seemed curiously reluctant to do anything that crossed inter-service lines of responsibility so I flew to St Louis accompanied by Commander Kenny Wilson USN. I found that the cracking was a surface crazing of depth less than a millimetre and of absolutely no structural significance. I said that I would accept the castings then and there on behalf of the Royal Navy, to the evident relief of the army inspector. That evening I saw my first professional baseball game in which the Pirates beat the Cardinals by a margin that I was told was unique.

The postscript to this story is that the sixteen castings for the cancelled fifth UK SSBN were subsequently resold to the US Navy for use in updating one of their earlier submarines

Vickers had the hands-on experience from building and commissioning three nuclear submarines and the Dounreay test reactor prior to their first SSBN whereas Cammells had not yet built a nuclear boat. Inexorably as time passed, the construction of the second submarine at Vickers gradually overtook the first vessel at Cammells and indeed the Vickers boats were commissioned 1 and 2; not without some protest by Cammells concerning the priority of sub-contract equipment deliveries to the yards.

I left the project in January 1966 on appointment to the Imperial Defence College for a year's study, followed by a research appointment. During this time I witnessed the minor drama of the launch of HMS *Repulse* at Barrow when the tugs were unable to secure her quickly enough and the hull grounded on a falling tide, eventually to be seen high and dry on the Walney Channel sands. It so happened that we had some time earlier looked into the stability of grounded submarines intact and progressively flooded in the context of escape and I knew that she would sit there safely upright until the next tide floated her off. I quite enjoyed the launch lunch. Some didn't.

I returned to DPT in 1970 by which time the first three SSBNs were in the patrol cycle and the fourth, *Revenge*, was working up and preparing for her DASO. Plans were already afoot to refit the first boat at Rosyth, earlier than needed but necessary to bring into force the required refitting pattern. Rosyth Dockyard had to be readied for this large task.

It had been estimated that there were nearly 200 equipments in each boat that would be refitted by replacement. Someone had decided that it would be advantageous to exchange 14 of these equipments at each inter-patrol period. It was quickly evident that more damage was being done to the equipment and to the submarine in general by moving the items in and out, notwithstanding the planned removal routes and the big hatch. So the procedure was stopped and "if it is not making a noise, leave it alone" became the rule.

The UK had contracts with US activities for assistance with the inservice support of the missile system. This included an arrangement with the Electric Boat Company for the missile-associated ship sub-systems under which equipments removed from the UK SSBNs were included with those from US SSBNs for refurbishment.

A problem to which urgent attention had to be given was the failure of the UK refitting activities to repair, or to have repaired, components removed from the submarines. Many of these were common in both SSBNs and SSNs. The project had purchased sufficient spare items to support the submarine force in all reasonable circumstances. What was not anticipated was that the dockyard would fail to assign priority and resources to equipment refurbishment ready for the next boat refit, and allowing for the stringent noise and vibration checks necessary before release for shipfitting. We sometimes had to call upon Vickers for assistance in assuring that deployment dates were kept while longer term arrangements to return equipments to the manufacturers were made.

Revenge's DASO was remarkable for the fact that the first missile she launched had to be destroyed some 50 seconds later. Study of the telemetry records apparently showed this to be due to something not previously encountered. The launch and flight of Revenge's second missile a day or so later was successful and the overall reliability of the system as demonstrated by the four British SSBNs conformed exactly to SP's prediction.

In addition to the essential work of supporting the SSBNs in service and in refit in Rosyth, the MOD at the highest level was now concerned with the possible need to make improvements to the overall perform-ance of the system in the light of known or conjectured changes in potential enemy detection or counter-measures systems. This study was brought about in part by the introduction of the Poseidon missile system in place of Polaris in US SSBNs and the possibility of the UK becoming the sole user and financial sponsor of the latter system sometime before the end of the useful life of the *Resolution* class. It was evident that the retention of expertise at Farnborough and Aldermaston was an important consideration for Ministers and approval was eventually given for the Chevaline programme.

In 1974 I was appointed to the (old style) position of Director General Ships and Head of the Royal Corps of Naval Constructors and thenceforth ceased to have day to day responsibility within the Polaris project.

This narrative is naturally concerned with the vehicle and some of the problems that loomed large at the time. I am mindful that the *raison d'être* was the missile system and I am lost in admiration for this US achievement and for the way Charles Shepherd and his teams, in both MOD and industry, transferred it to the UK, and indeed for the whole UK MOD/industry performance.

CHAPTER 18

The Weapon System
Charles Shepherd

Apart from the war years my twelve years in Polaris were the most challenging and satisfying of my forty years in the Royal Navy. I had the good fortune to start in Polaris on the weapon side then became Director Project Team (Submarines), and finally the Chief Polaris Executive himself, although by the time I got there the name had been changed to Deputy Controller (Polaris). This essay is mostly about the Polaris Weapon: others better qualified than I am have written about the other aspects.

I have been told that Polaris was the biggest single project the Navy had ever faced and at the very outset it was clear that our existing organisation would not do - too fractionated, too many independent authorities, too much democracy and too many escape routes.s

Now a little bit of personal background as to how I got involved at all in Polaris. Shortly after the end of the war a few Engineering Officers, (Steam) Plumber 'E' daggers, were press-ganged into Weapons. Yes, press-ganged. I was one of them and shortly afterwards became one of the Seaslug (Beam riding anti-aircraft missile) Project Officers. Were there more than one? Yes Sir, one for each department, and that was one of the first things to be avoided in Polaris. One Project, one Project Officer. All departments in the Admiralty became responsible to the Chief Polaris Executive (the first being Rear Admiral Rufus Mackenzie) for their Polaris work. Although these departments were still nominally responsible for professional aspects of Polaris, in effect their professionals were seconded to CPE to form the Polaris Executive. None of this Primus Inter Pares nonsense which had been in fashion for many years: no falling over backwards so as not to upset other departments. Admiral Le Fanu, then Controller of the Navy, directed that Polaris should be one organisation. I must say that I admired the way that the Heads of Department concerned conceded this point and agreed to the transfer of their own people to CPE - physically as well as in principle.

So there we were. A single organisation for Polaris. We strongly fought off rude remarks that we had thereby created an Admiralty within the Admiralty, but it was mighty like it. We sought advice from the US Polaris organisation in particular as to what shape our own single organisation should be. They had been through the same trauma themselves and were in a strong position to advise. Their advice was invaluable and freely given. Without this US advice I personally think we would have blundered on with the Good Old British Compromise philosophy.

As far as I can remember, Mike Simeon was the first Brit to be appointed specifically for Polaris. I was the second, in 1961 - nearly two years before the signing of the Anglo-US Polaris Sales Agreement - the key to everything in the Polaris weapon world. Throughout my time and probably since then the US were superb in their help, friendly and sincere. I can think of only one or two in their whole organisation who did not give their all in our cause.

From here on I will write only about the Polaris Weapon System. Others are more qualified than I am to deal with the submarine itself, nuclear propulsion, Polaris School, stores. finance and so on.

Perhaps here I should say something about the Polaris Sales Agreement itself. It was most ably negotiated by people much more important than I, and was a Government-to-Government political document. Broadly it said that the US would sell us the Polaris Weapon System including the missiles (but not the warheads), Fire control, Navigation, Launch System and Test Instrumentation. The design authority for the System would remain American and the Sales Agreement made no provision at all for transfer to the UK of any design information at all. At first I was not very happy about this but soon realised that it was a very good thing and greatly reduced the effect of British "WIBBIs" (Wouldn't it be better if ...?). Now Polaris even at that time was a proven system of great reliability and my experience had taught me that if a system works LEAVE IT ALONE, not the least reason being that we do not always know why a thing works and if we delve into its mysteries it may turn out nasty. I was very tough on our people in this respect and poured much cold water on our engineering and scientific acrobats and WIBBIs. This lost me some friends but kept Polaris on the rails - perhaps my biggest contribution to our cause. If we thought we needed design changes we agreed to submit them to the US for approval or otherwise. But it does not follow that since we were not a design authority all we needed was a team of mechanical monkeys to blindly follow installation procedures, testing and tuning, firing drill and the like. Ours was an independently operated deterrent and we had to get ourselves in a position to understand it thoroughly - indeed we were morally bound so to do with a weapon of this consequence. Far from having mechanical monkeys I was honoured to have some of the best technical people in the UK - in the RN, the Civil Service and in the very important teams from British industry.

As I have said, the Sales Agreement was a political document and my team had to make it function at the working level. We did this by translating the meat of the Agreement into what we called "Technical Arrangements" agreed with the US. This was not as easy as it sounds largely because the English and US languages are similar but not the same, eg take the expression "I am mad about my flat". In the US it means "I am furious about my puncture"; in the UK, it means "I love the apartment in which I am living". Drafting understandable Technical Arrangements was very difficult indeed. Interfaces between sub-systems and between UK ship systems and the US weapon system were most rigidly defined and controlled. Engineering disciplines in this region (known as "Configuration Control") was of a very high order. There was no other way. Discipline was a key word in Polaris and is just as important in a weapons system as anywhere else in life - including Rugby Football.

An early major task was to procure the Polaris Weapon System from the US. This sounds straightforward but we found it necessary to evolve a scheme of defining and grouping the various parts together with their ordering and delivery dates in a manner which could be computerised. Remember that this was over thirty years ago and computer ability was not what it is today. Nothing in this was new to us except perhaps in degree. But it all went very well.

At the time that the decision was made to go for Polaris (December 1962), the technical departments of the Admiralty and elsewhere were fully engaged in other work, and found themselves reduced in number by transfer to Polaris. They could not supply sufficient people for Polaris, so the Polaris Executive contracted with British industry for assistance. So that, in addition to getting the Polaris system working, we could get ourselves into a position to really know that system we requested from them a grade of engineer higher than would normally be engaged on Admiralty work. The Americans of course would have been pleased to do our installation, setting to work and testing and tuning for us, but this would have been against our policy of getting "with it". In November 1963 I therefore put it to the Americans that we were going to do as much as we possibly could ourselves. Some eyebrows were lifted at this but there is no doubt that having clearly stated our policy, the US did all it could to help us. To achieve this independence, it was necessary to send Admiralty people, both Naval and civilian, and UK contractors to the US for deep training at the US vendors works and to the Electric Boat Company (Groton) the lead yard shipbuilder with whom we had had cordial relations since the Holland boats of about 1900. Some of these courses were as long as nine months and I am happy to say that our chaps impressed the Americans. By June 1966 we had trained 250 people. As already mentioned we had contracted British industry to help us with the Polaris system. Contracts were placed as follows:

Vickers Barrow for the Missile Launch System

British Aircraft Corporation (as it then was - now British Aerospace) for the missile test equipment and the whole Polaris System as a system, particularly the analysis of shipyard test results.

General Electric Company for Fire Control and Test Instrumentation, the latter being test equipment put on board for initial testing and setting to work only, then removed.

Elliott and Sperry. Jointly for that part of the Ship's Navigation System intimately connected with the missile eg Ship's Inertial Navigation System (SINS).

EMI for Weapon Control Subsystem Simulation at our Polaris School in Faslane. This is the only time I have mentioned this School - I do not intend to mention it again as it was a major project in its own right and is dealt with elsewhere.

The above contractors were organised aboard the vessel in a way which had been thought about before but not implemented to any great depth. Basically our principle was that the shipbuilder should produce a complete ship and not just the hull and engines. So when working in the submarine at the shipbuilders our contractors were under the general direction of the shipbuilder - Vickers and Cammell & Laird - who also had a responsibility for co-ordinating the Polaris Weapon System tests in the later phases but not for actual missile firings. In addition to the contractors dealing with testing and tuning on board they acted as consultants to the Ministry of Defence. This was, I think, the first time that contractors and shipbuilders had acted in such an intimate capacity - and it worked very well indeed. It would be wrong not to mention calibration which was taken to a higher degree than anything we had practised before - again we followed US standards.

A feature I well remember was progress reporting to CPE once a fortnight. Special reporting techniques were introduced. Computer networks were produced and reports were set against these - in general we only reported what was going wrong - not on what was going right. Our thermometer-type charts we graded roughly as follows:-

In good shape   - no problems.
In minor weakness - Admiral, I have problems but I can cope with them.
In major weakness - Admiral, I have problems and I need your help.
Critical   - Admiral, you have problems and you need help!

I have been a bit wary about writing about people because I do not want to upset anybody. But I must say that Polaris succeeded largely because of the ability and extreme dedication of people on both sides of the Atlantic. Leave was a dirty word. I personally do not believe in taking a rest to "recharge my batteries"; if one does one finds that someone has pinched your job when you are not looking, or made a mess of it. At the pace Polaris was moving, even a week off made one out of date.

Everybody worked very, very hard from say 0730-2200 every day. On many occasions I rang my wife from the office and said "Sorry, I won't be home for dinner tonight". "Oh, why not?" she said. "Because I'm off to Washington, but I'll be home tomorrow!".

The Polaris set-up contained more non-conformists than is usual, and they were given their heads. They covered many levels of ability, many backgrounds and were strong-willed and determined; some to the point of pigheadedness. But a great sense of humour was present from the top to the bottom.

When a submarine was completed and tested and tuned, we went to the US trials base off Cape Canaveral, Florida and did live missile firings (dummy warheads of course) submerged. I had the honour of directing the first UK firings and they went very well, "Right in the pickle barrel" as Americans say. We were fifteen milliseconds late in a programme generated five years before. These firings were known as DASO (Demonstration and Shakedown Operation). Our sailors had a different interpretation which I am not going to tell you - but it related to the attractions of Cocoa Beach, just down the road, including "Topless Shoe-Shine".

Appendix - Things which have stuck in my mind

1   The top leadership on both sides of the Atlantic. Superb.
2   The followership of those beneath them.
3   Friendliness between the US and the Brits. The importance played by the Universal Social Catalyst (a wee dram).
4   Understanding wives who tolerated our crack-pot dedication.
5   The degree of toleration even between those of strong character (pigheads).
6   Great sense of humour on both sides.
7   The understanding manner in which Heads of Department "gave up" some of their best people to Polaris at the very start.
8   Detailed planning and progress reporting. I must say however that I am not convinced that it was as important as some thought.
9   Tough suppression of WIBBIs.
10   No truck with "The Great British Compromise".
11   The Mousetrap.

CHAPTER 19

Procuring the Weapon System
Peter La Niece

At the end of 1962 I was just over four months into a three to four year stint at the Admiralty (Bath) as Assistant Director Surface Weapons (G) when the news of the Nassau Agreement became public. The Royal Navy was about to procure Polaris.

The 1960 Le Fanu report was exhumed and I managed to obtain a copy to read. It was a complete blueprint for the establishment of a UK Polaris Project based as far as possible on the USN Special Projects Office with whom I had liaised during my previous time in Washington. The report was very comprehensive and fascinating reading.

The grapevine had already informed us that Flag Officer Submarines, then Rear Admiral Rufus Mackenzie, with whom I had served at Blockhouse in 1948/49, had been winkled out of his job to become the Project Leader and was already established in London. I decided that on my next visit to London I would call on Admiral Mackenzie and offer my services. I had in mind some unspecified position in the Polaris set-up in Bath. I found Admiral Mackenzie installed in a small temporary office; we talked briefly and I departed again to Bath and continued pushing paper.

The next development as far as I was concerned, was that, in my atomic weapons hat, I was instructed to join a joint Admiralty/Ministry of Aviation mission to the United States. This mission was to explore current progress of the A2 and A3 Polaris missiles and the related problem of fitting UK warheads. This became known as the "Front End" mission. The Admiralty was in no doubt that it wanted the A3 missile even though it was still unproven. The Ministry of Aviation was sceptical. I was to be the sole Admiralty representative and I set about preparing myself for the visit.

On the eve of my departure the phone rang. It was the Naval Secretary's office which dealt with Captain's appointments. I was informed that I had been selected to become Admiral Mackenzie's representative in Washington and was required to leave for the USA in two weeks time; would I come up to London on Monday for a briefing? I explained that I was due to leave early the following morning for a two week visit with the Front End mission. The answer was "come up as soon as you return; you will be leaving two weeks later".

I was told that my appointment might last as long as four years! I returned to West Meon that evening to pass this startling news to my wife. Next morning, Saturday 8 March, I flew with the mission to New York, *en route* to Washington.

In May 1958, shortly after I had returned from my appointment in Washington, I had briefed Commander Mike Simeon prior to his taking over my Polaris liaison duties as a full time resident within the Special Projects Office; he was given the short title of SPRN. He had subsequently been relieved by Commander Wid Graham, another gunnery officer. It was from him I was to take over in four weeks' time. On our arrival in Washington he took us under his wing and installed us in the Windsor Park Hotel in Connecticut Avenue, a few minutes away from the US federal buildings.

Our first call on Monday morning was on the Special Projects Office. We subsequently visited the Polaris prime contractor, Lockheed Missile and Space Company, at Sunnyvale, California, as well as other facilities around the USA. In the evenings there was much discussion among the "Men from the Ministry" who clearly remained sceptical about the A3 missile and showed a marked preference for the earlier A2. Needless to say I did not share this view; apart from other considerations the A2 would be obsolescent before our submarines were in service but that didn't seem to worry the men from the Ministry. By the middle of the second week we were back in Washington. In view of my impending preparations for returning to the USA in little over two weeks' time I decided to return 24 hours before the others and headed for the overnight flight on the Thursday night. The economy class part of the aircraft was packed and very stuffy; I had developed a heavy cold and the flight was at an unusually high altitude; at one point I experienced difficulty in breathing and nearly passed out. I was still feeling groggy when I disembarked and proceeded straight to the Admiralty to report to Admiral Mackenzie. He whisked me off immediately to the Ministry of Aviation for a meeting with the Controller General of Guided Weapons - an Air Chief Marshal. I was asked to give a verbal report on the mission. Having stressed that mine was probably a minority view, I recommended that we simply had to trust the Special Projects office's ability successfully to complete the development of the A3 and go for it ourselves; after all they were fitting it to all their own submarines; they had to make it work. Having said my piece I was released and repaired to West Meon to grapple with domestic problems.

We decided that the boys would remain at their boarding school and visit us during the school holidays. It was clear that my wife and daughter could not accompany me immediately and would have to follow later. Also we felt we could not again face letting the house and resolved to put it on the market.

On Sunday night I returned to Bath to spend the week clearing my desk and turning over. The following week was a frenzy of briefings in London and Bath. Since I had first called on him Admiral Mackenzie's title had been confirmed as Chief Polaris Executive. In London I met his assistant, Captain Rae McKaig and the two senior civil servants, Bob Lewin and Peter Nailor. In the short time available they all told me as much of their plans as they could. There was a twin challenge for the UK project; the first was a very demanding time scale and the second was to complete within budget. They also confirmed that, as Senior UK Polaris Representative in Washington, I was to have overall responsibility for everything going on there including, despite the long shadow of Samuel Pepys, financial matters.

In the Bath team the Weapons Director was Captain Charles Shepherd, a Weapon Engineer whom I had met briefly but at that time did not know very well. He was to provide me with two Weapon Engineering officers to join my initial team in Washington, with a promise of more to follow. I felt that it was essential that I had some administrative support and asked for a Lieutenant of the Supply and Secretariat branch to join with the time honoured title of "Captain's Secretary". There was initial opposition to this latter proposal from the Appointers. I also made courtesy calls on the First Lord of the Admiralty, Lord Carrington; the First Sea Lord, Admiral Sir Caspar John; other Board members and Directors of the civilian Stores Departments. Finally I was all set to go.

On the morning of Saturday 6 April 1963 in the Heathrow departure lounge I met for the first time the initial members of the SPRN team, the two Weapons Engineers, Peter Evans and Frank Elvy; the latter had just flown back from service in a Far East aircraft carrier. The third member, Chris White the Secretary, had been given little over 24 hours notice to join the party. We flew out of Heathrow on one of the first through flights to Washington's new Dulles Airport.

Following the Nassau conference between the President and the Prime Minister there had been a series of meetings on both sides of the Atlantic to negotiate the details of the Polaris Sales Agreement. This was signed in the British Embassy in Washington at noon on 6 April.

Above: Admiral I.J. Galantin USN, British Weapons Officer, Rear Admiral H.S.Mackenzie, Captain C.W.H. Shepherd, Rear Admiral Levering Smith USN.

Below: Keel laying of HMS *Resolution*, the first British Polaris submarine; Rear Admiral Horace Law (Flag Officer Submarines), Mr. Alfred Simms (Director General Ships, Admiralty), Mr. Len Redshaw (Managing Director, Vickers Shipbuilders), Rear Admiral H.S.Mackenzie (Chief Polaris Executive), Mr. Rowland Baker (Technical Director, Polaris).

Above: The Royal Navy Polaris School (with the tall tower) at Clyde Submarine Base, Faslane. A mock-up of a Polaris missile is in the foreground, and the size of the missile can be judged against the car parked alongside it. The buildings behind the school make up the massive stores complex that supports the submarine squadrons and parent establishment HMS *Neptune* that occupy the base.

Below: Admiralty Floating Dock No. 60 with base buildings behind.

Above: Polaris missile base at Coulport. As well as missiles Coulport handled all Torpedoes for the 3rd and 10th Squadrons.

Below: A missile in its transport capsule being raised for loading.

Missile capsules in place for loading.

Launch of HMS *Resolution* by HM The Queen Mother at Barrow. 15th
September 1966.

Above: HMS *Resolution* at launch.

Below: HMS *Resolution* at sea.

Above: Rear Admiral H.S.Mackenzie with the first CO of Resolution (Starboard crew) Commander K. Frewer and the Captain, 10th Submarine Squadron (Polaris) Captain Kenneth Vause (in khaki).

Below: The captain (in this case Commander Colin Grant) with The Key.

Above: Junior rates mess - studying tactics on the Uckers board.

Below: Commemorative plaque, 1996.

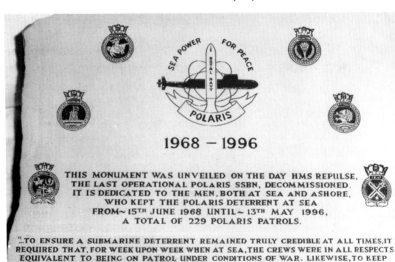

SEA POWER FOR PEACE

ROYAL NAVY

POLARIS

1968 – 1996

THIS MONUMENT WAS UNVEILED ON THE DAY HMS REPULSE,
THE LAST OPERATIONAL POLARIS SSBN, DECOMMISSIONED.
IT IS DEDICATED TO THE MEN, BOTH AT SEA AND ASHORE,
WHO KEPT THE POLARIS DETERRENT AT SEA
FROM~ 15TH JUNE 1968 UNTIL~ 13TH MAY 1996,
A TOTAL OF 229 POLARIS PATROLS.

"..TO ENSURE A SUBMARINE DETERRENT REMAINED TRULY CREDIBLE AT ALL TIMES, IT
REQUIRED THAT, FOR WEEK UPON WEEK WHEN AT SEA, THE CREWS WERE IN ALL RESPECTS
EQUIVALENT TO BEING ON PATROL UNDER CONDITIONS OF WAR. LIKEWISE, TO KEEP
THE SUBMARINES AT SEA ON A SCHEDULE PERMITTING NOT THE SLIGHTEST VARIATION
REQUIRED A SIMILAR APPROACH FROM ALL THOSE WHO WORKED ASHORE."

VICE ADMIRAL SIR HUGH MACKENZIE KCB DSO + DSC, 1995.

We touched down at Dulles two hours later. The Americans were impressed by the nice timing.

Once again Commander Wid Graham, who was to remain for a while as my Deputy, was on hand and we were quickly established in the Windsor Park Hotel. Next day, a Sunday, the first meeting took place with a visiting UK Polaris team. There was no time off at this stage of the project. At 0800 the following morning I attended for the first time, the regular Monday meeting of the Special Projects Office Management Centre. As was their custom with all new members joining their staff I was welcomed and then they moved on immediately to their regular slick weekly presentation of the project status.

The first Director, Admiral Raborn, had since been relieved and so after the meeting I was introduced to his successor, Rear Admiral Pete Galantin and his Technical Director, my old acquaintance, Levering Smith, by then promoted to Rear Admiral. I also met the heads of the various branches of the organisation. The Special Projects Office used the abbreviation of SP. The Technical Director was SP 20, his branch heads were SP 21 to 27. There and then I became SP 50.

After this, with my team of three, we crossed to the adjoining building to the offices of the British Naval Staff, of which I had been a member five years previously. There we met the Admiral, Rear Admiral John Bush. He offered us temporary accommodation in the British Navy Staff offices. We were provided with a table and four chairs, pencils and a stack of plain white paper. Talk about starting from scratch! We then met those Commanders on the British Navy Staff who were to become part-time members of our team providing support in their particular fields; they included Submarine Operations, Radio and Navigational aids and Ship Construction specialists. After that we got down to work.

A couple of days later I was requested by the Embassy to attend a full blown Press Conference at the US State Department. I was to "support" the Information Minister from the British Embassy. We duly assembled in front of the world's press against a background of US flags, eagles and all. The US side was led by Rear Admiral Mott, one of the USN's head legal officers, who had spent the previous three months negotiating the Sales Agreement. With only a few days in the Project I felt at a slight disadvantage. Even more so when the questions began to fly and the Information Minister displayed immense skill in deflecting them all in my direction.

The climax came when a correspondent from either the London

Times or the BBC, both of which at that time were antipathetic to Polaris, posed the following question -"The Polaris Sales Agreement says that immediately after the ratification of the Sales Agreement the first payment would be paid by the UK into a special trust fund. Has this been done?". We had not yet even got round to thinking about this so I gave a weasel-worded reply and returned to the office to draft a signal which effectively said "please send funds". To my astonishment I received a reply overnight to draw from the the Treasury Delegation in the Embassy a cheque for a million dollars. I knew exactly what to do. The man in the Treasury Delegation was the very same Teddy Baldock whom I had known in my previous tour in Washington. I rapidly had in my possession a cheque for the required amount. Proudly I approached the Head of the Finance Branch of SP and asked him to accept this munificence. He was sorry but he hadn't the authority to receive this type of payment so I retreated somewhat non-plussed. Fortunately on the Friday evening we were invited to a cocktail party given by the Chief of Staff of the British Navy Staff. At this party, I met a USN officer whom I had known previously, one Fred Salvia; he was, by chance, serving in the Pentagon department into which we directed our payments in 1958. After a couple of drinks I told him of my problem and Fred agreed to accept the cheque on Monday morning. I was off the hook. Eventually SP got their act together and future payments were straightforward - except for one occasion which I will recount later.

The following day, Saturday, I set off to find temporary accommo-dation for myself pending the arrival of the family. I discovered a studio apartment in Presidential Gardens in Arlandria, Virginia. Not very fashionable, despite the grand name, but good enough and better than a hotel. It was there that I very rapidly learned how to cook.

Very soon SP had made ready our office accommodation in their own areas and we rapidly settled in. I drew up a staff structure and allotted staff codes which paralleled those in use in SP. Officially the operation in which we were all engaged was a Joint Programme. In every respect SP took the "Joint" definition seriously and could not have been more helpful. In more ways than one we were fully integrated.

I was then asked to call on the British Ambassador, David Ormsby-Gore, later to become Lord Harlech. He was a great friend of President Kennedy and the US Administration. Despite this, to his considerable embarrassment, he had only been made aware of the imminent cancellation of the Skybolt project, which led to the Nassau Conference, shortly before the event. He was very charming and asked to be briefed about the Joint UK/US Polaris project and to return occasionally to bring him up to date. This continued for a while but eventually tailed off when I think he became confident that we were not going to "do a Skybolt" on him.

A further reinforcement to our team was a Ministry of Aviation Scientific Officer who had transferred from the Skybolt project. He was the first of a section dealing with the UK "front end" which was, of course, to be developed in Aldermaston. Being ex-Skybolt, and still rather smarting at the demise of that project, he was not particularly at home with the Navy and did not remain long; he was replaced by two other Ministry of Aviation Scientific Officers. The US Navy had traditionally been reluctant to deal with the Ministry of Aviation, which they always associated with the RAF who, they knew, had close ties with the US Air Force. Interservice rivalry in the United States being what it was, dealing with the Ministry of Aviation incurred the possibility of information finding its way back via the RAF to the USAF. To the USN this was tantamount to dealing with the enemy. Partly because of this and partly to match the SP management structure, it had been agreed that our team would be a fundamentally naval one with the Ministry of Aviation staff filling appropriate posts.

All business relating to the front end had to be conducted under the procedures laid down in the US/UK Atomic Energy Act. Although somewhat laborious both sides made it work. One of the areas into which I was expressly forbidden to stray was that of nuclear propulsion. This arose from the uncooperative attitude of Admiral Hyman Rickover, the US Navy's nuclear propulsion "guru". Up to that time the only RN officer with whom Rickover was prepared to talk was Admiral Mountbatten. So avoid Rickover I did; even to the extent, on one occasion at an Embassy Garden Party to celebrate the Queen's birthday to which we had both been invited, of doing a "hide and seek" evasion ploy around the shrubbery clutching strawberries and cream and a glass of champagne.

Because of the national importance and urgency of the Project, SP considered themselves virtually on a war footing. Accordingly, alone of all the Defence organisations in Washington, they wore uniform; all the others wore plain clothes. Unfortunately I discovered the khaki uniform acquired for my previous Washington tour of duty was showing signs of disintegration. It would have taken too long to have another made by Gieves in London and sent out; so I purchased one from the USN and wore that for the remainder of my time adorned, of course, with RN Buttons and insignia. Both the shade of khaki and the cut were slightly different and, occasionally, RN visitors gave me a rather sideways look when they noticed my hybrid dress.

Our task within SP was primarily the procurement of the weapon systems, missiles and various services; outside SP's province there was a formidable list of what, in the USN, were classified as Shipbuilder's items; these were to be purchased by the UK direct from the USN's Lead Shipyard for their Polaris submarines. The shipyard concerned was the Electric Boat Company at Groton on the opposite side of the river to the US Submarine Base at New London, Connecticut. A Constructor Commander and two draughtsmen were added to the SPRN team and installed at Groton to handle the purchase of these items.

Coincidentally I received an invitation to attend the launching at Groton of the latest US SSBN. I decided to travel there, killing a number of birds with one stone by attending the launch, meeting our new man and the Electric Boat Company team. My invitation was also extended to my wife. As she had not yet arrived in the USA I thought it would be a good idea to give Chris White an outing and, unthinkingly, asked if I could bring my secretary. Imagining my secretary was probably a nifty little blonde they seemed slightly taken aback. When I arrived with a handsome young bachelor Lieutenant they were even more startled. To avoid any further misunderstanding I decided to retitle his position as Administrative Assistant. There was an amusing episode relating to this launch. The submarine was to be named *Tecumseh* after a legendary Indian Chief. A descendant was invited to attend the launch and stand on the superstructure in full tribal regalia as the vessel went down the slipway. Unfortunately on the preceding night he partook of a great deal of fire water and was only just revived in time to take his place; he was a very sad and bedraggled looking Indian.

The submarine was duly launched. Although I had seen a Polaris missile it was the first time I had seen a Polaris submarine and I remember being mightily impressed by its size. The A3 missile was 31 feet in length and 54 inches in diameter. Each submarine carried 16 missiles. It followed that the hull was much larger than other submarines; the class to which *Tecumseh* belonged was 425 feet in length and displaced 7250 tons. Our submarines would be similar.

There was much food for thought.

A steady flow of visiting teams from the UK had meantime been arriving to cover such aspects as the design of the RN Polaris School and the UK Armament Depot. Later we also had the Front End team back again.

After I had debriefed on the subject of the choice of missile in London in March, the argument had rumbled on in high places with the Ministry of Aviation fighting a rearguard action favouring the A2; eventually, in June, a decision was made to go for the A3. I never discovered the extent to which my pennyworth contributed to the decision but I did point out that, on that occasion, I had stepped off an overcrowded flight virtually straight into an important meeting feeling well below par and could easily have made an unconsidered remark and harmed the course of events. As a result of representations made by me, and doubtless by others too, we were henceforth allowed to travel First Class across the Atlantic, provided we were working the following day. So, indirectly, some good came out of the Ministry of Aviation's prevarication.

By that time large consignments of documentation were being despatched to Bath where the demand for information was insatiable. Unfortunately the documentation did not always contain the depth of detail they were accustomed to work with on new equipment. There was a cliché running around Bath to the effect that "we do not know what we do not know"! With choice of missile made, the way seemed clear to place our order for all the other components of the system. Indeed SP themselves were becoming anxious because they were about to place contracts for their last batch of six submarines and it would clearly be to everyone's benefit if a combined order was made. Moreover, there was a clause in the Sales Agreement, stating that we should wherever possible arrange joint orders to achieve a better price. However there were misgivings in Bath who believed they were being pressured to give decisions before they had fully digested all the information they felt they needed. In this view they were supported by my opposite number, the SP representative by then in post on Admiral Mackenzie's staff with the title of SPUK. Make haste more slowly they all said. Fortunately Captain Rae McKaig was visiting the USA at the time with Captain Charles Shepherd and SPUK, Captain Phil Rollings USN. The matter was finally resolved at a long meeting at, of all places, a motel room in Charleston, South Carolina, over a bottle of whisky.

A start could then be made in processing our shopping list. Whilst the technical assessments were being made, the original SPRN, Commander Mike Simeon, had joined the London team. He had been across to discuss with SP the production of a computerised shopping list based on their own procedures. This was distributed widely on both sides of the Atlantic and was invaluable. It was regularly updated as orders were placed, contracted and eventually delivered. We felt happier now that we were underway with the ordering started for most of the urgent items; the only exception was the Navigation system of which more later.

While they were in Washington both Rae McKaig and Charles Shepherd stayed with me at my Presidential Gardens apartment where we could talk more freely. On their subsequent visits they always stayed at our house and we got to know each other extremely well. We did not always agree but the relationships were too strong to be strained by small differences. One of the lighter sides of the Project occurred one Saturday afternoon when all three of us were obliged to do a little personal laundry. We adjourned to a nearby Laundromat and continued our discussions while watching our smalls revolving majestically around.

One Friday evening at a party, Mrs Levering Smith told me of an unfurnished house to let next door to them in McLean, Virginia. I visited it next day, decided it was fine, phoned the owner, a retired USN Captain, and the deal was clinched. I bought a standard lease agreement from the local drug store for, I seem to remember, a dollar; I filled it in, signed and sent it off for countersignature. A good morning's work. British conveyancing solicitors please note. I then bought one bed, one plate, knife, fork and spoon plus a glass and a bottle of whisky, vacated Presidential Gardens and moved in.

I flew to the UK to attend a meeting which gave me the opportunity to help my wife pack up and put our furniture into store. We said farewell to our house, as yet unsold. We heard a week or so later that a purchaser had been found so that was a problem out of the way. Since I was already in the air on the way back to the USA, the family group, which included the dog, had to put themselves on board the *Queen Elizabeth*. I subsequently met them at New York and drove them down to McLean. Since moving in myself I had bought the minimum set of furniture. Our heavy baggage soon arrived and we quickly settled in, albeit in a rather rudimentary fashion. Our daughter was enrolled at a private school in Fairfax County, Virginia. The boys, then aged 10 and

12, who had come out with the others were, at the end of the holidays, to return to the UK, on what was to become for them a sequence of unaccompanied transatlantic flights.

Meanwhile, the SPRN team, mixed naval and civilian, was nearly up to strength. It eventually reached nearly fifty with representatives resident around the USA at Groton (Connecticut), Norfolk (Virginia), Charleston (South Carolina), Sunnyvale (California) and Puget South (Washington State). The office staff were recruited locally mainly from UK expatriates. I decided that I should follow SP custom and indoctrinate them all. The objective was to gain their interest and support so that they would have some idea of what we were trying to achieve, also the stress under which we were operating. We "anglicised" the SP "Road Show" which was a slick presentation all in glorious technicolor and, one Saturday morning invited them all, children included, to SP's Management Centre. The indoctrination was a great success and one civil servant's wife told me that it was the first time since they were married that she had any idea what her husband did at work!

There then occurred two tragedies. The first was the sudden removal from the Project of my opposite number in London, Captain Phil Rollings USN. Following a heart operation he had developed a blood clot which necessitated amputation of a leg. He was a great character and much missed.

The second was of major international significance. During the lunch break on Friday 11 November I was returning by bus from a visit to my bank; at the stop by the White House a passenger boarded the bus with the startling news that President Kennedy had been shot during a visit to Dallas. By the time I reached the office this had been confirmed and soon afterwards all Federal offices were closed and everyone instructed to return immediately to their homes. On my way back I passed the boundary fence of the home of Robert F Kennedy around which had already been thrown a protective ring of police. At home we watched events unfold live on TV. First the swearing in of President Johnson and the return of the late President's body by air to Washington. Then, the next morning, the shooting of Lee Harvey Oswald and, finally, on Monday, the amazing funeral ceremony with, amongst others the Duke of Edinburgh and General Charles de Gaulle walking in a disorganised group through the streets of Washington, in what looked more like a football crowd than a funeral procession. We returned to work on Tuesday morning with the realisation that we had seen history in the making.

On 31 December my new Deputy, Commander Sam Mulholland, was promoted to Captain. Immediately the Works Department arrived, removed all the furniture and the carpet square and replaced it with wall to wall fitted carpet as befitted his new rank. When, some time later, Sam's relief who was a Commander arrived, the same team returned with a pair of carpet scissors and cut two feet off each side of the carpet, thus reducing it to a carpet square again. The US services had their bureaucratic rules too.

In January 1964 there was a major indoctrination visit by the senior management of the UK contractors led by the UK Technical Director, Rowland Baker and Captain Charles Shepherd. There were ten in the party altogether. Because they were all highly involved at the time getting the project underway I was asked to arrange a whirlwind programme and whirlwind it was. They arrived on Saturday evening and on the Sunday we laid on a curry lunch at our house to introduce them to senior SP officers and our USN escorts. Due to a heavy snowstorm we had to depart somewhat prematurely for the airport bound for the US Polaris School at Norfolk, Virginia. After this visit on the Monday we were due to return to Washington and thence to New England followed by the West Coast. However Washington and the whole of the East Coast were, by that time, completely snowed in. The whole programme was therefore rapidly rescheduled and we caught the only plane that was leaving Norfolk that day which was bound for Atlanta, Georgia. From there we headed for Contractor's plants in California, initially two in the Los Angeles area, followed by Sunnyvale; then from San Francisco we headed back to New England visiting the General Electric Plant at Pittsfield, Massachusetts and the Electric Boat Company at Groton. On the Saturday morning, after a call on the Sperry Gyroscope Company at Long Island, we put our visitors on to a flight back to London. They were exhausted but more knowledgeable and had acquired some idea of the general atmosphere of hustle associated with the US end of the business. As a by-product we had all got to know each other a good deal better than we would have ever done at routine meetings.

For months a great argument had been going on in the UK over the choice of Ships Inertial Navigation System (SINS) to be fitted in the UK submarines. The alternatives lay between a US manufactured system and one being developed in the UK under the auspices of the Director General Weapons and one of his research establishments. To preserve the principle of commonality with the US, the Polaris Executive championed the US system while the Director General Weapons supported the UK version. The dispute had to go to the Controller of the Navy, Admiral Le Fanu, for decision. One morning I was summoned to see Admiral Bush; he had been phoned by Admiral Le Fanu who asked him to consult Admiral Galantin; after a quick briefing off he went and got the facts from the horse's mouth so to speak. The outcome was that the Polaris Executive won the day and the US system was chosen. Many of the discussions at our various meetings revolved around the principle of commonality; Charles Shepherd was from time to time heard to say "if the Americans paint it pink, we shall paint it pink".

Another area of concern was that of "interfaces". In nearly every boundary between the US equipment and the UK-built submarine there was an interface, whether it was piping or wiring, or power supplies; there were other examples too numerous to mention. The technical officers at Bath were, quite rightly, always concerned about this aspect and much attention was paid to it.

There was, in addition, an interface problem in negotiations. One of the difficulties experienced initially at meetings was the difference in official language used by either side. For instance, in the UK "tabling a paper" meant bringing it up for discussion; in the US it meant pigeon-holing it. National budgetary calendars were different as were contracting procedures. Both sides had very skilful civil servants in their teams and this, plus goodwill, soon ironed out such difficulties. A more intractable problem however was that, whereas in the UK a high level of technical detail was available at headquarters, SP had, from its inception, always relied on its contractors. Bath were often surprised that SP were sometimes unable to answer a query without seeking help from a contractor. This was not due to any lack of competence but simply the way it had always been. What hurt the UK team was that they were charged for having their queries answered; it was analogous to employing a consultant and being surprised when he sent in his account.

In February 1964 I flew to the UK for some meetings. Whilst I was there I was able to attend the keel-laying of the first UK Polaris submarine at Vickers shipyard at Barrow in Furness. This was a significant indication of progress.

In the course of the following months we had two VIP visitors whom I had to accompany on their tours. The first was the First Lord of the Admiralty, Lord Jellicoe. There were the usual briefings in Washington followed by a flight to Cape Canaveral, Florida, for a day at sea in a Polaris submarine, USS *Henry Clay*. During a tour of the submarine the escorting officer took us to the machinery compartments including a look through the inspection window into the reactor compartment. In the past all visits to this area by the British had been vetoed by Admiral Rickover. When I returned to the office I was questioned by the Staff Marine Engineering Officer as to what I had seen. Since I had been expressly ordered to steer clear of such matters and was pretty ignorant about nuclear propulsion, I was not much help. At the end of the day at sea which concluded with an official dinner in the Officers' Club, Lord Jellicoe, who was indefatigable, debriefed us all on the day's events over a night-cap. He concluded by saying brightly "Now who's for the bright lights?". I declined; I needed my sleep. But it might have been interesting to accompany him.

The second visit was by Mr Julian Amery, the Minister of Aviation, who was accompanied by his Permanent Secretary, Head of Procurement and Admiral Dossor, who was Admiral Mackenzie's representative in the Ministry of Aviation. This time our trip to Cape Canaveral was in Air Force Two, one of the President's planes lent for the occasion. It was very plush. During the flight, when we were at about 30,000 feet over Georgia, the Captain of the aircraft asked Mr Amery if he would like to look at the "radio shack"; this was from where the President kept in touch with affairs while he was airborne. "Would the Minister like to make a call?". He phoned his wife who was on holiday in Switzerland; she wasn't best pleased from all accounts since it was the middle of the night for her. Some years later I met Mr Amery again and reminded him of the occasion. He told me that a bill for the call was eventually sent by the USAF to the Ministry of Defence in London. Since by that time Mr Amery's political party was out of office, he said he had been obliged to pay for the call out of his own pocket. In addition to the Polaris facilities at the Cape, Mr Amery's party was also given a full briefing by NASA on their various projects. This included a tour of launch pads and assembly buildings of the then current series of satellite shots. The immense size was breathtaking. We also went to the West Coast and the visit culminated in a reception and banquet at the Fairmont Hotel in San Francisco. I had to hurry back to Washington and could only attend the reception but I remember that the small eats alone were so exotic and plentiful that I did not need any dinner. I later learned that the banquet itself was so lavish that the US contractor had to be admonished by Admiral Galantin for over-doing it; after all it was all going onto the contractor's charges somewhere.

These were but two of a stream of visitors who ranged from Admiral Mackenzie, whom I invariably accompanied, down to technical groups who were escorted by the appropriate members of the SPRN team.

SP had an extensive private telex network around their various activities throughout the USA. In 1963 this network had been extended to London with a spur in Bath. Between 0900 and 1200 British time the London and Bath offices could load this network with messages so that when we arrived at our desks at about 0715 (12.15 British time) a batch was already waiting. There was a daily challenge to try and obtain answers and reply by 1730, when we usually left for home and before 1800 when the London terminal closed (which was 2300 their time), The originator in the UK could therefore have a reply on his desk first thing the next morning. To be in our office at 0715 entailed leaving home a 0650, a little early for some, but at least it meant beating the Washington rush hour The lunch break was rarely more than 30 minutes and often omitted altogether with sandwiches taken at the desk. The pace was frenetic and the hours long. I think that our work output man for man was probably greater than our counterparts in the UK and incidentally the climate often more extreme. Above all it was important to retain one's sense of humour.

Some of the messages from Bath were pretty niggling and there was sometimes a tendency for the exchanges to become a little acrimonious. Inevitably there was a touch of "NIH syndrome". This was not unique. NIH ("Not invented here") was a common characteristic associated with any equipment not developed in house. The UK technical people were all accustomed to designing their own equipment and having to deal with a system they could on no account modify was hard to accept. As time went by mutual confidence increased, helped in no small degree by reciprocal visits on both sides.

One morning, soon after arriving in the office, I received a phone call from the Washington correspondent of one of the British national dailies. He asked me to comment on a contentious item concerning the UK Polaris programme contained in that morning's issue of his paper in London. I had some difficulty in disengaging without giving the opportunity to misquote me. Consequently I asked the London office, whenever an article on Polaris appeared in the future, to telex the contents to me so that at least I was aware of its existence the moment

I arrived in the office. This worked well and I was not caught out unprepared again.

While on the subject of the media, a team from the BBC were in Washington at about this time making a documentary about the work of the British Embassy and its numerous offshoots. They asked if they could film a meeting between the RN and the USN about the Joint Polaris project. The problem was that most of the work we were doing was classified. However, the Deputy Director of SP, one of the Branch Heads and myself agreed to discuss the rather mundane question of training. The camera team duly arrived, led by Mr David Dimbleby, then only a relatively junior reporter. The lights went on, the clapper-board girl clapped her board and off we went for a full 30 minutes. How we managed to get so much out of such a relatively barren subject I do not know. Most meetings with SP were crisp and brief. By the last few minutes we were definitely flagging. Needless to say it was a very short clip out of our last few minutes that was eventually included in the programme when it was shown on BBC Television.

Eventually a trickle of equipment began to flow. Most of the early items were destined for the RN Polaris School in which the first system would be installed. However, before this, not only the School instructors but also a proportion of the crews who were to stand by the first submarines during their construction, had to be trained in the use and upkeep of their equipment. We arranged with the USN that all this early training should be carried out at their Polaris School in Dam Neck, just outside Norfolk, Virginia. The first arrivals were officer instructors; they were followed by a steady stream of officers and mostly senior ratings reaching a peak of about fifty at any one time. They were all fully integrated with the USN classes and generally acquitted themselves well. On account of the markedly different living conditions in the US Navy most of them found the whole experience rather exhilarating although quite a culture shock. Absence of their tot of rum was hardly offset by the liberal quantities of ice cream available.

A General Election was looming in the UK and the press was full of reports of the likelihood of a Socialist Government, if it came to power, cancelling the Polaris project. In the event, in October 1964, they did win the election and we waited with bated breath to learn of the fate of the project. By that time contracts had been placed through SP with their manufacturers, for the bulk of the weapons systems for five submarines and the Polaris School, plus spares, so significant cancellation charges would be involved. After a period of uncertainty the only change was the cancellation of the fifth boat, with consequent revision of the shopping list. We were able to breath again.

It was at about this time, during a routine visit by Captain Rae McKaig, by then officially designated as Deputy Chief Polaris Executive, that Admiral Galantin advised us to give early thought to setting up a plan for orderly replacement of senior members of the Polaris Executive. SP had retained their initial team intact until the completion of their first submarine, at which stage a significant proportion of their best talent left for sea to further their careers. Rae McKaig and I discussed this principle and he carried back proposals for succession which eventually were put into effect. Ironically he was the first senior member of the team to be replaced in the following year. My own position was unclear, the original duration of appointment having been given as "might be four years". After some thought I concluded that the sensible time for me to be relieved was the summer of 1966, probably by a submariner. By this time the equipment would have been ordered and much of it on the way. Attention would then be turning to the planning for the completion of the submarines and their demonstration firings which would take place on the US Missile Range off Florida. Moreover if I delayed return to the mainstream of naval life much longer than this I would probably be destined for a "9 to 5" job for the rest of my career.

Transatlantic travel was by then becoming routine. I developed a pattern which went like this. My overnight flight to London was booked for a Thursday. In the two or three days prior to this I jotted down, in a completely haphazard fashion, short notes on items to report. Through flights to and from Washington had been discontinued by the British carrier and the internal connecting flight left Washington in the late afternoon. On arrival in New York I repaired to the first class lounge where, over a whisky courtesy of the airline, I assembled my debriefing notes into a coherent order. When the flight took off I waved off the proffered champagne, ended my dinner with the main course and instructed the cabin staff, on pain of death, not to disturb me until we were approaching Heathrow. Then sheltering behind the free-issue eyeshades, I slept or tried to. This way I felt more rested but, of course, jet lag cannot be entirely avoided. On the Friday morning I went straight from Heathrow to Admiral Mackenzie's office and spent the day, mentally on auto pilot, delivering my report based on the notes I had compiled. That evening I visited my parents; the following day I saw our eldest son, who was by then at Tonbridge

School; on the Sunday I travelled down to our younger son who was still at Westbury House. On Monday, jet lag overcome, it was back to London or Bath for meetings possibly followed by a visit to the shipyards or to Scotland. I usually flew back to Washington on the Thursday evening reaching home just before midnight, ready for a day in the office on Friday, picking up the reins again before devoting a weekend to domestic matters and, hopefully, a little relaxation. I did this fourteen times in the course of the three years.

On one of my return flights I just made it to La Guardia from Kennedy airport in time to catch the last shuttle flight to Washington. The aircraft lumbered seemingly interminably out to the end of the runway; it then stopped before take off and the cabin staff made the customary announcement welcoming us aboard the flight to Washington. The response from someone in the rear of the aircraft was a drunken wail of "I wanna go ter Bawston!". The aircraft then proceeded to lumber all the way back to the boarding gate and disembarked the tipsy Bostonian. I was amazed at the tolerant attitude of other passengers; having already been travelling for over eight hours I personally felt like lynching him.

When it was simply to attend a single day of meetings our trips to the West Coast were a flying marathon. For instance, for a meeting at Lockheeds, which occurred from time to time, I caught the 1800 flight from Washington to San Francisco. On arrival there, five hours later, at about 2000 local time I drove the twenty odd miles down the Freeway to Sunnyvale in a self drive hire car to be met at the motel by our local representative with whom I had a couple of hours discussion. Next morning it was on to the plant to spend the day at meetings, then the return drive to the airport for an overnight flight by the "Red Eye", as it was called, back to Washington. After a shower and breakfast it was the normal time to leave for the office.

On one occasion I boarded the Red Eye and was somewhat surprised when the take off rather resembled an aircraft leaving a carrier's flight deck. While we were banking into a steep climb the Captain came on the air and said "Good evening folks, in view of the very favourable flying conditions tonight, we are going to attempt to beat the record time for the flight to Washington". We did. But who wants to arrive in a terminal at five o'clock in the morning anyhow? There wasn't an airport bus or taxi in sight.

There were two other memorable flights. Memorable for different reasons. The first was one in a small company plane from Washington to Pittsfield, Massachusetts. The route was somewhat more inland than usual, clear of the urban sprawl of the numerous East Coast cities and across the foothills of the Appalachian Mountains, at relatively low altitude. It was a clear bright autumn evening and all that could be seen for miles and miles were trees in brilliant colours of reds and browns - a sight I shall never forget.

The second flight was a scheduled one on a minor airline from New York to Groton, Connecticut. The check-in desk was a small unattended kiosk with a telephone which had a recorded voice that said someone would be along soon. A man did appear and led us through a door through the back of the terminal building on to the apron where there was a small six seater aircraft. Having loaded our baggage in the nose of the aircraft the man asked us to board. Since there were seven of us and only six passenger seats, I was put in the co-pilot's seat. The man then climbed in behind us; he was also the pilot. We taxied off towards a remote runway, To get there we had to cross one of the main runways upon which, every minute or so, large jet aircraft were landing and taking off; it was like a pedestrian crossing a busy main road. Soon after we ourselves had taken off we were enveloped in a heavy snowstorm. Undeterred the indomitable pilot pressed on. Soon he took out a torch and aimed its beam at the wing on his side. He then passed the torch to me and said, airily, "see if we're icing up, will you"! Eventually we looked down and there, amazingly, was the runway at Groton. We splashed down on to about three inches of wet snow and I alighted with a feeling of some relief.

In February, Admiral Levering Smith replaced Admiral Galantin as the Director SP. Admiral Galantin went on to become the Chief of Naval Material, the equivalent of our Controller of the Navy. In company with other senior members of SP, I was invited to the change of command ceremony. This was a uniquely USN procedure; there were formal readings of "orders", followed by eulogies and finally a speech by the outgoing Chief of Naval Material which terminated in him becoming overwhelmed by emotion and having to be helped from the podium! I could not imagine a parallel to this in London.

By now our relationship with Admiral Levering Smith and his wife had blossomed from being just next door neighbours to a rather more intimate status of being firm family friends. I was punctiliously careful not to exploit the relationship in any of our formal dealings. We periodically met in each others' homes for a quiet drink and a chat. We were invited to their Thanksgiving dinner - a signal note of friendship in the USA. The Levering Smiths, who were childless, also became interested in the younger members of our household, particularly our daughter. On one occasion, at the age of eleven, she was given as homework a particularly abstruse scientific project. I was away and Admiral Smith, who was visiting, gave her some coaching. When I returned I also provided some assistance. All three of us then waited for her grading. It was B minus!

I also tried to ignore the comings and goings of various US officials to his house. One afternoon however it was difficult to ignore the approach of a large official car which stopped a couple of hundred yards down the road. From it alighted two rather sinister looking males dressed in long coats and fedora hats, who proceeded to "case the joint" in true Hollywood fashion. The car then moved up to my neighbour's house and stopped. Our stepped Admiral "Red" Raborn. He had just been summoned from his retirement job on the West Coast by President Johnson to become Head of the CIA.

Whilst Levering Smith sat on his porch and chatted with Raborn over a drink, I sat on mine only yards away, all three of us under surveillance of the CIA "minders". No doubt the CIA started a file on the La Niece family, if they hadn't done so already.

By the summer of 1965 we had broken the back of the procurement of equipment for the Polaris school and the submarines and emphasis was turning to the provision of spares. First the necessary scales of spares had to be assessed. Great assistance was given by the USN on the basis of their experience. It had been agreed that some categories would be interchangeable between the two navies; also that, although some repairs could only be carried out in a manufacturer's plant in the US, others would be done in a specially built facility at the UK base in Scotland. When the flow of hardware started, US Store Carriers carried consignments from Charleston, South Carolina, to Scotland. Because of some quirk in the US law, equipment had to be formally accepted at Charleston before transhipment, but once the property of the UK it could not be placed in the USN's outward shipping warehouse. The solution was for a warehouse to be leased to us at a peppercorn rent which made it UK territory. At least we found a legal term that meant the same on both sides of the Atlantic. The documentation was much less complicated than I had feared and I duly signed the "Peppercorn Lease" and became the nominal squire of a small piece of the UK situated within the United States.

Payments into the Trust Fund, after the initial hiccup, continued on a quarterly basis. One Friday our Finance Officer, having agreed the figure with SP, requested a cheque for three million dollars from the Embassy and awaited its delivery in a routine run by the Embassy shuttle car. The cheque failed to arrive and could not be traced. Since it was Quarter Day and it was a point of honour always to pay promptly, we asked for another cheque which arrived *post haste* by special messenger. The following week a letter arrived in the ordinary US mail in an envelope bearing a five cent stamp. It was the missing cheque. We fantasised for a couple of moments as to how far it would get us in South America, then returned it to the Embassy.

My next trip to the UK included a visit to the embryo Clyde Submarine Base where it was heartening to see that the Base, including the RN Polaris School and the Armament Depot at Coulport, was rapidly taking shape. Then to Barrow in Furness where the first submarine, to be named *Resolution*, was by then a complete hull on the slipway. All this was indeed progress.

There were still many consultations about installation of equipment and I can well remember one visit to the USA by Mr Len Redshaw, the Managing Director of Vickers Shipbuilders. With their great pride in workmanship Vickers had devised a significantly more elegant method of installing the huge missile tubes in the hull of the submarine. I stood beside him on the slipway at Groton while he looked at the Electric Boat Company's method, which was merely to cut enormous holes in the already complete pressure hull. In his taciturn North Country accent he uttered just one phrase - "They're just butchers!".

Counting the previous tour there, 1965 was the sixth Christmas the family had spent in Washington. As a useless statistic it was also the sixth in peacetime I had worked on Boxing Day! This time Washington weather showed how fickle it could be; on Christmas Day the temperature was 72 degrees F. A few days later we were buried in snow and suburban roads were blocked. I had arranged a visit to the West Coast and had to start my journey by trudging the mile or so to the main road through deep snow drifts. A delightful place though it was, Washington could be a hard place in which to work under pressure; this also applied during some of the more humid and stifling periods of the summer.

In early 1966 I accompanied Captains Philip Higham and Charles Hammer on an extensive indoctrination tour around the principal Polaris facilities in the US. Philip Higham, whom I knew well, had replaced Rae McKaig as Deputy Chief Polaris Executive. Charles Hammer was to be my own replacement in June, but first, because he was a submariner with no previous missile experience, he had to undergo a Polaris course at Dam Neck. To his credit he took this course very seriously but, with his maths very rusty, found some of the technicalities tough going; I was glad I had not had to do the same.

Charles Hammer completed his course and arrived for our turnover. We left for New York to return by sea. Unfortunately the National Union of Seamen chose that moment to call a strike and our sea passage was postponed indefinitely.

Whilst we waited in New York for the situation to clarify I reflected on the three and a quarter hectic years. As the UK Polaris Representative in Washington I had placed orders to the value of approximately 200 million dollars. Equipment was being delivered in a steady stream and according to schedule. It had been a most rewarding and interesting experience. The SP office was right in the forefront of technical and managerial expertise. They had conscientiously sustained their commitment to the joint project and they had treated us as members of their own team, although this had led some people in Bath to allege we, in the Washington office, were "too SP". However, the majority of the UK team appreciated that the bonds that had been forged were in the correct context. It took a long time for me to realise that, although we involved them in a lot of extra work, SP obtained much benefit from their UK relationship. I remember once apologising to Admiral Smith (in the office!) about the persistence of some of the questioning that we relayed from the UK, particularly from the Ordnance Board who in the UK were responsible for weapon safety. "Don't worry", he said "the Royal Navy are our best unpaid consultants". Overall, I reflected we had achieved our objectives. That would have pleased any Staff College.

Eventually we had to abandon any idea of returning by sea and caught a flight to London in the last week of June. Since leaving the UK in 1963 I calculated that I had travelled nearly a quarter of a million miles. Besides crossing the Atlantic fifteen times in each direction I had made a similar number of trips to and from the West Coast besides innumerable other trips around the USA.

We got back just in time for my wife and me to attend, on 30 June, the formal opening, by the Minister of Defence for the Royal Navy, Mr J P W Mallalieu, of the Polaris School at Faslane. Subsequently, on 15 September 1966, we were both fortunate enough to be invited to the launching at Barrow in Furness, of the first UK Polaris submarine, *Resolution*, by Her Majesty Queen Elizabeth the Queen Mother. It was an eventful day and a most fitting climax to this chapter of my career.

CHAPTER 20

The Propulsion System
Peter Hammersley

In mid 1958 Captain Tom Sanders, Chief Staff Officer (Engineering) to Flag Officer Submarines said to me "How would you like to be the first Engineering Officer of our first nuclear submarine, *Dreadnought?*". Needless to say, I was highly delighted. Shortly afterwards, Lieutenant Commander John Grove (as he then was) was selected as the first Electrical Officer and he and I went to Imperial College in London in October 1958 to do the one year post graduate Nuclear Engineering Course. Naval nuclear training at Greenwich did not then exist. We had a very good year and learned a lot about nuclear power stations but not much about Pressurised Water Reactors. We did learn the theory, however, and that gave us a sufficient base to qualify as nuclear watchkeepers with the US Navy later.

At that time, in 1958, the design of a propulsion plant for a British nuclear submarine was fairly well advanced. There had been a small team at the Atomic Energy Research Establishment at Harwell for some time under Captain Harrison Smith. There was a mock up of the machinery spaces at Vickers in Southampton and a team at Vickers, Barrow under Dr Forsyth had done a great deal of support work. But we were still at an early stage of the project and Admiral Mountbatten, as First Sea Lord, had been establishing a rapport with "that stormy petrel of the American Navy, Vice Admiral Hyman G Rickover" (*Mountbatten* by Philip Ziegler) since 1955. Largely thanks to Mountbatten, the Admiralty negotiated a contract to buy the entire reactor and propulsion machinery package for *Dreadnought* from the USN and the design agreed in 1958 was that for the USS *Skipjack* which was still being built. This design was the third USN Pressurised Water Reactor (PWR) design and so we bought enormous experience with it. In Ziegler's book, Mountbatten is quoted as saying that this gave us the ability to complete *Dreadnought* two or three years ahead of time. Without belittling the achievements of those who had been working on the British design, I believe that two or three years is an under-statement. I also believe, and have always believed, that we would have lost most of that advantage had we bought the American reactor and primary plant only to match to our propulsion machinery as was proposed by some in the MOD but opposed by Mountbatten.

While John Grove and I were at Imperial College, the Captain (Commander Peter Samborne) and other officers of *Dreadnought* were selected and we were all summoned to meet Admiral Rickover, with Admiral Mountbatten, in London. This meeting was twice cancelled and then reinstated and we afterwards learned that it was because Rickover wanted to select all the British officers just as he did with all USN officers. Mountbatten drew the line at this, so Rickover refused to meet us. Mountbatten persuaded him to change his mind; not an easy task but this signifies the respect which Rickover had for Mountbatten. He met us but with little grace.

John Grove and I went to the USA in October 1959, he to join USS *Skate* and I to USS *Skipjack* which had recently commissioned. Peter Samborne had already had eight months in *Skipjack* and our first Lieutenant, Tubby Squires, the same time in *Skate*. Two other *Dreadnought* Engineering Officers and a number of other key officers of the British nuclear programme went to other USN submarines and each officer had two senior engineer ratings, most of whom were destined for *Dreadnought*, with him. We all qualified as nuclear watchkeepers at our various levels and we all learned as much as our American friends could possibly teach us. Most of us have retained life-long friendships with Americans from those days and all of us are grateful to the USN. We bought not only the nuclear propulsion package but also practical experience and training. The result was that *Dreadnought* had a proven machinery design and a crew whose key members were nuclear qualified and had some practical experience.

We returned from the States and moved to Barrow where we helped Vickers in the building of *Dreadnought* and operated her machinery for them. The key Vickers people had also been to the States and learned all that the American shipbuilders could teach them about building nuclear submarines. So although we had many problems to overcome and much still to learn we in *Dreadnought* had a comparatively easy time compared to our successors. With our proven plant and some experience we had all the glamour and honours of the first in the field. Our successors had an unproven plant of British design and manufacture and no experience other than what we could give them. The USN gave our whole programme a base on which to build but the achievements of the British designers, shipbuilders, machinery manufacturers and the crews, from *Valiant* onwards, must never be forgotten because it is these which led to the first Polaris submarines and then to the *Swiftsure* and later classes.

The fundamental difference between the early British and American propulsion plants was that the British had steam feed pumps and separate condensers for the main engines and turbo generators. This meant that the British steam and feed systems were much more complicated and difficult to maintain. But a basic requirement of the British design was radiated noise reduction and it should never be forgotten that in this very important operation aspect, the British design was greatly superior.

Just before I left *Skipjack* to come home, I went to Washington to thank Admiral Rickover for all that he had made it possible for the USN to do for us. After keeping me waiting for a long time I was again received with ill-grace and told that we British would never get our machinery to work. I disagreed with him and then had a very pleasant and interesting quarter of an hour's discussion. He was critical of the British design and he was partly right. However, he was comparing our first unproven design with the third proven American one. The machinery for the Polaris boats was hardly our second design because the programme did not allow for it to be changed greatly from that of the *Valiant* class. The *Swiftsure* class was the first really improved British design and that, not surprisingly, bears a general resemblance to *Dreadnought* but with many fundamental improvements as well. But that is another story. The *Valiant* and Polaris machinery was operated successfully for nearly thirty years, a huge tribute to the designers, builders and crews.

I left *Dreadnought* in November 1964, after four and a half years, nearly three of them in Barrow while she was building and eighteen months at sea. Then I spent some three years in the MOD in Bath. The *Dreadnought* Project Team (DPT), under Rowland Baker, which had so effectively managed the building of *Dreadnought*, had been renamed the Directorate Polaris Technical (DPT) in brilliant fashion to avoid confusion. Later it became the Directorate Project Team Submarines (DPT(S/M)). I was head of the Marine Engineering Section covering the *Valiant* class in build and the *Swiftsure* class design. Commander Mike Dathan was my opposite number for the Polaris submarines and there was close liaison between our sections. The project management of the whole submarine programme, with the Polaris programme at the centre of it, was probably the most effective that the MOD had ever achieved then and, possibly, since. No feelings were spared at the monthly progress meetings in Barrow with Rowland Baker at the centre on one side of the table with his supporters and Leonard

Redshaw (later Sir Leonard) on the other side with his Vickers people in attendance, But there was also a great spirit of co-operation and friendship and many of those friendships continue today.

One of the main links for me was with George Standen who was Vickers Installation and Testing Manager and later Engineering Director. He had been at the Electric Boat Division of General Dynamics Corporation Shipyard in Groton, Connecticut, when I was in *Skipjack* and he and his team, closely supported by the Rolls Royce and Associates team, who were the reactor experts and the main links with the US Contractors, were the mainstay of all the British industry marine nuclear capability. They served the Royal Navy well and those two companies still do so today.

The Bath team made very frequent visits to Barrow and vice versa. Today travel is normally by air but we usually went by sleeper train from London in those days. We all became very used to the journey. Returning from Barrow to London the train started as a mixed sleeper and normal day carriage train and the sleepers were added to a Glasgow London sleeper train at Lancaster. At Carnforth the train stopped, went ahead from the platform and backed into another platform before leaving again for Lancaster. The real experts left the train at the first stop and had a beer in the refreshment room between the two platforms. They calmly watched the train pull out and back into the next platform whereupon they left the refreshment room on that side and rejoined the train. There are many stories of the "Carnforth Switch" as this practice was known. The best one concerns Commander (later Captain) Barney McHugh who was the Naval Engineering Overseer at Barrow, another who played a major role in the early programme. He was doing the Carnforth Switch one evening and rejoined the train at the last possible minute on the second platform. An elderly lady in the compartment looked at him in surprise as he leapt in and said "Oh dear, when the train pulled out for the first time I thought you had missed it so I quickly put your luggage through the window onto the platform". Barney collected it on the way back the next night.

CHAPTER 21

The Electrical System and the RN Polaris School
Herbert Fitzer (Fitz)

The Ship Department was designing a magnificent new aircraft carrier and I was enjoying my share in the development of its revolutionary electric power system when I was hijacked back to the world of submarines I had left not long before. I found myself, during a cold January 1961, in Washington DC with Sidney John Palmer, Charles Shepherd and Jeffrey Perks. We were there to discover what would be required if Britain should wish to build a squadron of submarines carrying intercontinental ballistic missiles, for which the missile systems would be provided by the United States. The American Polaris was already at sea in the submarine *George Washington*. For me this was a familiar exercise as I had been with a somewhat similar mission a few years earlier to prepare for the building of nuclear powered submarines using the propulsion system developed by Admiral Rickover.

The Special Projects Office led by Admiral Raborn was very helpful and made sure we had all the information we needed. There was little secrecy and they were keen to explain their philosophy: that a deterrent would only work if everybody knew about it.

After two or three weeks we flew back to England and, when we had written our report, resumed our interrupted duties. I was once more immersed in the problems of the surface navy, and the splendid carrier, but that project came to a sticky end and the great ship was never built.

Nearly two years later Kennedy and Macmillan had their famous meeting in Nassau and the Polaris Sales Agreement was made between the two governments in April 1963. That sparked off an explosion of activity within the Admiralty, not least in the Ship and Weapon Departments in Bath.

In no time the Director of Electrical Engineering whisked me back in charge of his submarine teams, but with secondment to assist Rowland Baker, the Head of the newly created Polaris Technical Directorate. I was very pleased to be working for Baker once more; I knew he was the right man for the job, one who seemed to thrive on crises, and found an answer to the most obstinate problem. Once, when I was with him facing yet another crisis, he quoted me a hymn:

> Father, hear the prayer we offer
> Not for ease that prayer should be
> But for strength that we may ever
> Live our lives courageously.

My first task was to augment my staff in order to take on the additional work for the Polaris Project. Much of the ground work had already been covered in the designs for the nuclear hunter-killer submarines, and although Polaris meant radical changes, the two were never formally separated.

The other task was to select a small team of the best engineers and draughtsmen with the right experience, to join for the duration the British Liaison Team in the USA, led by Captain Peter La Niece. They would operate from the Electric Boat Company in Groton.

The Liaison Team had to handle the vast amount of information which had to be transferred to Britain, and deal with many problems. Whenever I saw them they always seemed to be at full stretch. They also had to monitor the "Shopping List".

Although the British were going to build their own submarines there were, apart from the main weapon systems, a considerable quantity of items ancillary to those systems which were essentially part of the submarine. After a bit of argument it was decided that, rather than manufacture these in Britain, it would be better to take these from the American production lines.

Rowland Baker thought this was a job for me, so I found myself at the Electric Boat Company, with a very large number of people. charged with setting up a scheme to give effect to this so called "Shopping list". The List would be initiated by Electric Boat who alone had the knowledge. The whole business, though very necessary, was tedious and my chief recollection of it is that because of the number of people involved on both sides of the Atlantic, every smallest order needed 36 copies! Back in England, I continued to keep an eye on the "Shopping List", but apart from the odd hiccup, it seemed to work smoothly under the expert control of Harry Barnes, Head of Polaris Production.

In the meantime it had been decided that there must be in UK a Polaris school similar to the three schools in the USA. The crews of the first two boats would be trained in the United States, but subsequent crews in Britain. The school would also be needed to train many civilians involved in the Polaris Project from shipbuilders, other contractors, dockyard and scientific staff, and would therefore have to be ready for use well ahead of the completion of the first vessel. Captain Leslie Bomford arranged with the Ministry of Public Buildings and Works for the design and building of the RN Polaris School on a site within the main Polaris Base at Faslane.

I came into this in a small way by setting up a mixed discipline team under an electrical Commander RN to support the British Polaris School. Their task was to take the submarine systems and equipment on which the Polaris Weapon Systems depended and redesign them to fulfil the same purpose in the shore based school. It seemed to be fairly straightforward, but things got into a muddle.

The demands made upon this modest section rapidly multiplied and its Head found that there were seven naval Captains, RN and USN, who all thought they were entitled to tell him what to do. He was very conscientious and not surprisingly before long he disappeared from the scene for a couple of months with a nervous breakdown.

By then Rowland Baker had called me in and put me in charge of the Polaris installations in the School. That was interesting because the School was very much a Weapons Department commitment whereas I belonged entirely to the Ship Department. However, nobody seemed to object apart from one or two of my Ship colleagues who thought I should be running my proper submarine electrical teams. Those teams were well into their stride, were very competent and only needed me to hold their coats when arguments broke out.

I went off to Washington with Don Evans and Tony Wray to find that much had been done by the officers of the Liaison Team, each attending to his own part of the Polaris system: - fire control, navigation, launcher and so on. There was no special attempt to coordinate for the School.

That state of affairs was partly a reflection of the American arrangements for their schools which gave the impression of being an afterthought. Nevertheless they had one school in service at Dam Neck in Virginia and two others in hand. Recently they had brought in a somewhat unimpressive co-ordinating contractor called Howard Research for their schools; we found that this firm had as much to learn as we had.

A more structured visit to the States was made a few weeks later. Our team from the UK was the same as before but we also had the

engineer from Vickers who would supervise his firm's installation work
for the School. This time we were joined by members of the British
Liaison Staff in Washington, and set off on a tour of all the main Polaris
Contractors across America. We established what each would be
supplying for RNPS and met some of their people who would in due
time come over to Britain to stand by the installation and testing of
their equipment.

Some of us had already visited the first American Polaris School at
Dam Neck but this was well short of the facilities that would be needed
at Faslane. The other schools in progress were at Mare Island,
California and Pearl Harbour. "You must go to Pearl Harbour" said
the Americans, "that will be most like your School". We all flew off
to Honolulu and enjoyed the trip immensely; but were disappointed to
find that although the building was complete and ready, there was no
equipment inside. We did learn quite a lot; but I have at times
wondered since - was it just a jolly?

Back in the UK the Polaris School kept me going full time. The
School building at Faslane was a vast cavern of wet concrete and
scaffolding and not then for the likes of me. Mostly I spent my time tying
together what was going on in America and UK. I made frequent visits
to the States and on one of these happened to meet my boss, Director
General of Ships. He asked me what I was doing and I told him. He
said "Are you working for me?" I told him I was, but he was clearly a
bit displeased. There were times when I felt that I was in a three sided
football game between the Ship and Weapon Departments and the
Chief Polaris Executive.

I now became a regular attender at Admiral Mackenzie's fortnightly
planning and progress meetings. At the beginning I had to explain that
while everybody else was engrossed in the management programmes,
networks, status reports and the like, the planning for the School was
being based on the work that had already been done, and the only
reliable dates were those that had already been achieved. Gradually
however we fought back to orthodoxy and got the whole planning
process onto a proper footing. Dates which had at one time seemed
impossible began to look more attainable. I also became a regular
member of the Joint Steering Task Force in order to tell them how
RNPS was getting on - or not as the case might be. This was very useful
as I was able to meet American officers who could help solve some of
our problems. Captain Barrett had overall responsibility for the
American Polaris Schools and I found him a good friend and colleague.

We made progress. Orders were placed with the appropriate American contractors, not only for the various Polaris systems but also for many other things. There were simulators, some very elaborate, so that the functions of the weapon systems in the boats could be replicated in the School The wonderful navigation system could do nothing for an outfit which remained firmly anchored to a rock in Scotland, so in a way with the help of simulators it had to work back to front. We also wanted to be able to connect the whole system together, a facility which, as far as I know, applied to no American school. Another British requirement was for a complete outfit of test equipment which, with its miles of cable, would be used in the first place to commission the School and then for each boat in turn.

All these purchases, together with the mountain of documentation, specifications, drawings, installation and test procedures, were handled by the DPT Product Organisation which was well into its stride and needed no intervention from me.

I cannot remember that I had any comprehensive Polaris School team other than my initial section. I acquired a few officers who were able to concentrate on the School, one of whom started in the Liaison Team in Washington and then transferred to Faslane as Overseer.

Balernoch House within the Faslane Base area had been converted into a temporary headquarters, and there I called a meeting of all who were to be concerned with the fitting out of RNPS. Vickers, the prime installation contractors, were there with their project engineer, Derek Fletcher, and also the representatives of the American firms - General Electric, Autonetics and Howard Research who had already moved in to stay until completion. It was a scrappy meeting. Many there were meeting each other for the first time and the small meeting room was overcrowded. However the object was achieved in that each one knew, not only what he was doing, but what all the others were doing. It was not the last meeting but the one which set the whole thing going, and from then onwards as problems arose, they got solved.

I now had a bit more time to attend to my real job with the electrical submarine sections but did not drop my RNPS responsibilities. With Charles Shepherd and Don Evans, I went to Washington to give a presentation on RNPS to the members of the American Special Projects. We explained why in some respects our School differed from theirs, partly because we had to do everything in one School but also because of the differences in the methods of training and manning between the two navies.

For me that was almost the end. The Director of Electrical Engineering had other plans for me. My successor was appointed to take over all my submarine duties, including the Polaris School which was now on course towards the hoped for completion date. So I left the Polaris Project, having enjoyed it as much as anything in my career so far.

Later I was invited to the official opening of the Polaris school which took place, I think, one day before its programmed completion date. So that was that.

PART 4

BASE SUPPORT

CHAPTER 22

Support Planning
Ken Dunlop

I was just finishing my time on the staff of Flag Officer Submarines and had just been to sea in *Dreadnought* on the first occasion of a British vessel being underway on nuclear power, when Rear Admiral Rufus Mackenzie asked me to go with him as his Technical Assistant to the Chief Polaris Executive, a marvellous title which gave me a chance to put my finger into almost any pie. Put more simply I was the "submarine plumber" on his personal staff.

The Admiralty may have been ready for Rufus. They were certainly not ready for Dunlop. I spent the first week owning sometimes a desk, sometimes a chair and sometimes a telephone but never all three together.

The time set for the huge project seemed almost stupidly short and all elements - the missiles, the boats, the armament depot and the base - had to come together at the right time. Clearly an organisation such as CPE was the only hope of achieving this.

The Polaris Executive became an Admiralty within the Admiralty, remarkably self contained and dedicated to the Project. A vital part of it focused around Robbins, the Planning Officer, of whom more will be said later.

Necessity soon made me take on various jobs in which I had the necessary experience, so the framework was not rigid. As Polaris Logistics (P12) was not immediately available my first major task was to join in the selection team for the site for the Submarine Base and the Royal Naval Armaments Depot (RNAD) and the development of the overall design of the base.

The firm basis for the Polaris submarines was that they should be as nearly as possible *"Valiant"* class with a missile section inserted, in the same way as the USN had turned a "Skipjack" into *George Washington.*

Above all things the boat had to be reliable. One early and vitally important decision Rufus made was that we would complete *Valiant* and *Warspite* first to obtain experience and to meet both building problems and early running problems on them rather than on the Polaris boats.

I personally strongly supported this but there were those who felt that Rufus was favouring submarines generally rather than Polaris. However he proved absolutely right and the decision undoubtedly speeded up the readiness for Polaris patrols.

I was involved in one departure from "the same as *Valiant*" concept. Very early on I strongly recommended to Rufus to fit sonar type 186 long range passive search to Polaris boats.

My reason was that at the time 186 potentially provided the most distant warning of the approach of a ship. It was only usable at low speeds, but presumably Polaris on patrol would use low speeds most of the time. Others disagreed because they considered that machinery noise, particularly the main coolant pumps, would cause too much interference with the 186.   The final fit of Types 2001 and 2007 (improved 186) justified my approach.

Otherwise, the main achievement of the design and construction of the boat was that it was ready on time. Moreover, it seemed to me basically a good submarine.   *Repulse* had no difficulty in keeping periscope depth at three knots in bad weather.

I also tried to get a secondary role for the submarines in case nuclear explosives were banned or not needed. A larger headed shorter range conventional weapon seemed a possibly useful bombardment facility. Everybody was far too busy with the main task, however, and no money was likely to be available. So the idea proved a very damp squib.

The first job I had, within hours of getting to the Admiralty, was to join Rae McKaig's working party to propose the site for the Submarine Base and the Royal Naval Armament Depot for the missiles. At this stage I met Andrew McLeod, the representative of the Armament Stores Department and found him most helpful.

We quickly shortlisted:

a) Faslane/Coulport
b) Plymouth Area
c) Somewhere far out eg Kyles of Lochalsh, Mallaig.
d) Falmouth Area

I was strongly against c) on Jolly Jack grounds. People said we could provide splendid recreation facilities for him and wonderful canteens etc. But that is not what Jack wants. He wants pubs away from the service and away from his officers.

Plymouth and Falmouth had much to recommend them but getting the land for the RN Armament Depot (RNAD) could have taken a long time.

Faslane/Coulport had practically no land problems. Metal Industries, the ship-breaking firm, were keen to sell up at Faslane and most of Coulport belonged to the Government. One farmer objected at first but soon became quite happy to be compensated by the Admiralty. Most of his family subsequently got jobs with the builders of RNAD.

In deciding the location we were greatly helped by Mr Fairley, Chief Surveyor of Lands, who proved capable and sensitive to individuals who were affected by land acquisition.

Faslane also seemed to give a good exit and entry for the Polaris submarines as there was deep water from the Cumbraes to the open sea and they could go dived on either side of Arran or down to St George's Channel, so the chances of getting out undetected seemed good.

Having decided on the location the next major decision was quickly made. This was to have a joint base for the 3rd (conventional) Submarine Squadron and the Polaris squadron. It would have been far too costly to have two lots of facilities in different parts of the Clyde and clearly there was room for both squadrons at Faslane. I hardly remember any debate about it.

So the Ministry of Public Buildings and Works (MPBW as they were then called) took on the job of designing and building the new base. The engineer appointed for overall design was a man named Dobson. He was responsible for the next vital step.

In the initial sketches for the base we accepted that the existing main road would run right through it and divide it into two. About four of us were looking at these sketches when Dobson suddenly said "Why not divert the main road right up behind the base like this?" and he sketched a new run. Having no experience of such things we had no idea it could be done. I remember saying "If we can do that it will be the most important decision we shall make". We soon got agreement to acquire the land needed for the diversion and planning permission for the diversion itself.

Looking back now I shudder to think what would have happened if the base had been divided by a public road. Even excluding security considerations, the layout would have been vastly inferior. But the thought of having CND etc right in the middle of the base makes the mind boggle.

I do not think that Dobson ever really got the credit for his flash of genius. His image ought to be on a pedestal in the base, both for the proposal and the speed and skill with which he implemented it.

The content of the base was quickly listed and we had made considerable progress on overall layout sketches, when Captain Bomford, the new Polaris Projects Officer, came on the scene. He was understandably aghast at how far we had gone and keen to reserve judgement on the layout.

He felt that we had put in far too much detail already. In an ideal world he would have been right. We had to make far too many snap decisions without proper study. It was the only way of keeping to the programme. Fortunately "Bombers" was soon supplemented by Commander Ken Willis who quickly saw both sides of the problem, got confidence in what we had done so far and persuaded Bombers to accept it. As it turned out most of our snap decisions were right, and three valuable months were saved.

These were typical of the sort of corners that had to be cut in the whole project to make sure that it all dovetailed in and completed on time.

Then began the vast task of specifying all the services and equipment to be housed in every building in the place plus the floating dock, jetties etc. We had to work at breakneck speed. Fortunately Willis was at his best in this phase as he had an incredible capacity for detail. We also got a lot of help from FOS/M. On the other hand we had trouble with some odd branches in Bath and with the Treasury who had very little clue but the usual brilliant way of asking awkward questions.

Three recollections I have of this period are:

a)   Modular Repair Facility - This was a "dockyard level" outfit for fault tracing and repair of the printed circuit modules of the Polaris weapon system. We did not want to be totally reliant on the United States for this level of repair and it seemed pointless to site it at a dockyard when it would be needed, almost entirely, at Faslane.

Time was short, and we tried to bulldoze it through but came up against the Deputy Secretary of the Admiralty, Mackay. He was a good man but we had no time to be patient and I went to a very fraught meeting at which he said he had never before recommended anything for approval on such a thin case. Our reply was "true, but we have not got time to make a fuller one". We got approval.

b)   The very vexed question of whether the Supply organisation at the base should be naval or civilian. I was strongly in favour of RN manning, as supplies were too essential to the submarines to risk trades union involvement.

Shrewdly the Director of Naval Stores put their very best man into the project team. I liked and admired him but still disapproved of civilian manning and begged Rufus to insist on keeping it RN manned - without success.

c)   I attended a fascinating meeting between the MP for Dumbartonshire and the Civil Lord to discuss the effect of the base on the locality. The Civil Lord was Conservative, the Dumbarton MP good sterling working class Labour. It was obvious from the start that they were good friends, and there was quite a lot of leg pulling as the Labour party line at the time was against Polaris. However, the MP was thrilled that so much employment was coming to his constituency, which was even then feeling the pinch.

His final words to me were "I strongly disapprove and will do anything I can to help"!

We gave two presentations on Polaris in general which I attended as the support man. The first one was to Thorneycroft who was Minister of Defence. He was as dry as dust and did not follow up our urgent request for action. The second was to Healey and I had to show him a model of the Polaris School - the first building to complete at Faslane. I found him courteous and easy to talk to. He asked sensible questions and even listened to the answers.

The Base design completed ahead of schedule and the Base was ready on time and with far fewer problems than one could expect under the circumstances. This was in no small way due to the fact that Ken Willis was appointed as Overseer for the construction phase and worked wonders amongst the army of contractors on the site.

I only heard of one serious problem - the size of the Command Building. This had been designed for a fairly modest staff put forward by Ernie Turner when he was Commodore, Submarines. Later Admiral Law (FOS/M) and Rufus blew up the size of the staff considerably. By then the Command Building was too far advanced to alter it.

Several years later I came into Faslane in *Dreadnought* and as I had a few hours before catching my train to Chatham, I asked to be shown round the Base. A young Lieutenant took me round and gave flattering accounts of everything until we came to the Command Building. he said "I would love to meet the bloody fool who designed this". I introduced myself.

The Royal Naval Armament Depot soon left my world but we did have some problems of co-ordination between the Base and the Depot to work out. For instance did they take on the maintenance of other weapons? Also pilotage and security problems had to be linked together. My only concern was to make sure that somebody had the problem on his plate and that the whole supporting complex was going forward as an entity.

Programming and progressing was, undoubtedly, the secret of the success of this huge and diverse project. The main factors in the success were:

a) Robbins - the man who ran it.
b) The Programme Management Plans (PMP) system.
c) The reporting system.
d) The honesty of reporting due to the atmosphere created by Rufus and Robbins.

The programme system consisted of the use of network scheduling. This showed overall progress and the time by which each main activity had to be complete to fit in with the plan as a whole. It highlighted critical or near critical paths so that they could receive special attention. By 1963 this was a well known technique.

The new big success was the family tree of Programme Management Plans (PMPs) Each PMP was a simple milestone chart made out by persons responsible for doing the work. It contained only 8-10 key dates needed to complete the activity covered by the plan. Each PMP could be seen and understood at a glance.

The detail needed for the system to work as a whole was achieved by having several generations of PMPs, each PMP represented by just one milestone in the generation above it.

The first generation PMP would cover -

The Missile
The Submarine
The Base
The RNAD
The Refitting Dockyard

Just five milestones.

Each of these five would have a second generation PMP of its own giving the key milestones to be achieved and their dates: for instance to complete the Base. They in turn would be subdivided into further third generation PMPs and so on.

All these would be copied to Robbins who would fit them into the overall plans or say if they did not fit. Robbins also ran the PMP index.

So any PMP put up on a screen showed at a glance to any level of management how that particular activity was progressing. The one essential to make it a perfect system was that the PMP itself was made out sensibly with achievable milestones but not leaving too much time to make life easy. The personal factor played a vital part in the success of the scheme.

PMPs were the perfect system for reporting and reviewing progress on this complex project. We had a progress meeting once a month, when officers from all sections had their PMPs put on screen and they gave Rufus and the other senior members a brief account of their own particular activities.

Rufus always assumed that each man was doing his best and where help was asked for there was a genuine need for it. Nobody was put in the rattle for reporting bad progress. As a result reports were honest and we really knew where we were, and appropriate action could be taken.

The Polaris Project was a £360m scheme at 1963 prices. This must be one of the biggest and most complex naval projects undertaken in this country. The time scale from the start to completion was very tight by any standards.

Yet it was an immense success, it completed on time, things worked well and there was no post project financial uproar.

What lessons can be learned from the success?

a)   The right man was at the top. Rufus was at his very best all the way through. His personality permeated right through the whole team. Everybody therefore worked hard, worked together and was proud of being in the team.

b)   Most of the senior officers were basically co-operators. Rae McKaig in particular.

c)   Civilian departments put in their best men eg Lewin, Page, Dobson, McLeod, Fairley and Robbins.

d)   McKaig worked wonders in setting up the organisation.

e)   Programme and Progress reporting was run excellently so we knew where we were.

f)   The USN was most generous and helpful from start to finish. I suspect that Rear Admiral Levering Smith USN had much to do with this. But considerable credit goes to Peter La Niece. Information and goodwill flowed easily under his direction. I think, apart from other things, he spoke good American.

To sum up, the success was due to people. We had the right team and the right atmosphere.

CHAPTER 23

The Faslane Base(1)
Sir John Lea

Prelude

My introduction to matters Polaris happened when I was appointed in charge of the Submarine Maintenance Authority. The Authority at that time was in a wooden hut at Blockhouse and manned by about ten officers and senior rates. We were faced with the unexpected task of producing maintenance schedules for the Weapons System of the new Polaris boats. These had to be integrated into the USN system, and it seemed sensible to visit the USA to see how they did it. The subsequent visit to Corona, north of Los Angeles, threw into sharp focus how totally unprepared we were for the job. The contrast between FOS/M's wooden hut with its ten men and Corona with its hundreds of staff, computer aided and air conditioned, could not have been more complete. Partly because of this and partly because of the increasing complexity of the propulsion and other systems, the Maintenance Authority acquired a brand new building and more staff.

This job led into a new appointment, with the rank of Captain, as FOS/M's Staff Officer (Faslane) and the Deputy Superintendent, Clyde Submarine Base - designate. The size of the title was in inverse proportion to the support I had - which was none!

The job involved commuting between Blockhouse and Faslane with two or three days in each place each week, attempting to represent FOS/M's views and at the same time to prepare for the coming-to-life of the new Base. There were also quite frequent visits to Bath and London with discussion with the Polaris Executive.

Early Days

Accommodation at Faslane was a problem during these weekly visits. The Submarine Depot Ship *Maidstone* had nothing suitable, and the future Base was a muddy building site. Embedded in the new base was a pleasant old house called Balernoch House. It was empty and unfurnished, but it had a garden and I was able to put a caravan there with an electric supply from the house. It was far from ideal, and pretty chilly in winter, but it was handy. The old house was potentially comfortable, and I tried hard to persuade the responsible department to take it on and refurbish it as a residence for the Deputy Superintendent who was to have the responsibly of running the Base.

Even though it would have been cheaper than building a new house, and was ideally placed, I was not successful in spite of having the support of the Polaris Executive, and the house was allowed to decay and was used eventually as sub-standard offices for the Civilian Administration department.

At this stage, in 1965 and early 1966, Faslane was a complete building site and not a pleasant place to be. It seemed incredible that it would ever be finished in time to receive the first Polaris submarine. The fact that it was ready was a real tribute not only to the contractors, but more importantly to the co-ordinating efforts of the Polaris Executive and, in particular, to their resident representative, Commander Ken Willis. He was on top of every detail, and completely unflappable. The whole project was indeed fortunate to have two such formidable organisers as Ken, and his boss in Bath, Captain Leslie Bomford. His title was Resident Officer, Polaris Executive (ROPE). When he left there were inevitably a few loose ends to be tied up and he was relieved by a Lieutenant Commander who rejoiced in the title of Co-ordinating Officer Residual Development (CORD).

During the time leading up to the completion of the Base, the support of the resident squadron rested with HMS *Maidstone*, under the command of Captain Derek Kent. He had already been appointed, designate, as Commodore Clyde and Submarine Base and as Superintendent of the Base and so was more than a little interested in the preparations for the operational opening of the Base. We agreed that it was important to have all the terms of reference of the various organisations, naval and civilian, which were to make up the Base, cut and dried and agreed well in advance.

On the face of it, this seemed to us both to be a pretty straightforward task. It proved to be quite otherwise and was never really resolved until some time after I had left. From the outset it became clear that the weakness in the organisation was due to the insistence of the civilian departments that they would only answer to the top man - the Commodore - for their performance, and in this attitude they were strongly supported by the headquarters departments in Bath. The situation was further confused by their insistence that for much of their performance they were responsible directly to their headquarters departments. The Commodore, with his regional and operational responsibilities was clearly too busy to oversee the efficient running of the Base itself, which was why I was appointed. It is sad that the naval authorities from the outset did not insist on my being appointed as Superintendent of the Base, and not as Deputy, with the authority that would have carried. As it was, FOS/M was very aware of the difficulties of running a mixed naval/civilian operation base, and he understandably thought it important at this time not to rock the boat by having a confrontation over who was in charge.

There was nothing personal in all this, and in the event I got on well with the senior civilians concerned. With all the naval members of the team there was, of course, no problem, except in an unexpected way which I learnt about only after I had left. I learnt that the naval staff who were involved in the support of the two squadrons at Faslane were upset, touchingly, on my behalf not only by my complete lack of formal authority, but also by the lack of trappings that would have gone with it, such as residence, car, driver, steward, entertainment allowance etc. To be honest I was not greatly fussed, particularly as my fellow Captains who did enjoy these things were all close friends, but I can understand my people regarding the situation as they did. It was only on the personal insistence of Commodore Derek Kent that I even had a Secretary!

Towards the end of those early days there occurred one of those events which gave great pleasure to all those concerned with the project. The big floating dock, which was needed for the docking of the Polaris boats, was built in one of the locks in Portsmouth. It was planned to tow it up to Faslane where it was to be secured by two huge hinged arms to two large concrete pontoons built by the contractor into the land at the edge of the Loch. The arms had forked ends which were designed to go over a lug on each pontoon. When the great moment came to lower the arms onto the lugs and to fit the securing pins, the fit proved to be exact to within 1/16". It was extraordinary what this small but impressive success did to morale on the site. As a by-product there had been great problems over docking the early nuclear submarines in the graving docks, because of the rigidity of the docks. The floating dock proved to be so flexible that it took up the contour of the submarine and the stress problems disappeared.

The Base in Action

The Base consisted of the four major departments and its sole *raison d'être* was the maintenance, repair and timely turnaround of all submarines in the two attached squadrons. The Naval Technical Department, under a Commander, was responsible for all repair and maintenance, calling for extra help as necessary from contractors or the Engineering Services Department. It included a most effective naval-manned planning and co-ordinating organisation which provided Ship Managers who acted as a focal point for all Base contributions to the maintenance period.

The Engineering Services Department was responsible for all the shore services such as cranes, jetty facilities, power supplies, emergency diesel generators, compressed air etc. Their parent headquarters department was Director General Dockyards and they brought with them much of the unwillingness to work closely with men in uniform which was then the norm in the dockyards. My task of trying to coordinate by consent, but without authority, was at its most difficult in this area which was a problem in view of the vital importance of the Engineering Services Department to the successful completion of our task. In the event we were all so clear about the task of the Base that the problem was overcome.

The Stores and Transport Department in contrast were well used to working closely with naval personnel and, with the Base Supply Officer's outfit, had a most effective organisation for the de-storing and storing of submarines in maintenance and for the provision of spare gear, victuals and fuel.

The Royal Naval Armament Depot at Coulport had it own Superintendent and was to all intents an independent organisation, though it answered to the Commodore and depended on the Base Engineering Services Department for the same services it supplied in Faslane and similarly on the Stores and Transport organisation.

The Base started its operational life when trades unions were at their most powerful and, being a new site. there was intense recruiting by both the AEU and the TGWU, both of whom had so many grades that they seemed to be indistinguishable. The local AEU convenor on the site was a particularly difficult customer and he produced more problems than we really needed. When the last Polaris boat from Vickers was due, her completion and timely arrival at Faslane were threatened by a strike organised by a notorious communist union leader at Barrow. She was finished by supervisory staff who effectively broke the strike, but on her arrival at Faslane she was blacked by AEU members in the Engineering Services Department.

Fortunately half the ESD staff belonged to the TGWU, and I was able to persuade them that it was absurd of them to react to a sympathy strike call by a different union, and the programme was saved. We realised, though, from this early incident that we were particularly vulnerable to strikes by the civilian crane drivers and I was able to persuade the unions to allow the training of naval people to drive the cranes, ostensibly in case of a nuclear accident.

On the domestic front, fine accommodation and facilities were built for both naval and civilian personnel. In the early days there was a bit of a potential problem with the Wardroom. There is a world of difference between the naval definition of an officer and the civilian definition. For example, a civilian Clerical Officer equates to a Leading Writer in the Navy. There was early pressure for all civilian officers to be allowed to be members of the Wardroom. It was resolved by an edict that the Wardroom had been built entirely for naval use and that no civilians could be members except by invitation.

A large new officers' married quarter estate was built on a lovely hillside overlooking the loch above Rhu village. It was an estate of quite extraordinary ugliness and was soon known as Moon City. Its building demonstrated the amazing tolerance of the local people, who not only put up with all the upheaval and damage to their little bit of Scotland, but even went to great lengths to welcome and to be friendly to us early arrivals. We still count amongst our best friends many whom we met at that time. Though my job was undoubtedly professionally frustrating, domestically it was one of the happiest and we owe a great debt to the local folk.

For all the naval people, the highlight of our time was the formal naming of the Base as HMS *Neptune* by Her Majesty the Queen Mother. One hears much about what a happy and gracious lady she is, but the reality far exceeds the reputation. It was a wonderfully happy day, with the Royal Yacht secured alongside and the sun shining.

From the outset we tried to contribute to the local community. We joined in and raised a lot of money for local charities with the local fifty mile walk, though I personally only did 45 miles because we were due out to dinner! We made our facilities - particularly the swimming pool - available locally as soon as possible, and after the hurricane of 1968 we made a big contribution by clearing roads and providing emergency food services. I believe all these things made us more acceptable.

We had our fair share of CND protests. They received very little local support, rather the reverse, and we eventually found that the most effective way of clearing the approach road of a sit-down demonstration was by flooding the road with hoses.

It is now nearly thirty five years since I arrived at Faslane and, with hindsight, it was a great privilege to have been associated in however small a way with such a huge and successful project which against all the odds got the first Polaris boat on patrol on time and serviced on her return. It was a triumph of co-operation between Navy, Civil Service and contractors.

CHAPTER 24

The Faslane Base (2)
Nick Howlett

The introduction of the British Polaris programme to the Royal Navy in general and the Submarine Command in particular, brought about the single most revolutionary aspect of the project programming and subsequent in-service management organisation since the Second World War. This was achieved not without considerable upset to the many traditional procedures and habits as well as changes to the more traditional aspects of manning and training. Most important, within the Submarine Command, by nature previously a somewhat inward looking and family orientated organisation, there was an almost overnight need to "get its ass into the act" and to quickly dispose of many of its out-of-date methods and practices. Part of this essential updating had already begun with the introduction of the first SSN - HMS *Dreadnought* - and whilst on FOS/M's staff in the early 1960s, I was involved in the manning and training arrangements for our increasing nuclear fleet. Luckily for me, this led in 1966 to my being appointed to the Clyde Submarine Base at Faslane as the first Principal Technical Officer and where I remained until 1968, once HMS *Resolution* had been deployed operationally.

In 1966, the Clyde Base was firmly in the hands of the Chief Polaris Executive and his on-site representative, Resident Officer Polaris Executive (ROPE). The latter's sidekick was inevitably called CORD. ROPE, Commander Ken Willis, and I had previously met while on FOS/M's staff, during the many and detailed discussions we had had on the design and operation of the Base. I like to think that he and I had an immediate rapport, essential if we were going to get the Base ready on time for the initial deployment of *Resolution*. In the early stages, we both faced some opposition to the whole project; some from apathy, some from hostility and much from ignorance. However we were both of the same mind to see that the British deterrent took its place as the most important task set the Royal Navy, and our excellent relationship for the next two years stemmed from that premise.

Prior to settling down in Faslane, myself and two other officers obtained permission from the USN to visit the USS *Simon Lake* at Charleston USA. This was the USN's most up-to-date Polaris support ship and was destined to take over from the existing support ship for the US Polaris Squadron at Dunoon. Thus besides seeing an actual Polaris support ship at work, we were able to make some very useful contacts for the future. During our visit we were able to see for ourselves the whole of the support ship operation, including the missile support section and the adjacent floating dock. The latter had recently sunk itself at its moorings just prior to our arrival and there were red faces all round. We were also allowed to watch and visit the USS *George Washington* undergoing her between patrol maintenance period. During missile loading, armed marines manned the topside of the support ship, prepared to shoot anyone who approached the ship's side before the loading hatches were shut - a reminder of the seriousness with which the Americans took the viability of their deterrent.

The sheer excellence of the support ship repair facilities, the dedication of the crew, made us realise how far behind we were in the RN, from the standpoint of modern management and methods. I was determined that the Clyde Submarine Base would at least emulate what we were shown in the USA and hopefully match their skills and dedicated approach.

Faslane, home to the Third Submarine Squadron based upon HMS *Maidstone*, was not the most attractive base in the early 1960s. Alongside ROPE and CORD, we deposited ourselves in Balernoch House, moving eventually into a small Nissen hut so as to be seen as the embryo base staff. Conditions were pretty basic and there was a certain amount of "them" and "us" between the Clyde Submarine Base and the Third Squadron. In hindsight this was bound to happen as the base requirements gradually encroached upon the operational squadron's facilities. In the end common sense prevailed and the problem got sorted. I was joined in the base repair organisation by Ian Hiley, who did sterling work on the build-up of our personnel, eventually rising to some ten technical officers and about 450 ratings of all skills and trades.   Tommy Lamport arrived and took over the huge mechanical workshop arrangements and as usual was worth his weight in gold. Roger Lambert, ex *Valiant*, joined as the Head of the Nuclear Repair Facility.

I cannot speak too highly of the continual efforts on our behalf by Ken Willis (ROPE) and his team. Not only had he to contend with the conflicting requirements of the Base and the Third Squadron as the former began to take shape, but inevitably there were quite serious changes required to the initial layouts of certain of the repair facilities.

They took all these in their stride. Over-riding the whole scene was the urgent need to meet the date for the first deployment of _Resolution_; much of the success in meeting this date was undoubtedly due to ROPE and his staff.

One of the highlights of the base programme was the arrival of the new floating dock from Portsmouth. John Lea has covered the main aspects of its arrival and berthing arrangements. Once secured this monstrous sight in the Gareloch caused considerable consternation amongst the locals who objected to the massive impact this black monster had upon the environment. After a great deal of acrimony I agreed that when the dock was due for its repaint, we would make every effort to camouflage it - knowing full well that this would be very many years in the future.

The actual securing of this huge dock to its fixed pylons was overseen by a Senior Constructor from DGS in Bath. The gentleman concerned was well over six feet tall and he arrived in a very small Mini. After the operation was successfully completed, he drove off towards the Wardroom for a celebratory drink and disappeared down one of the jetty inspection wells, Mini and all. No damage was done and he was so very pleased with the berthing success that he took it in good heart.

One of the least attractive aspects of the Clyde Base was the weather. In a major construction site this could and did cause us all considerable problems. A particular meteorological phenomenon of the Dumbarton district, was that every forty years or so, a major gale strikes the area. Needless to say this took place in January 1968; the gale struck with full force and caused structural damage to some of the buildings. This coincided with _Resolution_ alongside for unprogrammed repairs, coupled with a complete failure of the Scottish electrical supply to the Base. Discussions on this situation and how best to resolve it took place in my office by candlelight! Eventually the system righted itself but a lot of nailbiting took place before we were out of the woods. Quite a lot of damage was suffered locally, in Helensburgh and Glasgow. We sent teams of naval personnel to help clear up, for many of the local roads were impassable. This was a most useful PR exercise _vis-a-vis_ the local residents. One married quarter in Rhu had its complete roof blown off, leaving the occupants, who were in bed at the time, staring at the sky.

Once the Polaris School had been commissioned, as the first major milestone achieved, crews could be trained in the UK rather than the

USA. The next milestone was to commission the workshops so as to meet the important date of *Resolution*'s deployment. The organisation of the Technical Department was based upon both Squadrons (3 and 10) being served by a common workshop and afloat service. Squadron Engineering Officers had offices either side of my own and they were both served by a maintenance control room where all the repair plans were displayed in a simple form of PERT network. This ensured that there was no great conflict between needs and resources. This office, under the excellent charge of Dan Leggatt, operated as a sort of technical operations office, co-ordinating all the squadron repairs underway as well as planning for the future. DGS supplied us with a constructor who led a small party of quality control experts, essential in overseeing the materials used in repairs as well as standards of subsequent testing. There were at times, regrettably, some glaring examples of incorrect materials used in some of the submarine machinery spaces.

I touched upon the relationships between the Base and the local residents. This was a most important issue and in particular, relations with the local civic authorities. The Third Submarine Squadron had previously over the years established a good working relationship with local people and many lasting friendships were created. The Faslane Base with its nuclear deterrent concept was a rather different matter and initially placed some strain upon individuals' attitudes with regard to the overall concept. CND, et al, saw the Base as an opportunity to publicise their opposition in much the same way as they did during the arrival of the US squadron at Dunoon. Many Scottish people were concerned that the establishment of the Base as a permanent feature, opened the possibility of the area being a major target in the event of a nuclear attack on the UK. Some, not many, were just objectionable for the sake of objecting. Traders in Helensburgh took a more pragmatic view, especially after seeing the significant improvement to the trading lifestyle of their counterparts in Dunoon.

One or two regrettable incidents such as forgetting to include the Provost and the Town Council of Helensburgh on the invitation list for one of the major base public functions, did nothing to improve matters, but by and large an acceptable, if not always entirely happy relationship was established in the early days.

During one of the summer holidays my eldest son and daughter, with two young German pen-friends, were becalmed in Loch Long in their yacht. Eventually having gained the shore, they landed adjacent to the Top Secret missile base at Coulport, and managed to climb, in all ignorance, over the security fence, approaching the guard house at the entrance from the inside. This caused absolute consternation amongst the armed Admiralty Police, accentuated by the sound of guttural accents from the two German girls. Red faces all round amongst the police contingent and a rapid increase in patrols.

No documentation on the UK Polaris Programme could be completed without special mention of the part played by the late Admiral Derek Kent. During the Base build-up he was both Captain SM3 and Commodore Designate for the Clyde Submarine Base. A kinder, more considerate senior officer one could not hope to serve under and his calm, diplomatic leadership whilst fielding these two often disparate commands contributed significantly to the ultimate amalgamation of the 3rd and 10th Squadrons under one operational command and repair organisation.

CHAPTER 25
Engineering Support
Peter Hammersley

In February 1968 I took over as the Base Engineering Officer of the Clyde Submarine Base at Faslane relieving Nick Howlett whose task had been to oversee the building of the Base and plan the organisation. My appointment was timed so that I could take over in time to set the organisation to work for *Resolution* and the rest of the Polaris boats. *Resolution* arrived for her first maintenance period a few days after I did. My main task for the next two and a half years was to support the Polaris Squadron of four boats.

The Base had been well planned and well organised except that the scale of the support which would be necessary for the nuclear submarine fleet had been greatly under-estimated. I spent a large part of my time there pleading and writing papers to justify extra people. Many were eventually provided and thus extra accommodation and work areas were needed. But, apart from that, the facilities were superb. The Electronic Workshop was a huge improvement on anything that the RN had known before. Such facilities are now taken for granted and rightly so, but their provision then was another tribute to the planning and foresight of the Chief Polaris Executive and DPT. The Periscope and Mast Workshop was also a superb improvement, largely due to the officer in charge of it, Commander Tommy Lamport. He was an outstanding example of the best type of Special Duties Engineering Officer. Loyal and highly professional in every way, he worked very long hours to support the submarines. He was also a very keen fisherman and did not get as much time as he would have liked for that. Partly to compensate and partly for the sake of his fellow submariners, he used to run fishing training classes (out of normal working hours) in the Periscope Workshop which was long enough to cast a fly as far as most of us were capable.

Resolution's arrival at Faslane was soon followed by *Repulse* and the others and they were all delivered on time. Our workload built up rapidly. The Base played its full part and they all deployed on time. *Resolution*, known as BN01, carried out a number of patrols before *Repulse* was fully operational. I well remember the day when she, *Repulse,* sailed on her first patrol. Tommy Lamport was standing at the end of the jetty pretending he was running a boat hire business. He looked out to sea and shouted "Come in Number One, your time is up".

CHAPTER 26

Base Supply Organisation
Mark Jones

The support mission for the Base being built at Faslane on the Gareloch, Dunbartonshire, was defined by the major task of ensuring that the four Polaris boats were never late on patrol and never had to end a fifty six day patrol prematurely because of any shortfall in supply. Each boat throughout its patrol had to be self-supported and self-contained. The second major task was the support of the Third Squadron of Fleet nuclear and diesel powered submarines.

Having returned from eighteen months at sea as an Admiral's secretary, mostly with aircraft carriers in the Far East during the confrontation with Indonesia, I was told that I was to get a job at Portsmouth near my family. Thus in the early spring of 1966 I joined HMS *Dolphin* at Gosport and found that I was to be one of a small team on the staff of Flag Officer Submarines (FOS/M) working on detailed planning for the new submarine base being built at Faslane in Scotland.

The work began in a hut office in *Dolphin* with desk space provided by tables against the walls for people who came and went. There was much to absorb about the intended method of working and much discussion at Gosport and during visits to the naval equipment and supplies departments in Bath. Resources were being secured and committed for the new base and its submarines to achieve the date already fixed for the sequence of Polaris submarine patrols to begin. Everyone was helpful. Wherever one turned for advice or commitment there was a nominated Polaris Liaison Officer whose task, in addition to his full-time normal duties, was to smooth the way and get things done.

Despite the apparent simplicity of the plans for the supply system already in place, I found, during the many visits and discussions, that I was acquiring an increasingly long list of difficult items that would be the responsibility of the Base Supply Officer (BSO). I was beginning to understand why no-one else had taken this job.

The Faslane designated supply staff with FOS/M had, in addition, to wrestle with all of the discussions and paperwork that involved any aspect of support for the base. For instance the Base was to be provided with housing for families in the nearby towns of Helensburgh and Rhu based on estimates of the numbers of families to be expected to move to Scotland. This also entailed securing the enlargement of local schools based on an assessment of the primary and secondary places that would be required. One of the more obscure and fascinating pieces of research was to get and agree the numbers, particularly as the secondary school age figures were quite surprisingly low.

An unexpected problem was that husbands were expecting to be so busy in their new jobs that their families anticipated seeing too little of them to make it worth their while to move from England to Scotland and the married quarters which were being built there for them. This in turn entailed an extra demand for more "single" accommodation in the base than had been forecast.

While most of the crew of a diesel submarine moved out of the boat when in harbour and required beds and meals in a depot ship ashore or afloat, there was less need for such facilities for the large nuclear submarines. The Polaris submarines had the new concept of having two crews which swopped round at the end of each patrol, so the accommodation in the base being built for them assumed they would similarly swop beds ashore as they did onboard. The accommodation swopping idea did not work as well in practice as it did in theory and was another factor in necessitating additional accommodation blocks being built as soon as the base was opened.

All the visits, discussions and reconnaissance were to prove valuable many times over, but neither in *Dolphin*, when picking brains there and getting advice, nor similarly with *Maidstone* at Faslane, did I ever really get an idea of, and of the need to provide for, items of stores customarily traded and swopped between boats along the jetty at any submarine base. These are important items, otherwise efforts would not be made. As the transactions were unrecorded in any formal way which was visible to the supply system no allowance was made for them.

As each Polaris boat was completed it would begin a longish period of testing and working up, culminating in a missile-firing test off the Atlantic coast of the USA. During this period some of the storeroom space would be occupied with test gear which would be removed before deployment on patrol, and called for careful planning of storage needs. Having one of my naval officer or civil servant members of the supply staff ride in the boat for this period was valuable to sort out the systems and records.

Social and working visits to the USS *Simon Lake*, the American

Polaris submarine support ship berthed further down the north shore of the Clyde estuary at Holy Loch, were made to study the similarities of their system for getting replenishment from the USA by sea and air. We examined their computer with its big memory drum and watched the officer 'designated for supply duty' himself wielding a crowbar to open the packing cases of spares newly arrived from the USA for his SSBN before she went on patrol. His comment was "they just work the ass off me". The Captain of *Simon Lake* strongly stressed in our discussions that "Supply is a gut function".

The naval supplies and transport organisation had now arranged the supply support concept so that a parent ' equipment' generated the lists of spares required. Adding a new piece of equipment to a boat's outfit automatically provided its schedule of spares; removing one caused its spare to be removed from the lists of those to be provided. For instance, many items of machinery onboard required 'spare gear' supplied from the factory. If these were awkwardly shaped and needed special stowages these features could be specially recorded. On the other hand many radio and electrical systems were supported by the same kinds of component, even though there are thousands of types of them, mostly relatively tiny, many of them supplied already installed and tested on circuit boards. Here the need was to know from equipment lists what was wanted and to be able to find it quickly. The missile systems themselves required a whole range of spares support as did many other new systems onboard. Criticality of need had to be balanced against space, cost and ease of retrieval.

For the thousands of small items their stowage onboard was in arrays of small aluminium boxes, each a cubic foot in size, loading into shelving racks. Each box had a list of contents and was labelled with a reference number so that each item could be tracked to its lair by lists held on board. The stores computer system in the Base made the allocations and held the master record of the locations in each submarine. Thus as each item was recorded as having been used during a patrol, supply of a replacement would be made with a delivery note which showed to which box it belonged. All very simply planned and described but this description omits the humble and exhausting task of actually putting the initial outfit of thousands of items into the boxes and making the record of each location. It had to be done only four times!

One of the early concept changes was the decision, towards the end of 1966, to adopt the American Polaris Force practice of designating one of its officers onboard as the Supply Officer to act as the single-point-of-contact for all supply matters between the boat and the base. This was to give a valuable link for all the many ideas that we had to develop and implement. It also enabled us to find out quickly just how serious a delay in supplying a "critical" item really was, involving a process of much co-operative bargaining. The boats had a stores Petty Officer in each crew and, although the stores outfits for each boat were virtually identical, they soon made many of their own differing improvements. The Base supply computer systems had assembled lists of all the spares needed in each boat and then sorted them to eliminate duplications according to criticalities, but the essentially "dumb" system and its allocations of stowages onboard responded quite soon to intelligent use of the system though it took hard and detailed work to achieve.

The new Polaris boats were designed to be self-sufficient at sea and submerged for months at a time thus creating an important morale problem for both Chef and Supply Officer; when a man is on duty 24 hours a day for two months his meals become very important to him. Thus the meals that would be provided for the crew during their patrol had to meet many needs, not least being variety to sustain interest and good morale. It would be their choices, conveyed to us by their chefs, that must govern the selections, this flexibility being governed by the overall catering budget for each boat.

With each crew a two-month menu for each meal every day was worked out and agreed with the galley staff. Built in also were choices and extras which they could find at any time to make changes in the menu and provide extra or changed choices on the menu of items becoming more popular amongst the crew. The drawings and diagrams of each storeroom were used to plan the storing of all the foodstuffs so as to use every inch of the space available, the key being to ensure that those items needed first would be at the front of the store. As the chef onboard had a complete list of everything, selecting changes and special choices became easier as the storeroom was "eaten into". Above all something needed at any time must never be at the back and inaccessible.

In the short period before deployment for the 56 day patrols, a significant constraint was that access into the pressure hull of the Polaris submarines was by a single 33" hatch which had to be shared by people and stores. The main volume of stores to be embarked in this period would be the foodstuffs, much of it in packages of varying shapes and sizes. Tony Kemp, on the victualling side of the base staff, spent a lot of time devising and evaluating methods of assembling the stocks, passing them through the single hatch and dispersing them to their stowages within the boat. The scheme which emerged was to assemble the food items into individually suspended loads less than 33" in diameter. These would be transferred, while still suspended, into a lorry in the Base warehouse. When the lorry arrived at Coulport, the missile supply base some miles away, the loads would be lifted off the lorry by crane and swung across and lowered down through the submarine's hatch. They would then be clipped onto the overhead rail within the submarine to travel along the passageways to the individual storerooms.

However, within these main constraints of space, cost and access, changes could be rung by use of the cold, cool or dry storage spaces. Milk is an example that illustrates the interlocking options for the stowage of foodstuffs. Fresh milk is of course preferred and will last a few days chilled but takes up much space; it will of course last even longer in cold storage but meat had priority there. "Long Life", or UHT treated, milk lasts much longer but spoils if chilled too long before it is required so goes in a "dry" space and moves to the "chilled" space when the fresh milk has been used. The less popular dried milk had to provide the bulk of supply as it needed a relatively small volume of "dry" space, before being reconstituted with water and put in a chill refrigerator. A fortunate effect of television at the time was that it had made "instant" milk more popular even though in those early days at the Base we could not use our TV sets in that area of Scotland.

Commander Tubby Squires in his Fleet nuclear submarine, *Warspite*, took a great deal of interest in what we were attempting and volunteered to try out the menu-driven food system in his boat for us when setting off on a long deployment through the South Atlantic. He provided much sage advice and many useful lessons as well as building confidence in what we were doing.

The meals for the naval ratings in the Base and the submarine crews were provided by the main galley building up the side of the hill above the main road through the Base, close by the blocks of offices where we kept the pay and other accounts. In common with the food supply chain for the submarines we confined the purchase of all foods to naval supply and NAAFI, declining all offers from civilian commercial suppliers, despite some pressure. As a single exception we did later on replace half-pound blocks of butter with the small foil-wrapped pats of butter in the interests of hygiene and economy, though the sight of burly sailors grasping these by the handful made me doubtful about economy if still assured on hygiene!

The pay of those living out with their families included an allowance for food so that if they wished to eat the "free" meals in the dining hall they were supposed to pay in cash. I was advised that adequate control could only be ensured by having a system of tickets. I decided, having read much research on this subject in preparation before coming to Faslane, to run an "honour" system instead. We had one of the base staff, often a Wren, sitting at a table at the top of the steps by the entrance to the dining hall ready to receive payment. After all everyone knew who should pay to eat and this way was very flexible as no-one needed to make their mind up about eating until the last minute. The numbers involved did not cause awkward fluctuations in the numbers of meals required. It seemed to work well.

The support services for the naval families moving into the area with their husbands included a large and several smaller new estates of housing near Helensburgh and Rhu some miles from the base as well as enlargement of local primary and secondary schools. But there remained many problems; for instance in persuading the local buses to serve the estates, or that frozen New Zealand lamb was more attractive to naval families than expensive Scottish beef. An organisation of wives representing all the naval wives became active with access to senior officers in the Base. A primary concern was loneliness as not only were many young wives now hundreds of miles from Mum and their old friends, they were also without the support of their husbands when they were deployed at sea for long stretches of weeks at a time. A young wife might be detained in her quarter by illness of herself or a child, without a telephone, a car, a bus service or even a corner shop. My wife and others devised a scheme whereby assistance could be sought by a simple sign in a window which neighbours and others would know meant "someone inside needs help" and would then knock on the door and get someone to do something. The sign chosen was a drawing of a fish, an ancient Christian symbol. Thus was born the "Fish" scheme.

To ensure that no-one was left without help, each street, or each block of flats, had a co-ordinator, usually chosen because she had a telephone. Any passer-by seeing a fish sign in a front window knew that help was needed and would notify the co-ordinator. The scheme was linked to the doctors and hospitals in the area and was of comfort not only to the families but also to the husbands away and out of contact throughout their patrols.

When Commander Mike Henry took the "first-of-class" *Resolution* out for a three day shake down and tactical appraisal, before becoming fully operational, he arranged for me to go too. Here was an opportunity to share the meals and sleeping arrangements, to feel the boat running, to watch the operation of the nuclear power plant, to watch the galley staff preparing, cooking and serving all the meals, and to explore the boat from end to end, inspecting and checking the storage and accessibility of the foodstuffs, stores and spares which had been selected, labelled and prepared for loading with such care.

Immediately on return to harbour, after briefing the Base supply staff on various aspects, nearly all satisfactory, we concentrated on the need to ensure the separation of the "clean" and "oily" halves of the boat fore and aft of bulkhead 99. Astern of this bulkhead was the nuclear power plant, with the turbine to convert its steam into electrical power for the main propulsion, pumps and all other services, as well as diesel machinery with its special fuel smells and the steering gear, all typical of a normal submarine.

So as to prevent any oily grime reaching the main and forward parts of the boat with their clean areas for the missile and command systems and living quarters, any footwear and heavy safety boots which might be oily had to be taken off on passing through bulkhead 99. Suitable footwear for the clean side was needed. Our solution was to provide clean "house" slippers, one pair for each man in the crew, coloured red for one crew and green for the other, the crews being known by these colours (Port and Starboard). This required some rapid shopping and a transaction through the base's cash clothing account so as to make a "loan" issue of the correct size and colour for each man.

The Polaris submarines started their patrols exactly on their long-planned dates and none suffered from supply shortages. Meanwhile we got on also with the tasks of supporting the Fleet nuclear and diesel boats, seeking to serve them by the same standards and principles. But the Polaris force continued to teach us many very simple lessons.

Resolution had had a good and arduous shake-down and work-up before deployment and was in hand with catering money so decided on a special treat by ordering "oven-ready" pheasants, a demand which had not been exactly anticipated but was met, apparently successfully, in the few hours' notice before they arrived - there was just a small matter that the pheasants had been properly gutted but still had their feathers so, undismayed, the chef plucked and cooked them well to time but alarmed the ventilation engineer when the feathers clogged the filters.

It was all up and running when I left in January 1969, took the family back to Hampshire, and got into an aircraft to Cyprus where I was to join an assault ship - the Navy still full of surprises.

CHAPTER 27

Material Support
Basil Page

"So where were you when John Kennedy was assassinated?". I had been in the US one week having joined the RN Special Projects cell in Washington DC to arrange for the procurement and supply of the considerable quantities of American spares required to support the specialist missile fire control, navigational and many other equipments involved in the UK Polaris Project. I was at my first provisioning conference at Sperry's, Long Island, when the news came through. The meeting was abandoned and we returned to our hotel in Manhattan to find Broadway blacked out.

As a member of one of the civilian manned supply departments for the Navy (later to be integrated into the RN Supply and Transport Service), I had been given a job different from anything I had experienced before - even in war. The RN is almost alone among both the British and other nations' armed forces in the extent to which its supply services are civilianised. The shore supply depots and corresponding HQ organisation are entirely civilian manned with the RN uniformed Supply Branch providing the "front-line" service aboard HM ships and shore establishments and dependant upon the civilian main depots as their wholesalers.

My welcome in Washington - from the RN - was, shall I say, "different" in that it consisted mainly of "What on earth are you here for?". The welcome from my US Supply Corps opposite numbers, both uniform and civilian, in the US Polaris Special Projects Office was quite different - "Thank goodness you've arrived!". To be fair, the essential nature of spares support for the Project did dawn upon my RN friends before long - meanwhile they were too engrossed with the equipments required for actual incorporation in the submarines whilst building to worry about their back-up support.

Limited secretarial support was shared in the UK office but no other help was available and frequent week-long absences at the American main equipment contractors across the States to decide on and order (with USN advice and assistance) the large range of items expected to be required to keep the US equipments operational at all times meant long hours when back at base. Memories are of ten, eleven, twelve hour days starting soon after 7am (we could not, of course, be seen to be less diligent than our American friends in starting work!), Saturday and Sunday work - or travel; of frequent flights to the West Coast and "red-eye" flights back east and straight into the office or sometimes further "red-eye" on to the UK and immediately into joint US/UK meetings in London or Bath.

At the same time domestic situations needed resolving. My two sons aged 9 and 11 (the eldest just started at grammar school) were found places at the British Embassy recommended "private" school in Virginia and withdrawn from their English schools. We had not wanted to send them to boarding schools in UK for up to three years. However this soon turned out to be an unwise move in view of the differing syllabuses and timescales in the two educational systems so, by mail, with great difficulty and not a little worry, the boys were found places at a boarding school in Surrey after about six months and returned home. Heartbreaking periodic farewells became the norm, but we were right to do it although our US friends have never fully understood why.

When the stage of physical movement of stores and equipments to UK was reached the need became obvious for a UK officer within the US Naval Supply Center at Charleston, South Carolina. One of my Department's civilian officers was duly appointed and the USN, for a peppercorn rent of $1 a year, agreed to build a modest UK designated transit shed at Charleston within their Base from which all our material was subsequently shipped to UK by USN auxiliary vessels going to Holy Loch.

Not long after my deputy settled into his post in Charleston, with his wife and two small daughters, and despite the warm welcome and hospitality accorded, the problem arose of his civilian status within a primarily military and uniformed complex. Inevitable difficulties arose in such areas as the use of the Officers' Messes and his status as the UK's liaison officer in the area could have been affected. Mountains were moved and it was eventually approved that the occupant of the post should be given a temporary commission in the RN so that he could wear uniform on duty. This was a unique step in peacetime although in wartime, in war zones abroad, officers of our departments were routinely temporarily commissioned into the RN. So after a short leave in the UK, including 48 hours at HMS *Excellent* to learn how to salute etc, he returned to Charleston as Lt Cdr RN (Special Duties). Another Polaris "first" and a similar situation applied to the incumbent of the post under the Polaris/Trident programme.

Meanwhile life in Washington continued apace. Endless air travel (100,000 miles were clocked up in 18 months), innumerable self-drive cars at airports and freeway travel to contractor's works: the occasional visit to cities squeezed in (San Francisco, Los Angeles, Milwaukee and, of course, New York), but otherwise airport to contractors, or to USN facility such as the Spare Parts Distribution Center, Great Lakes, or the US Polaris Material Office Puget Sound, Seattle.

Visitors from the UK were frequent and constant social activity was very much part of the job. The unpaid efforts of one's wife became very important - and arduous - as assistance with resulting costs was (with a local Treasury cell present at the Embassy) necessarily strictly within the rules! (Grants were made on a limited basis for entertaining foreign nationals ie US - never for our constant UK visitors). Fortunately, being attached to the Embassy we had access to duty-free alcohol though "my man in Charleston" had obvious logistical problems in this respect. My luggage on my frequent visits to him was largely liquid!

Another deputy was eventually appointed to help me in Washington and as progress was made and results in the form of hardware began to appear on the shelves in UK, at our RN Store Depot at Copenacre Wiltshire, life became less frenetic and settled down into more of a routine. Expectations of a more traditional posting at the end of my third year in Washington were shattered, however, when I was invited to move instead directly to Faslane in Scotland to start up the Supply Organisation in the Clyde Submarine Base under construction. I was needed there "urgently" - a familiar Polaris term - and it did not need a lot of thought! With what I had seen of the workings of the Americans' own Polaris material support organisation across the country and the contacts made, the move seemed logical. My wife and I did have our first real break before sailing home (itself a welcome change from flying) a few months before my three years were up: a glorious two weeks' holiday in the (then) unspoilt Caribbean.

Thoughts of the "American Experience" must be primarily of the really tremendous help and kindness of the USN Special Projects (Polaris) Organisation and the main contractors. It was not help just because it was required by the Polaris Sales Agreement; there was genuine enthusiasm. One of the most remarkable aspects was the way that our UK team was totally integrated within the US organisation. We wandered almost at will into each other's offices and developed relationships which undoubtedly contributed greatly to speed and efficiency, and the friendships which endure to this day. The "special relationship" was undoubtedly to the fore: corners were cut and assistance given well "beyond the call of duty". How right and proper it was when an honorary Knighthood was subsequently conferred by Her Majesty on the Head of the USN Polaris Project Team.

Arrival at Faslane in October 1966 was a salutary experience. HMS *Maidstone* (Captain SM3) was Depot Ship for the Third Submarine Squadron of "O" and "P" class conventional submarines and the nuclear HMS *Dreadnought* and HMS *Valiant*. HMS *Narvik*, a Second World War tank landing ship, was accommodation ship to the embryo shore base which was simply a building site. There was quite literally mud everywhere and "wellies" essential to get anywhere.

The store complex was barely started and an advance party which consisted of a stout-hearted Senior Store-Keeping Officer, two or three store staff and civilian motor transport drivers taken over from *Maidstone's* pool, operated from a tiny existing out-building. The only building of the new Base finished (almost) was the Polaris School, and by courtesy of the Officer-in-Charge, a desk was found for me therein and shared use of a telephone. (Partly blackmail on his part - in exchange he persuaded me on to his list of regular lecturers.)

I was warmly greeted by Captain SM3, but within a day or so after a very convivial evening welcoming party on board *Maidstone*, was told by the then Squadron Supply Officer that "You'll never do it old chap!". Not the sort of encouraging noises that were needed by me at that time, but an entirely understandable warning from an officer who knew by experience that where "stores" were concerned - as in other areas - submariners were a bit of a law unto themselves! The RN Supply and Transport Service - with myself as the guinea pig and at the sharp end - was to have its first experience of supporting submarines directly, without the "buffer" of a depot ship or shore base; and not just conventional submarines, but a new breed of Polaris nuclears with the need for near perfect support if their operational capabilities were not to be impaired. Stores, machinery repair parts, whole new ranges of spares for sophisticated British and American electronic equipments, atmospheric control (an irreparable defect could require the submarine to surface and "abort" its patrol), and at last but by no means least, food for two months submerged, all as a 365 day, 24 hour service, The Base itself, workshops, module repair and calibration facility and accommodation areas also required support, and in the transport task alone it would prove difficult to keep all customers happy, day or night (not that one ever could, as all car drivers are experts on the subject of transport management!).

The task posed very interesting problems for a civilian-manned department associated more with a "nine to five" dockyard organisation, and not a little scepticism arose in certain places. Perhaps as a direct result of what I had seen of the American Polaris organisation I was fully convinced of what was necessary and, after some argument, not a little tact, and some sheer cussedness, firm objectives were finally accepted: but the practical difficulties we experienced in the early stages were no help!

Most problems could (and were) overcome by dedicated staff working very hard, but undoubtedly the major difficulty was to be the computer systems. Back in the sixties "state-of-the-art" computers were little more than electronic calculators and slow printers, vast machines needing cosseting in special air-conditioned rooms, and fed by staff punching cards from basic documents.

The system planned would, whilst working with the other (different) systems operating at the established shore organisations elsewhere in the UK, enable rapid supply and replenishment of Faslane's own holdings. In addition information would be held about expected usage and degrees of essentiality or criticality to a patrol (using American experience where applicable). This would assist in determining those items, particularly of machinery or electronic spares, which it was necessary to hold on board the submarines.

The issue process from Faslane to the submarines and Base workshops was planned on a daily processing basis, and it was here that the system proved weakest. Routine supply and replenishment of outfits of stores to be held on board was straightforward, but day to day requirements whilst in port, under maintenance, could not usually wait for 24 hours. They were more numerous (seemingly always urgent, and always vital(!)) than anyone (perhaps outside the submarine service with its somewhat freebooter attitude to stores) could have envisaged. So these invariably had to "by-pass" the system and be caught up with later. In so doing, manual reference to stock records entailed "reading" punched cards of which there were over 120,000 in the stock-record file alone, and some misfiling was inevitable despite the strictest discipline. This was one sure recipe for disaster.

On top of that, the hardware of the computer installed temporarily about two miles away in a converted canteen belonging to the BP Oil Company proved so unreliable that despite the permanent presence of two resident company engineers the computer was out of action

50% of the time. It was a very worrying period, but after much nausea and high-level inquests it was decided by HQ that to save re-programming the entire system for a different computer a duplicate of the existing equipment would be procured, presumably on the theory that twice 50% availability would equal 100% (unless of course the two machines were "down" at the same time!) The second machine was eventually installed in the designated space as soon as the new office block was ready, whilst the first remained in its "temporary" accom-modation; hardly ideal for management purposes.

The shortcomings of the basic systems remained and not until after I left in 1970 and all four Polaris submarines had become operational was a new generation computer installed, capable of random access and interactive processing at any time. It was the dedication of my staff both in the office and in the stores and understanding (sometimes with a little difficulty) by our customers that enabled the department to provide the type of service that was required. This was greatly helped by the setting-up, with the full co-operation of the Naval Base Supply Officer, of a unique "Base Replenishment Team" (a misnomer because it was intended to provide assistance with stores and food replenish-ment to the submarines, and not to the Base). The team was headed by one of my civilian officers and staffed by naval supply ratings. It was located within my office complex so that contact at all levels was easy, and provided an excellent liaison and service to all submarines: it undoubtedly smoothed out many of the difficulties and problems of those early days.

Buildings rose; stores arrived and were stowed; victualling and freezer stores filled; tanks in the diesel "farm" filled; new cars, lorries, mechanical equipment were all being delivered. However the need for more staff was evident and no sooner were the offices as planned completed but approval was given for a third floor extension: we all worked literally underneath pneumatic drills for many months.

In fact the biggest spur to the building programme was the visit of HM The Queen Mother on 10 May 1968; even the roads appeared, and the mud disappeared as if by magic.

It was a great moment when HMY *Britannia* berthed alongside. Later, after all the ceremonies, the senior officers of the Base and their wives hosted a splendid lunch in the Wardroom of HMS *Neptune* for Her Majesty and the very many VIPs who had descended on us for the occasion. It was a busy time all round with all the visitors from various HQ departments including innumerable Admirals being transported, accommodated and entertained. Motor transport was fully stretched between the Base and Glasgow Station and Glasgow Airport, but I saw that all our drivers still found time to be interested in the royal Rolls Royce parked in our garage overnight.

Life rapidly returned to normal: more problems and, somehow, solutions. Because the Polaris (10th) Squadron attracted top priority, the conventional "O" and "P" class submarines of the 3rd Squadron sometimes felt - sometimes with reason - that they suffered by comparison in the service we gave them. And so it was that early one morning I was sent aboard HMS *Onyx* by Captain SM3 for a day of trials in the Clyde and adjacent lochs. It was a memorable day for me, involving as it did various manoeuvres including, of course, diving, and I found the drill for changing from diesel to electric propulsion and *vice versa* particularly dramatic. The day became famous throughout my department; *Onyx* became known as the "Boss's Sub" and she at least got the best of attention thereafter. Actually I like to think that the standards for which we were aiming eventually rubbed off onto all our non-Polaris customers as well.

The big day for *Resolution*'s first patrol was looming; actual sailing date secret of course. Our task to ensure that the prescribed outfit of food, and thousands of items of stores and spare parts was virtually 100% complete. The political pressures for a successful full length patrol of the UK's "new" nuclear deterrent were tremendous and felt by all concerned. An aborted patrol for whatever reason would be at best a very great disappointment. One of the most important aspects of life on board whilst submerged for long periods was atmosphere control; a failure would inevitably mean aborting. Despite all efforts of the manufacturers, there were still a very few bits and pieces of spares for this equipment not on board. Discussions with Captain SM10 and the Commanding Officer only served to emphasise the pressure the CO was under and his natural unhappiness at any risk of failure - and it was my department in this particular "hot" seat. All weekend effort continued: *Resolution* was at Coulport embarking missiles and on Sunday afternoon we were due to have a final look at the position at a meeting on board. I have to confess that I fortified myself and my deputy with a couple of pink gins from my office cupboard before being driven to *Resolution*. However, after considerable discussion the CO said he would "go" - and had indeed gone by the morning. The patrol went its full period (daily we worried, as I am sure many others did), but all was well and *Resolution* returned on schedule to a huge welcome. Few people not closely involved could ever appreciate the tense atmosphere pervading during that time and, for me, that Sunday afternoon before the first patrol is quite unforgettable.

One of the biggest problems a civilian Head of Department had to face was that of industrial relations. Our industrial (store) staff, apart from a few senior transferees from other depots, were all recruited locally. Unlike staff from "dockyard" towns, there was no tradition of working for, or loyalty to, the Royal Navy; we had no alternative to recruiting from anywhere in the Clydeside area, and many of the people we got were used to "downing tools" to get response from employers and quite unable to understand the slow working of the established governmental Whitley negotiating procedures. Our need, as mentioned before, was to operate a 24 hour, seven day a week service calling for comprehensive shift working; pay, hours and allowances loomed large, with men expecting management locally to be able to respond. Many were the rumbustious meetings we had, many the threats to strike. On two occasions I found myself literally standing on a packing case addressing two hundred irate Clydeside Scots and several more times similarly meeting my thirty or so drivers; my reasoning and quasi appeals to them must have done something, though my senior Foreman told me he overheard one group saying "What the ... is the old man talking about?". However, apart from one weekend when the drivers worked to rule - with no ill effects! - we avoided dislocation. Indeed there was a later more memorable occasion when addressing the staff in the newly built cinema of HMS *Neptune* on the touchy subject of productivity that, to my great astonishment - and no little delight - the antagonism turned to applause. It was only later that I realised that it could have been because I had tripped and nearly fallen flat on my face on the way to the stage; but maybe not.

I have hardly mentioned before the victualling task for all the submarines, especially of course the Polaris boats with their special requirements. This is perhaps because it gave me personally by far the least of my worries (dare I say one reason being it was "ex-computer" and dealt with on traditional lines?). Much work by equally dedicated staff (and again with the very active co-operation of the Base Supply Officer), went into devising suitable menus for the long patrols of Polaris, testing new foods, and new methods of packaging and physically embarking and storing the bulk on board. Food obviously meant a great deal for morale and, though the traditional rum issue had only recently been dropped, a fair quantity of canned beer had to be provided in lieu.

As so, following *Resolution*, the remainder of the Squadron, *Repulse*, *Renown* and *Revenge* commissioned and took their place in the patrol cycle, all, remarkably, within the planned time-scales. Our own long term difficulties were now met with well-established routines to overcome them and, thanks to the support of the RN Supply and Transport Service's back-up from Rosyth Dockyard, and stores departments at Eaglescliffe and Copenacre (involving not infrequent out of normal working hours activity for them) our objectives were achieved. We now had our two duplicate computers operating, and the important step of the design of the replacement system had been initiated and the equipments, and new buildings, ordered.

After seven of the most demanding but interesting and rewarding years of my career, and having seen all four Polaris submarines operational, it seemed appropriate for me to hand over to my successor and resume more normal duties. I was "dined out" in traditional manner by the Wardroom of *Neptune* although this turned out in the end to have been a rather doubtful honour: in the fairly typical horseplay after dinner, those Polaris COs present managed to involve me to such an extent that I suffered from a bad back for some years afterwards. But I would not have missed any of it.

Throughout it all - uprooting to the States, then to Scotland, finding accommodation (six addresses in seven years), changes of school for our sons, much entertaining of all varieties with no help, my everlasting thanks are due to my dear wife, who always supported me in everything and put up with my moods in the bad times.

CHAPTER 28

The Royal Naval Armament Depot
Andrew McLeod

The story of RNAD Coulport is really a story of people, hundreds of people on both sides of the Atlantic, who contributed to this part of the Polaris project. Unfortunately, I can't write it that way. It would need a book on its own and even then would inevitably omit due tribute to many. This is therefore a more or less personal view and very largely omits reference to individuals except in the early days when they were thin on the ground!

The RN Armament Supply Department had very little direct involvement with the Polaris missile system prior to 1963. The Department had studied reports on the US development of Polaris, but with the UK apparently wedded to an airborne nuclear deterrent, it seemed unlikely that we would be involved. This was dramatically changed by the signing of the Nassau Agreement.

The setting up of the Polaris Executive with Rear Admiral Mackenzie in charge has already been described elsewhere in this book. Norman Luscombe, Director of Armament Supply (and later the first head of the combined RN Supply and Transport Service) allocated me to the Executive to deal with the Armament Depot planning. I was fortunate in having previously been Head of the Guided Missile branch which included atomic weapons. I had also, until a year previously, been responsible for torpedoes, a subsidiary but by no means minor task for the Polaris Armament Depot.

Norman Luscombe had decided views on the importance of continuity in planning the Depot, monitoring its construction, installing and checking out the equipment, training and work-up staff and finally full operation in support of the Navy. His stated intention to me was that one officer should be responsible throughout, becoming Superintendent of the new Depot in due course and remaining in post until the fourth submarine had been deployed. A marvellous prospect; but not one without its trials and tribulations on the way.

I had twice in my career suggested that a Scottish appointment would be very acceptable. The first was half way through our training course in 1937. I was told they would bear it in mind and I was happy to find what a considerate outfit I had joined. I was posted to Woolwich Arsenal. The second was when I was about to leave Malta in 1958. This time the appointment was to West Wales (Trecwn and Milford Haven - previously separate establishments). I am not complaining, I enjoyed my two years there. Here I was, getting my wish (admittedly in two or three years' time) and getting the best job in the Department. Opinions may vary about these last words: "most challenging" might be more apt.

I was shortly joined by Charles Tavener on the engineering side and Ron Lavers on the administrative. We had worked together before; both had missile experience and both stayed with me throughout all the toughest times of the programme. It is sad that neither is here to tell their own story.

CPE set up a small committee, chaired by Captain Rae McKaig, to recommend the best site for the Polaris shore base. The Navy Works Department representative was an old acquaintance, Burnside. We were jointly concerned in the mid-fifties with recommending Glen Douglas as the site for a NATO Armament Depot. Coincidence brought us both back to the Highlands - and to the same area.

Out of ten possible locations considered, the Committee strongly recommended the Clyde - with extensions to the Submarine Base at Faslane on the Gareloch, and the Armament Depot on Loch Long at Coulport where the Admiralty owned some 600 acres of land. This recommendation, besides other advantages, avoided possible delays in site acquisition which might have seriously prejudiced a tight timescale. It was accepted by the Board of Admiralty.

Coulport lies on the western side of the Rosneath peninsula, about five miles north of Kilcreggan. It is at the end of the road which runs more or less round the shoreline of the peninsula. It looks southward to the widening Clyde estuary and westward across the deep waters of Loch Long to Ardentinny, to which it was once connected by ferry. A minor road, the Peaton, now much improved, crosses back to the eastern side of the peninsula, climbing to 600 feet and cutting some ten miles off the main road distance to Faslane.

The peninsula, in the mid nineteenth century, was a favourite location for retirement or holiday homes of Glasgow businessmen. It had easy access by water, an advantage which it lost with the coming of the motor car. To some extent it has stayed still since. Rosneath had two very reputable boatyards - I was shown round and offered "Silver Trident" for £200,000 - £6m in today's currency! Cove Kilcreggan had a reasonably thriving social life, an active church and a very good literary society. The rest of the peninsula's housing mainly consisted of large mid-Victorian mansions in substantial grounds, many rather run down, elegant but outdated.

Coulport had a dozen or more houses spread out over the half mile south of the ferry. The hills facing it to the west across Loch Long rise to over 2,000 feet and Creachan Mor looks a particularly fine sight with the top 1,000 feet under snow. It is heaven on a good day; it is a severe shock for a townsman on a bad one.

The Polaris tasks at Coulport would be broadly similar to those of the US Depot at Charleston, South Carolina, except on a smaller scale. They would entail:

a)   receipt of missiles, guidance, spares and support equipment from the US and warheads from UK manufacture; assembly and test, loading into submarines;

b)   receipt of missiles from submarines for storage, repair, modification, periodic overhaul and surveillance testing.

If the timescale of some five years for Polaris deployment were to be met, it would be essential to give very early preliminary instructions on building requirements. Navy Works (to be absorbed by the Ministry of Public Buildings and Works (MPBW) on 1 April - a complication for both departments when we could most do without it) - put a deadline as 31 May.

In meeting this deadline, Captain Phil Rollings USN, an armaments specialist, was invaluable. He was the first US Special Projects Officer (SPUK) and his early invaliding was a great loss to us as well as to the US Navy. Phil was able to provide the concept document layout and detailed building drawings for POMFPAC (Polaris Operating and Maintenance Facility Pacific), the new missile depot being built at Bangor in the State of Washington. He was also able to answer most of our queries.

Based on these documents, it was possible to specify, in considerable detail, building requirements for the Coulport Armament Depot. In April/May 1963 these were examined in the States in conjunction with the US Navy and with Lockheed, the overall "Missile Systems Manager". This was a joint visit with Captain Reg Burrell (Weapons Inspectorate) a programme laid on by Captain Peter La Niece, SPRN.

At Charleston, we saw the "hardware" for the first time and the depot organisation and tasks - most impressive! In Washington we spent much time with the Missile Branch SP27. It was agreed that representatives of DAS and DGWI (Weapons Inspectorate) should be posted to SPRN's staff by 1 August when trials of the new A3 missile were due to start, including "slow run through" of missile assembly and testing. Bert Vinter was our first "man in Washington" followed shortly by Ron Lavers and then John Muir. DGWI's representative was Commander Jim Barwood. All gained very valuable experience - all joined Coulport later. All were befriended (as I was) and helped by Lockheed contacts and by Rear Admiral Ralf Metcalf (retired) (Mr Metcalf in Lockheeds - their depot facilities man).

We met the Polaris Technical Director, Rear Admiral Levering Smith, who stressed the need for common US/UK standards in testing and quality assurance. This remained an aim, which was enforced, fairly ruthlessly on occasion. It was tested most effectively and, as far as we were concerned, successfully, at Coulport, six years later by a joint US/UK Capability Review team of some fifty US and UK experts in their individual fields.

The main alterations to our tentative building plans recommended by SP and Lockheeds were:

a)   missiles would be stored and transported in the "liner" (a large and strong tubular container, which is locked in vertically to the submarine for embarkation or landing of the missile). This would give better protection in transport and avoid the necessity for dehumidification in storage buildings and the extra headroom required for straddle carriers;

b)   inserting the missile in its liner would be carried out horizontally in the Missile Assembly Building as at Charleston, avoiding the need for an extra, very tall, building for vertical "canning" employed at POMFPAC.

We were back in time to get the final building requirements, including those for the torpedo workshops and stores, to MPBW by the deadline of 31 August, but it was a close run thing! Layout of buildings on site was a joint effort with MPBW to ensure requisite explosive safety distances, permissible test cable lengths and appropriate traffic flows. It entailed tramping through the heather - being paid for something I do for pleasure. It was reviewed by a departmental work study team.

The site had its own fresh water supply, Lochan Glas, with adequate pressure for firefighting in the event of a mains failure. In Loch Long, only a short distance north of the old ferry, depths were adequate close inshore for a submarine jetty. There was a small area of relatively flat land at the southern end of the site, suitable for offices, non-explosive workshops and stores. There was an area of former arable land sloping upwards to the north - then hill and heather. The explosives buildings were, necessarily, on this higher ground, most of them of "bunker" construction.

Site plans were drawn up during the summer and the MPBW team, headed by Sandy Sing, visited the States with us to clarify points of uncertainty. In September/October the first detailed building and installation plans were reviewed by MOD(N) and MPBW, with technical vetting by US contractors. A contract was placed with Costain in the spring of 1964 with forecast completion March 1967 and beneficial occupancy of most buildings approximately six months earlier. Work on site started in earnest in August 1964.

The DAS team had grown by this stage. Ted Richardson, the first Chief Engineer, had joined, Other important additions were Principal Foreman of Stores, Jim Murray, who earned the MBE for his work and George Scantlebury, Principal Technical Officer, who was responsible for overseeing the UK manufacture of missile trailers and other handling equipment. At a later stage they were, amongst other duties, to run all jetty outload operations, stores, transport and handling equipment maintenance. In due course they arranged transport of HTV missiles (inert, correct for size and weight) and AIM missiles (identical to the tactical missile, but without explosives) for test purposes at the building yards, Barrow and Birkenhead and to Chatham where RFA *Fort Langley* was fitting out to carry tactical missiles from the States. These journeys, at 10mph, on erection trailers, with police control and escort, took some organising. Jim and George were also heavily involved in recruitment of local staff, often interviewing south of the Clyde in the evening after a day's work at Coulport - and sometimes missing the last ferry and having to be rescued by a duty driver, a journey of about forty miles via the Erskine Bridge.

That, of course, was for the future. The immediate tasks were to monitor MPBW's progress at Coulport and resolve queries on specification requirements. At Bath the tasks were to arrange with the

US suitable future delivery programmes for test equipment and missile.

The milestones of the overall programme were set out and monitored from PERT (Programme Evaluation Review Technique) charts. Programme Management Plans (PMPs) were used for reporting to CPE in London. Bill Everitt reminds me that the first PERT chart was so long that he had to complete it on his lounge floor - after his wife had gone to bed.

Considerable travel was involved. Apart from the Bath-London interchanges, Bath-Coulport visits were frequent for some of us. Four nights a week in a British Rail sleeper were not unknown. Mangotsfield Junction could look like a stage set for the "Ghost Train", ill-lit, draughty and empty.

There were also continuing American visits, Washington, Sunnyvale (Lockheed) and Charleston being the usual destinations, but there were also POMFPAC, Pittsfield (GE, Guidance), Sacramento (first stage motor), Bacchus, Utah (second stage motor), Nortronic LA (test equipment). Often it was late back to the motel, eat, write up notes, plan for the following day, fall into bed. It was not all work and no play however. The odd weekend included visits to Yosemite National Park, a game of golf at Cyprus Point, a sail on the Potomac. The Americans are very hospitable people.

All Polaris contracts required the vendor to provide full parts breakdown with estimated failure rates and repair recovery rates. This formed the basis of initial provisioning. For major missile components 95% confidence was required against stock-out during the re-order period. The main missile spares provisioning conference, which took into account modifications under consideration, took nearly a week. For downstream replenishment US Milstrip procedure in coded format for machine processing was used, transmitted in due course, from the depot's own Autodin. The system could also provide the status of any item immediately.

In April 1966, the first DAS staff were permanently stationed at Coulport. They set up temporary offices in Milnavoulin House. This was a private dwelling just outside the depot perimeter, which we had been able to buy and which later became the Superintendent's residence.

Recruitment of local staff was started and steadily increased in numbers over the next two years. Neither Faslane nor Coulport had a plentiful supply of local labour readily available and from the start it was the concept that Faslane would draw mainly from the north of the

Clyde and Coulport mainly from south of the Clyde. About 60% of our staff came from Port Glasgow, Greenock and Gourock. We ran five bus services on that side of the Clyde with ferries from Cardwell Bay and Gourock to Kilcreggan and buses from there. The remaining 40% were drawn from the Rosneath peninsular and some, mainly specialists, from as far afield as Glasgow. An assisted travel scheme was necessary and flat rate "travelling time" over the first hour each day. In total the depot employed over 1200 by 1969.

Police quarters and some thirty-odd houses were built or purchased at Coulport for key staff. To help house staff appointed from other depots, various housing estates were built: those at Rosneath and Cove/Kilcreggan were almost entirely occupied by Coulport staff.

My residence , Milnavoulin, was magnificent - it you can put up with the inconvenience and heating costs (and rent) of an early Victorian mansion. One American guest, listening to my wife's fading footsteps on the wooden floor between dining room and kitchen (passing library and entrance hall) likened it to an Alfred Hitchcock suspense movie. We had lots of visitors from Admirals to Government Ministers (left and right), An entertainment allowance would have been acceptable. However the site and the view were quite a consolation. Sadly, the house no longer exists.

Another rather larger house, Ardpeaton, a quarter of a mile down the loch, was divided into five flats. I am told that its magnificent view had the added advantage that one could see the rainstorms approaching over the loch in ample time to nip to the garden and get the washing in!

Later in 1966 we were joined at Coulport by a sizeable number of professional and technical staff, after training in the States, in readiness for installing and checking out the vast array of test equipment.

Construction work was running late, mainly due to the difficult terrain. Geological faults led to flooding in elevator pits and in basements which required a maximum humidity of 50% - at least our use of basements for cable runs, rather than conventional floor trenches and fitted covers as at POMFLANT, made it easier to rectify the effects of flooding. Anti-static floors cracked and had to be replaced. The delays were to some extent reduced by remedial action through the Project Management Team, but clearly the time for test equipment installation was seriously reduced.

The assistance of engineers from the various US contractors was vital in testing equipment installation particularly as each missile depot was a "one-off" and not so well documented as other areas of the project. The overall direction of US contractors' staff by Lynn Jones was even more important. We were very fortunate to get him as the Senior US Navy representative at Coulport and to draw on his experience as the senior Lockheed representative at POMFLANT.

The US team also played a very considerable part in specialised training and work up. Much of the equipment was sophisticated and required considerable skill and practice for efficient operation. This can readily be appreciated when dealing with simulated flight testing - and maintaining the equipment which does this. Similarly, checkout of the guidance capsule, which requires an almost inconceivable degree of accuracy, clearly calls for extremely high standards. The guidance inertial components, which are heated slightly, require to be maintained within a temperature range of $+-1^0$ at all times, storage, transport and operation. They have to be individually alarmed and continuously monitored. For transport the insulated shipping container had visual and audible alarms and a plug point for power. Other skilled operations are not so readily appreciated - even elevating the missile/liner on the jetty and locking it on to the submarine missile hatch requires the co-ordinated skill of erection trailer driver, craneman and submarine crew.

One considerable task is the regular non-destructive testing of missile motors which requires, among various other tests, x-ray examination of the propellant. A 25 million electron volt Betatron is used, housed in its own heavily protected cell, with its own remote controlled lift and turntable. For the first stage motor alone some hundred x-rays are needed, each requiring a very experienced operator to interpret.

Missile motors and assembled missiles had to be kept at the earth's electrical potential at all times by earthing leads having no more than 1 ohm resistance. This was of paramount importance. Lynn Jones reckoned that our earthing system, designed by Steve Shipilov (US) and George Scantlebury with critical reviews by Rebar Hazen (US) was superior to the systems at POMFLANT and POMFPAC at that stage.

We had a considerable set back in January 1968. I think it was a Sunday night. A hurricane ripped across a narrow belt of central Scotland doing considerable damage, including uprooting many thousands of trees. It damaged roofs of important buildings at Coulport including the main missile assembly and test building (MAB) and the missile guidance test facility (ICPB). This type of damage would have been much more widespread were it not the fact that most of the explosives buildings were of "bunker" construction. It did considerable damage to the jetty, where catamarans broke partially loose damaging piles and severing water mains. It severed grid supplies - providing a realistic test of our own generators which in addition to providing sixty cycle supplies for test equipment also provided a fifty cycle emergency supply for depot essential services. At Greenock the wind brought down 300 tons of dockyard crane across the middle of RFA *Fort Langley*, just about to sail for another missile load after dockyard repairs. It interfered considerably with her programme - and performance. Just four hours previously I had parked my car (and my wife) under this crane while going on board to check that *Langley* would sail on time.

The depot duty officer, Pat Hughes, the police with Sergeant Meldrum in immediate charge, staff in local quarters, all turned out to help secure and protect buildings and equipment. It was a long, cold, wet and hungry night. Access to Coulport was cut off for a couple of days with trees across the roads. Many staff managed to make it on foot however, even from as far afield as Helensburgh, climbing over obstructions on the way. We were very grateful; there was a lot of work to do.

In some areas it was two shifts a day, twelve hour shifts, six days a week. Morale remained high however, despite pressure of work and the problems many had with wives and families on their own for long periods four hundred miles or more from home. The well supported Civil Service Club helped and the splendid sports facilities at Faslane made available to civilian staff as well as the Navy. A great boost came from an all day visit to the Base by the Queen Mother. She spent nearly two hours at Coulport, met many of the staff completely impromptu and when the Royal Yacht left Coulport jetty she remained on the after-deck waving until nearly out of sight.

HMS *Resolution* sailed to programme (and to the bagpipes from the jetty) in early June 1968 with a full complement of missiles prepared in the States but with warheads and guidance fitted and checked at Coulport. In February 1969 at Demonstration and Shakedown Operations (DASO) off Cape Kennedy, each crew of *Repulse* successfully fired a missile and subsequently a full operational outfit was embarked, all fully prepared at Coulport. *Renown* followed some three months later and *Revenge* in early 1970, both after successful DASO firings. In between, of course, were the surveillance landings after each patrol and their replacement by new missiles; one of the continuing daily tasks of the depot.

There was quite a social life too. Trafalgar Night in the Mess; Burns Night in the Police Canteen; St Andrew's Night in the Civil Service Club; dances in the Depot Canteen; the annual dinner of the former Greenock Torpedo Depot with John Fieldhouse, then Captain SM10, as Guest of Honour, were all memorable.

Even in an article on Polaris I cannot omit reference to torpedoes and the efforts of the staff involved in their maintenance and repair. In addition to supplying torpedoes to the Polaris submarines, the depot assumed the tasks previously undertaken by the submarine depot ship, Maidstone, in supporting the 3rd Submarine Squadron and other submarines working up in the Clyde area. This involved, in total, a throughput of some 2,000 torpedoes per annum. Coulport also assisted in the trials of the new Mark 24 torpedo and eventually in March 1970 assumed control of the Arrochar torpedo range and trials facility. This enabled a major reorganisation of work and transfer of staff.

It was with quite a lump in the throat that I handed over in mid 1971 to John Langrish, the Deputy Superintendent. I had stayed rather longer than even Norman Luscombe had intended, but it was a fascinating job.

Chapter 29

Management of the Base
Peter La Niece

Having been involved, on and off, with Polaris practically since its inception in the USA, I was greatly pleased to be appointed as Commodore Clyde. I was to relieve Derek Kent, the first Commodore who had endured all the "blood, sweat and tears" (and mud) during the setting up of the Base to the plans of CPE and FOS/M.

I took over in May 1969 with the full realisation that the job had many facets and not a few bosses and superiors with a finger in the pie!

My appointment was officially designated as "Superintendent Clyde Submarine Base and Commodore Clyde". The latter was the title most generally used. My responsibilities covered a number of functions.

First there was overall charge of the Base, which comprised all the facilities on the Gareloch at Faslane for supporting submarines and also the Armament Depot at Coulport situated on the shore of the neighbouring stretch of water, Loch Long. The naval establishment which was an integral part of the Faslane Base had the ship name of HMS *Neptune*; I was its Commanding Officer. Secondly all ships and submarines operating within the Clyde Sub Area, which extended across the whole of the west coast of Scotland came under my operational command. Thirdly, across the Clyde at Greenock was a subsidiary Naval Base at which was based the civilian manned Port Auxiliary Service comprising a small armada of tugs, water boats, naval ferries and miscellaneous other craft; this came under the local command of a Commander. Finally all other naval shore facilities in the Clyde Sub Area came under Commodore Clyde's administration in varying degrees. These included a NATO Armament Depot, a Boom Depot, torpedo range and various embryo war headquarters such as at Inverkip on the south side of the Clyde and Altbea at Loch Ewe.

There were two submarine squadrons based at Faslane; the 10th comprising three Polaris submarines, *Resolution, Repulse* and *Renown;* the fourth, *Revenge,* was reaching completion and about to join. The other squadron was the 3rd and comprised the nuclear attack submarines *Warspite* and *Valiant* with *Dreadnought* refitting, plus four or five diesel electric patrol submarines, mostly of the Oberon class. The 3rd Submarine Squadron also provided workup assistance for submarines from other squadrons.

The overall command set-up was complex. Operationally the Base came under Flag Officer, Submarines at Gosport. Flag Officer Scotland and Northern Ireland, with his headquarters at Rosyth, had overall responsibility for all northern waters which included the Clyde Sub Area. Individual civilian departments within the Base had professional links with their headquarters departments. Finally Rear Admiral Trewby, as Assistant Controller Polaris (the revised title of Chief Polaris Executive) still had a "project" interest in the Polaris element of the Base.

I found that the set-up within the Base was equally complicated. There were three Captains; of the two submariners John Fieldhouse, Captain SM 10, was in command of the 10th Squadron and the RN Polaris School, whilst the other Tom Clack, Captain SM 3, commanded the 3rd Squadron and other submarine training facilities. Each of the Captains SM had dual responsibility, primarily to Flag Officer Submarines and locally to myself. The third Captain, Jim East, was an engineer and was in charge of the naval technical facilities and responsible directly to me. In addition there were senior civilian officers each in charge of their own armament stores, naval stores and civilian manned support facilities. There was also a sizeable unit of the MOD Police.

To enable the Navy to exercise legal jurisdiction over waters which were of such importance to it, the Gareloch, Loch Long and the Holy Loch, where the US Polaris squadron was based, had been designated by Act of Parliament as a "Queen's Harbour"; it was an area bounded by sixty miles of coastline. Captain SM 10 doubled as Queen's Harbour Master. Although we were effectively "landlord" to their anchorage, we had no jurisdiction over the US squadron in the Holy Loch, other than co-ordinating harbour movements. Captain SM 3 doubled as Chief Staff Officer Operations.

As regards HMS *Neptune,* I was fortunate in having an excellent Executive Officer in Commander George Hayne, another Gunnery Officer. The day to day running of the naval establishment and the 1160 married quarters was largely in his hands in conjunction with the Base Supply Officer, who was also an old acquaintance. There was a separate medical block, really a mini-hospital, under a Surgeon Captain with a substantial medical and dental staff. In addition there was a quite separate Radiological Protection Unit, headed by a Surgeon Commander, responsible for radiological safety, both personnel and material.

Having met most of the heads of departments within a couple of days, I set off on the obligatory round of official calls. The first of these was to Rosyth to call on the Flag Officer Scotland and Northern Ireland, Vice Admiral Sir Ian McGeoch. He was a former submariner and had been Flag Officer Submarines during the period that the Clyde Submarine Base was under development and it was comforting to know that he had a full understanding of the Base's task and the complex lines of responsibility.

Our overriding priority was the support of the Polaris squadron. Very soon *Resolution* returned from patrol and all departments swung into action. The procedure was generally always the same. The movement of Polaris submarines was highly classified and, with the exception of a very limited number of officers, the first intimation of a return from patrol was when the submarine appeared at the entrance to the Clyde Estuary. Included in the Port Auxiliary Service was a fast despatch boat which had started life as an RAF rescue vessel. It was primarily used for trips to the outer reaches of the Clyde where distance and sea conditions were unsuitable for most of the smaller craft. This despatch boat would take Captain SM 10 out to meet the returning submarine which would proceed direct to a jetty at Coulport to unload one or more missiles for routine inspection. At the Coulport jetty she was met by a contingent of Base staff and the replacement crew. The families of the incoming crew were also allowed to attend. They had an uncanny knack of always being ready, despite the short notice. The replacement crew immediately took over and the patrol crew proceeded on leave. The work list was rapidly evaluated and the submarine came round to berth at Faslane for her maintenance period.

At the end of the period alongside, the submarine proceeded to sea in the Clyde exercise areas to prepare for her next operation, returning to Coulport to replace any missiles and torpedoes that had been unloaded for inspection. They also topped up with victualling stores sufficient for the duration of the forthcoming patrol. The final departure for patrol was as inconspicuous as possible.

When the off-crew had completed their leave they reassembled to indoctrinate replacements and undertake refresher training at the RN Polaris School and elsewhere. They also provided a welfare link with the families of the on-crew.

In between the intensive periods of turning round each Polaris submarine, the Base also had to provide support services for the boats of the 3rd Squadron and itinerant visitors from other squadrons. This all required careful planning.

Some time prior to my taking up the appointment I had been made aware that the management structure of the Base was unsatisfactory. The original scheme had provided for no less than twenty senior managers reporting direct to the Commodore. Some slight reduction had been achieved but my first management meeting illustrated how impracticable the set-up still was. I therefore recast the management structure principally by giving the Engineer Captain who already had the title of Deputy Superintendent, responsibility for co-ordinating all the support functions, naval and civilian. This left me dealing, on a day to day basis, mainly with just the three Captains and Executive Officer. Individual departmental heads still had the right of direct access to me and, in order to preserve personal contact I, for my part, made frequent informal visits to their departments. I also scrapped the old fashioned round-the-table style monthly management meetings and replaced them with more positive presentation type meetings with slides showing programmes, targets and progress charts in the USN style.

I was told that relations between the Base and the local press were unsatisfactory and so I invited them to a briefing. I also told them I would always keep them informed when I could but sometimes security limitations might preclude this and I asked for their understanding on such occasions. They seemed impressed by my initiative in inviting them and providing some unsolicited information; the more so when I asked them to partake of a "wee dram"; we finally outflanked them by producing our Naval Base photographer and taking a group photograph of them all, cameramen included. Although always inclined to be volatile, press relations improved thereafter. I was even invited to make a return call on the Helensburgh Advertiser and had my photograph taken operating a linotype machine, although this nearly precipitated a walkout by the relevant trade union.

It was time to give some attention to the problems of the civilian staff, particularly the industrial grades. As is customary in all Government departments all negotiations were conducted through the medium of a Whitley Council of which I was the Chairman. The Vice-Chairman was the Convenor of Shop Stewards, a Mr Danny MacAteer. Danny was the Naval Base Ratcatcher! He was a member of the Transport and General Workers' Union; the most obstreperous members of the Whitley Committee in those days were from the

Amalgamated Engineering Union. When he was not being goaded on by his engineering colleagues, Danny was a likeable fellow, although conversation with him was not easy since he spoke in an almost unintelligible Glaswegian accent. The vast majority of the industrial staff came in by bus or ferry from the Glasgow or Renfrewshire areas. All were, in their previous employment, used to rather more militant (with a small "m") negotiations with management associated with shipyards and similar industrial companies. Working in the Base, the Government were their Top Management; locally their face to face dealings were principally with Naval Officers; myself and Captain Jim East, supported by the civilian Heads of Departments. It was all a little strange for them. Our major problem was that a situation had developed where there was a progressively increasing dependence on overtime working. Something had to be done to restore working hours to a more stable level. Fortunately Jim East had considerable experience in industrial relations dealings in the Royal Dockyards. Thanks to his initiative we started a drive to gain the acceptance of the work force for a productivity agreement. In those days such an approach was still fairly novel. The union side was clearly lacking in knowledge of such a scheme and we decided to hire a hotel suite in Dumbarton and have an all day joint teach in. It was a classic beer and sandwiches session in a smoke filled room. With both sides better informed we resumed negotiations.

This all took time. On my return from our summer holiday Jim East was able to announce that agreement had been reached. Future prospects on that front appeared more promising.

September 1969 saw the arrival of the fourth Polaris Submarine *Revenge*. She had made a brief appearance a few weeks earlier during her contractor's sea trials wearing the red ensign. She was now in full commission and brought the 10th Submarine Squadron up to full strength. It was the only time we had three boats of the class alongside at the same time.

Thereafter a steady routine developed as the support cycles of both squadrons progressed. This work was punctuated by having to look after a continual stream of visitors, many of them VIPs. Such is the price of success. I was finally relieved in February 1971 content that I was turning over a fully working organisation.

Chapter 30

A Working Base
Martin Wemyss

By one means or another I had been in touch with progress in the
Polaris project but it was one thing to be an observer, another to be
amongst it at its home base. I grew up in the 3rd Squadron starting in
1947. Before Polaris came on the scene, the base for Britain's latest
and best submarines was a depot ship, *Maidstone*, alongside a crumbling
wartime jetty at Faslane in the Gareloch.

In 1970 as Captain SM3 I occupied a comfy office in an integrated
command building housing Commodore Clyde and his staff, SM10 and
both squadron staffs, an operations room, communications centre and
base and squadron engineering staffs. From west facing windows I
could see the new jetty complete with lofty travelling cranes and every
form of overside power, fuel and water supply. To the north was an
enormous stores building, the Command Team Trainer, also housing
the tactical development group, ship control and reactor control
simulators. Nearby were extensive engineering machine shops of all
kinds and the Base's independent power generators. Further up the
Loch side the Wardroom and senior and junior rates' messes were
roomy and well appointed with lovely views; down the Loch were
villages of married quarters. Over the hill to the west, Coulport
housed and maintained Polaris itself and the cleverest sorts of
torpedoes. The transformation was complete and it was immediately
apparent that it worked.

I remember in the sixties, the Americans advising that the co-
location of Polaris submarines, not only with other nuclear but with
conventional diesel electric ones as well, was a recipe for friction and
disaster. Many wise heads wagged in Bath and London in prospect of
the split loyalties which were bound to occur in a base manned partly
by civilians and partly by uniformed personnel, the whole commanded
by a Commodore. Coulport and the stores complex were civilian
establishments whose bosses were in Bath and London. Many of the
Base engineers and maintainers were locally recruited civilians.

In the event each sort of submariner, Polaris, attack nuclear and
conventional considered he had the best deal. Polaris, not only
because he had national survival in his hands but, for once in his life, his
programme was within fairly fine limits. The Launders' bar chart was

in force and next year's holidays could be booked with confidence. The attack nuclear men knew that they were the spearhead of the Navy. They had the power, the speed and freedom from the surface which no other submarine had and soon would have weapons to match. Not for them the Polaris restrictions of creeping about to maintain invulnerability to detection and to keep in constant listening touch with headquarters. Everything was new and exciting, and the men of the conventionals knew that they were the only real submariners, the inheritors of a tradition who even smelt right and certainly would not have to put on a tie for supper.

There may have been problems between civilian and uniformed staff in the early days but by 1970 they were over. Flesh pots and senior officers were miles away, everyone lived within minutes of the Base. There could be and was a twenty four hour service throughout the year. Everyone's first aim was to satisfy the needs of the customer and there he was, clearly visible day and night, lying alongside the jetty.

The joy for my squadron was that all these services were there for them too, and for submarines coming to us for post-refit, crew training, nuclears and conventionals straight from building, and for surface visitors; frigates, minesweepers, the lot. If Polaris had the highest priority for stores and workshop space, very seldom would this be apparent to anyone else.

If the Polaris Executive was the outstanding managerial success story I believe it to have been, then so too was the design, construction and setting to work of the Faslane Base as part of the total project. In the seventies we reaped the harvest of the pioneers of the sixties. A measure of their success was that, while the nuclear element of the 3rd Squadron trebled in my time from two to six and life was very exciting indeed, nothing disturbed the steady patrol cycle of the four Polaris submarines of the 10th Squadron. Happy days.

PART 5

THE POLARIS FORCE

Chapter 31

**Providing the People (1)
Henry Ellis**

On a miserably wet and cold morning, in January 1963, I was about to duck gratefully into a snug office in Flag Officer Submarines' Headquarters in Fort Blockhouse, when I was stopped by Commander Ken Dunlop, an old cricketing friend. "Rufus is looking for staff to set up a Polaris project in the Admiralty, how about putting in for it?" he grinned sheepishly. "We can toss a ball about in St James Park in the lunch hour". "Isn't that where all the spies practice?" I replied doubtfully.

I had spent the previous four months working for "Rufus", as Rear Admiral Mackenzie, Flag Officer Submarines, was respectfully and affectionately known; and not unknown to open his staff meetings with some batting practice with a rolled-up chart. I had been trying to put together an operational programme for the first-of-class sea trials for *Dreadnought*, our first nuclear powered submarine, and leaning heavily on her captain, Peter Samborne, for nuclear initiation. He was now off and running, and London sounded a great idea. Two weeks later I was appointed to the Polaris Executive as the Manning and Training Officer, a post to be known as P23. Rufus Mackenzie and John Grimwood, his secretary, set up an office on the ground floor of the Main Admiralty building, and I joined Ken Dunlop in a dusty room next door. We had a tall, yellowing ceiling, two worn leather-seated chairs, a desk, and an old furred-up electric kettle. And the inestimable Vera Cole, who operated it, in stolen moments when she was not purloining second-hand Nelsonian cardboard covers in which to set up the Polaris filing system. My wife, Susan, still uses the quite irreplaceable ironing board which Vera gave us on our marriage shortly afterwards.

The first un-nerving problem was that I knew nothing about Manning and Training. Par for the course the cynic would say. It had just not been my thing; I had been too well served by people who had been good at it. But Rufus had recently reported in my "flimsy", with traditional generosity that I was "incisive, determined and confident"; and I had, after all, not long before, as ANA Moscow, been quite competent in counting the number of telephone poles between Moscow and Leningrad, by night. So "determined" it was. But zeal without knowledge is a runaway horse, as the Russians would say, and

Ken and I crossed a rain-swept Whitehall to see George at the Silver Cross, the submariner's local bolt-hole.

Fortunately, shortly afterwards, we were joined by Captain Rae McKaig, who was to become a marvellous leader of the pack, fly-half and full-back. We could never have wished for a more tolerant, supportive and decisive Director.

The shape of the task for P23 was simple enough. To provide repeat crews for *Dreadnought,* who had undergone the new-found training in nuclear propulsion, and including a completely new category of technicians, who for the most part would not have served previously in submarines. These latter were to operate the on-board Polaris weapon system, an American invention with a scope and vocabulary more revolutionary than the transition from the cross-bow to the long version, the Mark VIII torpedo to the rocket. It was a new world of PE plans, interfaces, networks, critical paths, inertial systems, the inviting SINS and the taboo mysteries of "bottom" navigation. And above all project management. It required a new breed of furrowed-browed commuters to Washington, Dam Neck and Charleston; a crocodile file of jet-lagged black brief-cases. Missions to the oracle. We questioned American practice at every turn. We thought we knew better ways to skin a bear. So does every submariner worth his salt. We believed we could economise, and use only one crew for each submarine; less high-priced technicians, less "redundancy of equip-ment" (an American concept for replacement units). With a burst of American nuclear security and British national pride we made life more difficult by building our own warheads. In the end the experience and advice from our staunch American submarine friends was usually overwhelming, let alone the looming demands of Admiral Rickover in the background. Their support and encouragement was far beyond the technical requirements of the Nassau Agreement governing the project.

An early introduction to this relationship came in the form of a day at sea in the Clyde, in the Polaris submarine, USS *Ethan Allen,* together with a number of eminent pressmen. These included Chapman Pincher and Alun Jones, then the Defence Correspondent of *The Times,* who did much to foster our future liaisons by a generous and perceptive address to the Captain at the close of play. It was to all of us a new world, a whispering town of a ship whose gently inclining decks and conditioned atmosphere suggested the innards of a luxury yacht rather than a weapon carrier that could single-handedly destroy many of the major cities of the Soviet Union or devastate its military potential.

We now had to try to sell the programme to the rest of the Fleet, who were to be invited to cough up large numbers of the best qualified weapons technicians, let alone numbers of surface ships that would need to be withdrawn as a result. We were nobody's flavour of the month. In the early days of the recruitment from the surface fleet there were some long faces. Submariners were ungenerously considered to be an elitist, scruffy, overpaid lot who hot-bunked and lived on baked beans between bouts of playing "Uckers", a highly sophisticated version of Ludo. They went deep when the weather was bad and smelt of diesel in the pub. In foreign ports they invaded the canteens and bathrooms of the accompanying frigates, like parasites on a whale's back. They never drank at sea, except for a modest ration of beer after rum was withdrawn, but in harbour they were wont to become insensible.

Commanders Bob Ward and David Porter, in the Directorates of Manning and Training, and Don Evans from the Polaris Technical Directorate in Bath, were of endless help in defining and satisfying P23's requirements. We stood before frowning audiences as we stumped across the land, enticing audiences who were not at all persuaded to become instant submarine "volunteers". The Submarine Service was after all exclusively volunteer, and Polaris service was going to mean housing in a remote loch in Scotland, with long family separations. Neither were the moral issues of "deterrence" entirely clear in the 60s. What is the point of a deterrent, our audiences would demand, ominously, which you can only use when deterrence has failed? Dick Barton to the rescue. My old and respected Snotty's nurse, Rear Admiral Brian Brayne-Nicholls, taught me to play bridge in the Gunroom. "Never fart against thunder", he would murmur with a wag of his nurse's finger, when I would double a seven no trump contract with a single ace in my hand. Is that what Polaris was doing?

It is fair to say that our existing weapons artificers were more technically qualified than their US counterparts, as a result of that American policy of "redundancy" of equipment and the reduced need for in-depth running repairs. As a result we tended to send over-qualified officers and men to the Polaris training courses in the States. Be it as it may they did very well over there, and by the time we had built and commissioned our own Polaris Training School in Faslane, run with the wonderfully civilised instruction of Willy Waddell, we had already received back a nucleus of highly trained weapons crews. The Royal Navy's Artificers and Mechanicians were in any case a breed unto themselves. In submarines they were gilt-edged. Many a young submarine officer owes his reputation to the control room crisis management of the "outside" Engine Room Artificer in particular. Such a man earned my unqualified loyalty; one of his tasks was to maintain that Da Vincian masterpiece of engineering imagination, the old submarine air-pressured water closet. For the uninitiated this device relied virtually on the non-return feature of the upper flap of the "thunderbox", which came into operation at the moment that discharge-to-sea pressure was introduced. The Polaris launch tube owes much to its concept.

Two issues caused more contention than persistent bumpers or picking the seam. Did we need two crews of each boat? And did we require four or five boats to maintain one permanently on patrol in a firing position? Solutions fell like soiled confetti over the planners' desks. Everyone had an axe to grind. Not least the Royal Air Force, who were fiercely contemptuous of the Navy's ability to take over the long-cherished and proudly held deterrent role of the V-bombers. In the nicest way (well, usually) they were waiting with bated breath to see Polaris fall arse over tip onto its own nose-cone. It was an unconscious stroke of fate that found me in the Plans Division five years later, conveying by hand to my opposite number in RAF Plans the signal stating that on the very day ordained the Navy had assumed responsibility for the UK Strategic Deterrent. I knew, and he certainly suspected, that it had been a close run thing.

By that time the fifth boat had been axed, in March 1966, and the view had been taken that with patrols running into months it would be impossible to maintain the submarines, let alone the crews' morale, without doubling up the crews. So we came, sadly in my view, to Port and Starboard. Sherlock and Holmes would have been a worthy tribute to that hospitable establishment across Whitehall from which post-prandial inspiration derived. It was not to be. The Navy, bless it, likes things neat and tidy.

Little strokes fell great oaks; and the Evil Empire. Polaris will take its place among those strokes, with V-bombers, the Cuban missile crisis, the Berlin airlift, the Eighties and the Iron Lady. "That which is far off and exceeding deep, how shall ye find it?" asked Paul of the Corinthians.

Footnote

I recollect a budget of £360 million to build and commission the Polaris project. I understand it was never exceeded. A miracle of control in the galloping inflationary climate which reigned elsewhere. And thinking of great oaks, ten years later I took early retirement and with my golden bowler I bought a chain-saw. The good life beckoned. I quoted to cut down some trees on Rufus's land near Guildford. He graciously declined my estimate. "Woodman, spare those trees" he said, with the stern face of Scottish deterrence.

Chapter 32

Providing the People (2)
Dennis Mills

On return from the Mediterranean in November 1963, instead of the promised course at Henley Administration Staff College, I found myself shanghaied by FOS/M to be his first Polaris Staff officer (later changed to the grandiose Flotilla Ballistic Missile Systems Officer!). This seemed inevitable in view of my missile enthusiasm of four years earlier as Staff Officer Plans and Intelligence. My job description as FOS/M's representative on the Polaris Executive covered every aspect of the programme except the warheads. This involved spurring the efforts of about forty staff officers on the Admiral's and Squadron's Staffs most of whom were much concerned about their perceptions of the effect of Polaris on other submarine developments. However Vice Admiral Horace Law as FOS/M and Rear Admiral Rufus Mackenzie as Chief of the Polaris Executive (CPE) were most agreeable joint bosses to work for.

My first task was to educate the rest of the Staff in the principles and practice of the Programme Management Plan (PMP) system and get sometimes grudging acceptance of their responsibilities in achieving the agreed milestones towards the completion of each Plan. Every fortnight, alternately in London and Bath, those of us responsible on behalf of the various authorities involved had to report progress to CPE himself giving reasons for any delay in meeting our milestones.

Very soon I was almost exclusively concerned with the development of the Faslane Base from a greenfield site. The original specifications had been hastily cobbled together by FOS/M's excellent Work Study Team but with insufficient input from professional submariners. For example after study of the initial plans, I had hastily to redraw the Administration Building to cater for double Polaris crews and spare crews of all classes. This led to an interesting forenoon confronting the Civil Lord and his mandarins in order to get the Administration Building quadrupled in size.

Where there was no FOS/M Staff Officer concerned I found myself, for reasons of speed, designing, for example, such facilities as the boat maintenance facility. A fascinating aspect of the programme was that whereas the cost of the highly technical Polaris School went through on the nod there was ferocious argument over details of married quarters. Nevertheless the higher levels of the Ministry of Public Buildings and Works were on the whole very understanding and co-operative when problems were explained to them in simple sailors' language.

It was a relief to get away to the Clyde from time to time. On one such occasion I accompanied Admiral Horace Law on a visit to one of the US SSBN's just back from a deterrent patrol and her depot ship USS *Hunley* in the Holy Loch. The "special relationship" was much in evidence and our generous hosts explained anything we asked about.

After nearly 18 months of fascinating work as a jack-of-all-trades, in March 1965, I was translated to the post of Flotilla Personnel Officer and Submarine Drafting Officer. My predecessor was Commander Paddy Gowan who had had the Polaris programme thrust upon him to add to the problems inherent in all the other new developments - later he returned to be a much respected Welfare Officer at the Faslane Base

During my five years in the job we had to increase our population by 40% while Denis Healey was reducing the rest of the Navy by 10% overall. As in both World Wars we therefore had to resort to the "press gang" especially for the highly qualified technical people; fortunately history repeated itself and most of the conscripts elected to remain in submarines after their initial five years.

Being personally responsible for the career planning and appointing of seaman officers up to selection for command, my very early concern was to persuade several good officers to withdraw requests to resign their commissions and offer them all a career opportunity planning service and so ensure that they understood the great opportunities offered by the Polaris expansion. Thus it was that for the first two years, apart from policy decisions and tricky individual problems, I delegated the day to day running of the Drafting Office to my excellent Assistant Drafting Officer, Vic Gunson. He and his team of writers did a magnificent job. Fortunately also I was soon helped by the appoint-ment of my erstwhile Third Hand "Bosun" Grieg, as Training Planning Officer who took on the enormous task of scheduling the great variety of courses necessary to prepare people to man the Polaris and other submarine programmes. Close relations with the Submarine school were maintained throughout.

It was also valuable that the Captains (SM) and Commanders (SM) of the Squadrons were old friends from earlier appointments and many of the COs had been First Lieutenants or Third Hands in the

Mediterranean when I was Staff Officer Operations to Captains Jackie Slaughter and Phebe Van der Byl. A particularly fine generation, some of whom became household names later. This helped two-way exchanges of ideas.

Drafting preference cards having served the various drafting officers well for many years, the idea was adapted for seaman officers and later followed by other branches. This helped to plan careers and in general gave satisfaction to the customers. Regular reviews of the whole spectrum ensured that nearly all our people followed their desired careers.

For the commissioning of *Dreadnought* the experiment had been successfully tried in appointing Long Course qualified Torpedo/AS and Navigation officers to cope with the sophisticated technical equipment being developed for the nuclear powered boats. This served as a useful precedent to get submarine officers doubly qualified for the mutual benefit of the submarines and these officers. This move was popular with both our people and the specialist schools. Moreover it helped to ensure a steady flow of volunteers to fill our expanding needs.

A particular concern was to look after the interests of the Supplementary List officers. These short service commission officers served us well and I was anxious to give them every opportunity to gain recommends for permanent commissions. To further this aim, they were treated in every respect like General List officers, trained and appointed to Fleet and Polaris nuclear boats. With the willing cooperation of the TAS and N Schools several were so qualified that they did very well in the later promotion stakes. Unfortunately a minion at the MOD discovered that this was "not by the book" and later we had to wait until they were recommended and transferred to the General List before continuing the scheme.

Since 1956, with a shrinking navy, those promoted to Commander were placed on the "Wet" (seagoing) or "Dry" (staff) Lists, apparently in reverse proportion to their previous sea-time. The aim was, no doubt, laudable - to provide the maximum number of senior officers qualified to drive ships. In the case of submariners all those promoted to Commander had already had command on at least four occasions, some more, and were experienced ship-handlers. To be placed on the "Dry" List was, therefore, a somewhat humiliating and frustrating experience and resulted in some resignations. When the problem of finding enough Commanders for the double crews of Polaris arose, this was a golden opportunity to offer the "Dry List" a chance to get back to sea and it was seized with alacrity, thereby enhancing the career prospects for submariners.

The philosophy outlined above pervaded the other branches and where practicable was fed into the drafting system for the ratings with mutual advantage. Momentum having been developed through Polaris double-crewing a scheme was developed to ease the strain on Fleet submarines crews; by expanding schemes of complement on a sort of five watch basis with six-monthly changes so that one watch was under training and one left ashore to rest.

It is noteworthy that during this period of expansion the Royal Australian and Royal Canadian Navies sent their people to be trained by us before taking over the O Class submarines built in this country for them. This fortunate circumstance, combined with the measures outlined above, enabled us to man the Polaris Squadron and shore support without paying off a single conventional boat before her planned time - a fundamental fear which had caused the early objections to taking on the Polaris project.

Other points of interest. The submariners were the first branch of the Service to be put on the new drafting computer at Alverstoke. With the help of FOS/M's excellent Work Study Team proposals were made to modernise the Seaman Branch structure which were later merged with the Navy-wide scheme. The FPO visited all squadrons to explain the scheme and to hear the comments of ratings of all categories which were generally very favourable. Again something needed to be done - and it was. Submarine Drafting Instructions were completely rewritten.

My final task before retiring was to prepare a vast Manpower Plan for 25 years to 1995 based on "state of the art" developments in submarine material, assuming that boats of all classes would be replaced after twenty years' service. It is to the eternal credit of the designers, shipbuilders and the people who manned and maintained the submarines that so many have given excellent service for so long beyond those predictions.

Chapter 33

The 10th Submarine Squadron
Lady Margaret Fieldhouse

I shall always remember the day we heard that my husband, John Fieldhouse, was to command the 10th Submarine Squadron, and that Scotland, and the Clyde, was once again "on the cards for us". It was a Sunday and, as normal, we went to the Church of St Ambrose at HMS *Dolphin*. We were both feeling rather pleased with life, as John had been told, in a roundabout way, that he was going to be Naval Assistant to the First Sea Lord, Admiral Sir Michael Le Fanu. It was something quite different for him, and I thought the odd visit to London for parties and get-togethers would be great fun; we were both looking forward to this new job very much.

As we went through the gate at HMS *Dolphin*, the Quartermaster stopped us and said that FOS/M wanted a word with John after church. Surprised, but not alarmed, he duly went to see FOS/M and was told that, due to the illness of the present Captain SM10, Ken Vause, his appointment as Naval Assistant to the First Sea Lord had been cancelled and he was to go to Scotland to relieve him. I covered myself with glory by bursting into tears as we went out through the gate, and howling all the way home. I couldn't believe that we were going to the Clyde again - but we were.

We made preparations to let the house and John did a month's course at HMS *Dolphin*; then on 1 April (April Fool's Day) he joined HMS *Neptune,* and the family went into Quarters at Bannachra Drive, in Helensburgh. Mark was at prep school and Amanda and Sarah were to attend a local day school. Being a new base, all seemed total confusion. Two new type II houses were being built at Shandon for Captains SM10 and SM3, but were nothing like ready. Only the foundations were down, so Bannachra Drive was our temporary home.

Gradually we began to settle in, as did all the other families, most of whom were living on the Mackenzie Estate, known affectionately as "Nightmare Alley". It was, for all of us, absolutely uncharted waters. It was the first time, of course, that our submarines, *Resolution, Repulse, Renown* and *Revenge*, had two crews, Port and Starboard, manning them and no-one really knew what to expect. In fact, it all worked very smoothly after a few initial teething troubles. None of the wives enjoyed the idea of seeing their men off to destinations unknown for eight weeks at a time. I remember going with the wives to Rhu Spit, where we were closest to the submarine as she thundered down the loch; to wave *Resolution* off. One young wife was in tears, and I tried to be comforting, saying, "It won't seem too long, you'll see that time will pass very quickly. "Oh, that's fine for you, isn't it?" she said sharply. "Your husband will be home every night for his whisky and soda and his supper. Heaven knows what mine will be doing".

I took the lesson to heart and thought very carefully before coming out with more platitudes to any of the wives. In fact, the time did go very quickly and the Base got into full swing. It was a great Wardroom, and a splendid Senior Rates Mess, and many were the parties and events. Scottish dancing was a great favourite with many people, and we had some Highland Balls. When a Port crew was at sea, Starboard crew kept a careful watch on their wives and families and saw that they were managing without their own men around. They coped with many of the little things that always seem to go wrong when your man is at sea, and indeed, some of the bigger things too. Somehow, there was always a grave shortage of Base workmen to come out and do necessary house repairs. I cannot remember a single incident when there was any bad feeling because a Port husband paid too much attention to a lonely Starboard wife, or vice versa. It was all very friendly and matey and certainly seemed to work very well.

One of the great events was the sending of the "Familygram" to the men at sea. It was limited to thirty words and, although wives thought they were sent "unseen" by other eyes, they were all checked for security reasons. The thing that amused my husband was that, almost without exception, the major worry and talking point in the Familygram was the family car. It always seemed to be in trouble - "broken down", "in a slight accident" "wipers not working" "Dad's forgotten the HP payments"! It was amazing how much the car preyed on the minds of the wives left behind on their own, but even these problems were often put right by the opposite crew. There was a feeling of great co-operation between everyone on the Base which was an almost tangible thing.

The climate on the west coast of Scotland was dreadful (the second most mentioned thing in the Familygram), rain day in and day out. At one time I really believed that my children went to bed in their wellies and sou'westers, ready to get up for school the next day! It could be extremely depressing, because we had double British Summer Time then and, as we were quite far north, it was great in the summer but dreadful in the winter, as it was only light for about five or six hours a day. The children went to school in the dark and came home in the dark.

I remember one particularly super Midsummer Night's Ball in the Mess, and I was having a great time, dancing my feet off; my poor husband (never a dancer) finally came to me and said it was time to go home, as no-one felt they could leave before the Captain in those good, old-fashioned days. "Don't be silly, love", I said "It's not even dark yet". "It's been dark" said my husband "but its light again now, it's three-thirty in the morning!" I didn't stay to argue!

One of the things that amazed me was the tremendous range of talents we found, often among very unexpected people on the Base. We had a thriving dramatic society, a wonderful choral society, dress-making classes to a very high standard indeed, coaching in squash, tennis, badminton, indeed almost any game you could think of. There were language classes, cookery classes, you name it, there was someone to teach it.

Another bonus was the way the local people of Rhu, Shandon, Helensburgh and Garelochhead took us to their hearts. At first they were justifiably suspicious, as it wasn't always easy to accept this huge number of sailors, their wives and families as a permanent addition to the population. They became. however, incredibly friendly and supportive. John and I were always amazed that there was so little trouble between the sailors and the locals. Somehow "Jack" managed to limit his propensity for drunken runs ashore, which was good for all of us. Friendships were made which have lasted to this day.

One of the great moments, of course, was seeing in the home-coming SSBN up the loch. All the wives gathered, looking as glamorous as possible, and I well remember the slight shock-horror we all felt when the men finally came ashore, looking pasty-white. Wherever they had been, it was most certainly not to the sunshine, that was for sure; and they weren't going to get much more in un-sunny Scotland either. But who cared? They were home, and safe, and about to turn over to their opposite crew. That night was always party night and what a party! It was unforgettable.

We had a very good liaison with the US submarines in the Holy Loch and, again, we made friends with whom we are still in touch, all these years later. I was pretty unpopular with their Captain though, I remember on one occasion. NASA had just made their fantastic trip to the moon and everyone was glued to their televisions sets, riveted by what we saw. At 3.30am I rang their Captain SM, a friend of ours, and said "Congratulations, isn't it wonderful?".

"Goddammit, Midge, I've just got to sleep" he said "What a helluva a time to wake me up". Ah well, you can't win them all.

But one thing I think where we did win was the laying down of the future foundations of the 10th Submarine Squadron. There have been many Captain's SM10 since my late husband, and I am sure things are very different, because life must change and move on. I am equally sure that those early days were special in so many ways, and those of us who were fortunate enough to share them will never, ever forget them.

Chapter 34

A CO's Story
Michael Henry

I had settled comfortably into my appointment as Staff Officer Submarines on the British Navy Staff in Washington DC when, at the end of 1962, the Nassau Agreement, heralding the sale of Polaris to the United Kingdom, was signed. As the only British submariner around, I had notions of grandeur about the importance of my role in the subsequent planning and got together with Commander Wilfred (Wid) Graham, the only British officer (but a gunnery, not a submarine, specialist) on the staff of the Director, Special Projects - Mr Polaris USA. We very soon learned just what minor players we were on this big league.

In January 1963, a major meeting was held in Washington between SP and a team including Rear Admiral "Rufus" Mackenzie, the newly appointed Chief Polaris Executive for the UK. I sat far down the table from the great men and marvelled at how many British naval officers and civilians seemed to know so confidently what they were going to do and to be so anxious to convince their American hosts of their credentials (even though, I thought to myself in parenthesis, apart from Rufus, with his distinguished career in war and peace, few of them had probably ever been in a submarine).

So I curbed my enthusiasm and got on with other aspects of my appointment. However, I was given an SP designation - SP511, thus answering directly, not only to Commander, British Navy Staff, but also to SPRN (or SP50), Captain Peter La Niece, and thereby directly to the USN Director. As SP511 I was sent for by SP11 (Head of Plans and Programmes), Captain Gerry Clarke USN, and told to get down to Cape Canaveral (at that time uncomfortably renamed Cape Kennedy) and learn about the "Demonstration and Shake Down Operation" that each crew of all the 41 American Fleet Ballistic Missile Submarines underwent before being cleared for deployment, and during which each crew fired one or more instrumented missiles with dummy warheads down the Atlantic Missile Range.

Now I had my niche and my role. I had already been to sea in several American nuclear attack submarines for periods of up to two weeks and had gained, I like to think, the trust that I was (a) a competent "submareener" and (b) not likely to try and cheat on restricted data, the caveat applied to all US nuclear propulsion and warhead information. I was able to spend hours, days, weeks even, happily immersed in and identified with the problems, worries and successes of FBM crews, with freedom to range through their submarines (except the propulsion areas); question decisions and even criticise procedures; relax and play with them ashore. Little wonder that when I came to put together my own crew, they were in the American as much as the British mould. Too much perhaps for some.

A reminiscence which is out of chronological sequence, illustrates the support I got from my USN colleagues. Those responsible in the UK for the Polaris Navigation Sub-System had concluded that it was too deeply technical for a seaman officer to understand and operate, ergo the navigating officer must be an electrical officer. The said colleagues tipped me off and I was appalled, as were they. Navigation was the province of the Seaman, or "Unrestricted Line" officer. Fortified by their support I challenged the decision and persuaded Captain Philip Higham RN, then deputy to CPE, to agree with me. We got our way, but with the proviso that if the first candidate failed the course at Dam Neck (the Guided Missile School in Virginia) the decision would be reversed. He passed, and set the benchmark for future RN Polaris navigators.

The training of British officers and senior ratings - mostly Artificers - was an early priority. It was agreed that enough would be trained at Dam Neck, in all aspects of the Polaris weapon system, to form the staff of the RN Polaris School at Faslane, and until that was ready, to train the first crews. The future officer-in-charge of RNPS, Instructor Commander Willie Waddell, arrived in the USA, and we spent a busy week or so introducing him to Dam Neck, buying him a car, and finding him a house, and generally settling him in. In the early days of the British "Polaroids" at Dam Neck there were problems of pay, accommodation, dress and discipline. I will only say that the Brits were accepted as I had been; were given no special treatment; and acquired their new skills with honour. The RN Artificer system was one which the Americans came to admire, even envy.

At the end of 1964, Vice Admiral Horace Law, then Flag Officer Submarines, told me that I was to be the first Commanding Officer appointed to a British Polaris submarine, but not before I had returned to the surface navy for a spell. I spent nine months as Executive Officer and Second-in-Command of HMS *London*, one of our early County Class guided missile destroyers, under a Captain who had transferred from the Polish Navy after the war. It was an appointment upon which I shall not dwell. Suffice it to say that my subsequent time in command of another County was much happier.

"It is a submarine as big as a cruiser, as expensive as an aircraft carrier and potentially as destructive as a squadron of V-bombers. It requires men of that calibre to man it. See that you do not fail in this respect."

Thus ran the rather pretentious opening to my Captain's Instructions to Officers, written while standing by the building of HMS *Resolution* at Vickers Shipbuilders Ltd in Barrow-in-Furness.

After HMS *London* I had undergone a shortened nuclear propulsion course at RN College Greenwich (even though it was the simplest of nuclear courses I found it hard going) and a prospective Commanding Officers' Course at Dam Neck, which I was the only British CO to attend, the rest going to RNPS, before reporting to the Building Group in Barrow in the spring of 1966. We found a lovely Victorian house to rent, but could not move in until it had been redecorated from top to bottom at our expense, in lieu of rent. Meanwhile we lived - self, wife and up to five children - with a friend from my days as a Midshipman, and now working at Vickers. To Derek Tuson and particularly his wife Mickey, this is a belated public "thank you".

The Building Group included *Warspite, Resolution* and *Repulse*; my combined crew for *Resolution* amounted to something under fifty officers and men, mostly senior ratings. My Marine Engineering Officer, Lieutenant Commander Tom Brinkley, had already been there for a year or more. I had the two commissioning Executive Officers, Lieutenant Commanders Dick Husk and Francis Ponsonby, earmarked for Port and Starboard crews respectively. I should observe that, asked the question what to call our crews, Admiral Law had decided firmly against the American Blue and Gold and in favour of the more traditional British designation.

Dick administered the crews, their accommodation, welfare and discipline. At that stage, we worked in temporary office buildings, in plain clothes, and lived in "hirings" if married accompanied, or with various landladies if single, and the administration and payment of the latter took up a lot of Dick's time. Francis was tasked with the editing (and to a large extent writing) of the *Resolution* Class Standing Orders to which we all contributed with the aim of producing a set of Orders which would be common to all crews in the Polaris squadron. As an aside I found to my distress when eight years later I took over the 10th

(Polaris) Submarine Squadron, crews had been allowed to diverge from this common standard, and I count it as one of my two achievements as SM10 that I got all eight crews back into line. The other was to set up the "Mini-DASO", conducted in Loch Long.

New crew members were arriving all the time and the problems of accommodation grew, There was a limit to the number of Barrow landladies who could or would accommodate *Resolution* (and *Repulse*) sailors and so we looked for another solution - one which also needed to address the emerging requirement for instructional space. In our favour had been the decision to keep the crews together as one unit; indeed we did not start to separate the crew until after my opposite number, Commander Ken Frewer, had arrived to take over the Starboard crew.

There was a substantial Vickers building with the potential for accommodation, messing and classrooms, left over from the high-test peroxide submarine programme (HMS *Explorer* and *Excalibur*), on the dockside in Ramsden Dock. We looked at it, decided what we wanted to do with it, and put up our proposals. I cannot recall the financial ramifications of the deal except that, like everything else in the British Polaris programme, it was only time, not money, that was in short supply and that the latter would be forthcoming if we could make a case.

The man from the Ministry of Public Building and Works announced a date for his visit and we prepared our ammunition, fearing that there would be ten reasons against every one we had in favour. To our surprise and delight a bubbling enthusiast of a retired Colonel arrived, approved every one of our ideas, and improved on not a few of them. His only concern was where to site sufficient "lats for the troops". Evidently his military service had convinced him that latrines were top of the list for soldiers' welfare and sailors must have the same needs. And so *Woodbridge Haven* was born - or rather reborn - the original having been a splendid little support ship that had looked after the 3rd Submarine Flotilla in Rothesay during the refit of the depot ship *Montclare*. And as far as I know "Woo-Ha" looked after both *Resolution* and *Repulse* until they finally left Barrow and must have accommodated hundreds of senior and junior ratings (each crew had some 125 ratings) and fed even more. With the commissioning of *Woodbridge Haven* the crews went into uniform.

At the same time the crews' increasing demand for office space were met by the loan to Vickers of the Algerine class minesweeper

Rifleman prior to her disposal. This gave me a relatively luxurious day-cabin and the officers of the Building Group a Wardroom (though we still ate in the Vickers' lunchrooms).

When I had arrived in Barrow *Resolution* was still on the slipway, and *Repulse*, even less recognisable, stood on the adjacent slip. Both, incidentally, were out in the open, as opposed to the modern enclosed building practice. Such was the speed of construction however that *Resolution* was to meet her launch date of 15 September 1966 although I believe I am right in recalling that some of her pre-launch fitting out was behind schedule, and she launched lighter in displacement than originally planned.

We had discovered that the Bishop of Birmingham had been a chaplain in the last *Resolution* so I presumed to write and ask if he could conduct the launching service. He agreed, even before we knew that Her Majesty Queen Elizabeth the Queen Mother was to launch the submarine.

Came the day, and the great and the good were seated on the launch platform, while lesser folk, including the crews and their families, stood on another platform with (I think) a better view. The Bishop declined to bless Britain's first deterrent submarine; Her Majesty however had no such qualms and firmly called for God's Blessing "on her and all who sail in her". And so the largest submarine in the western world at that time slid into the water to the usual cacophony of horns and sirens, and the rattle of chains; dipped a curtsey to her Royal sponsor and floated safe and serene in the Walney Channel (unlike her sister *Repulse* who, launched a year later, evaded her tugs and drifted aground).

After the launch and the lunch I drove down to where *Resolution* was lying alongside and looked at my future command. The casing, a term which now embraced the missile deck, towered above me, and I remember marvelling at just how big she was and hoping I was indeed a "man of that calibre",

Fitting out, and static trials of every sort continued against the calendar. The reactor core was loaded in January 1967 and there followed "cold ops" and "hot ops" - operating the primary and secondary water systems firstly using steam from ashore and then from the reactor itself. "Power range testing" where the reactor was brought up to a proportion of its capability took place in Ramsden Dock opposite *Woodbridge Haven* where the submarine could safely be secured and her propeller turned without risk to herself or other vessels in the fitting out dock

Dominating progress, or any delay to it, was the "tidal window". It so happened that in 1967, *Resolution* could only get out of the Barrow Docks and into the Walney Channel on a couple of days in June and back again on a day or so in August. Otherwise there was not enough water to get through the intervening lock. The sea trials were planned for an eight week period and had to be completed within that time or go by default. Nor could bad weather be allowed to disrupt the departure from Barrow, and so a false bow was built onto the floating dock in Vickers so that, if the worst came to the worst, *Reso* could be transported through the lock system and out to sea, there to be floated out when the weather served.

In the event the floating dock was not needed and *Reso* left on time. But not many people knew that when the lock sluices were open, water ran out, and Britain's first deterrent submarine, with her reactor in operation ("critical" is the technical, albeit emotive term), sat on the bottom. We knew, because we were watching the draught marks pretty closely. However, the tide rose just enough and Dick Husk was able to pump out just enough, and we came safely out. There is a splendid picture of this departure, all formal except for Bill Timms, the Vickers' Ship Manager, in dirty white overalls, emerging from the door on the side of the fin. However it does not show one vital item. When conning from the "bridge" on top of the fin, orders were to be passed to the helmsman below via a microphone on a "suitcase" - a portable affair on the end of a lead plugged into a socket in the fin. I was deeply suspicious of this system and had, before sailing, insisted on a "voicepipe" constructed of two tin funnels, one at each end of a long plastic tube, as an emergency back-up, to be run through the open conning tower. Sure enough the suitcase failed and I gave my orders on departure down the green plastic pipe.

Mention of draught marks reminds me of the basin dive earlier in the year. We had been pressing the constructors in Bath for a Trim Statement - a list of tanks and how much water they should hold to maintain a neutral dived buoyancy - for weeks. By the time one arrived, Dick Husk, as any good submarine First Lieutenant could and should, had worked it out for himself. After all the principles are no different; you just measured in tons rather than in gallons for this submarine which weighed nearly ten times the wartime S class in which some of us had served.

Dick's trim wasn't bad; in fact it was damn' good considering how little help he had had from the proper source. The constructor responsible, whom by chance I had had as a junior officer in HMS *London* and reported upon unfavourably , accepted the result with ill grace and returned to Bath. After the Sea Trials he came up with the requirement to add ninety tons of ballast in the after trim tank. We knew he was wrong but were powerless at that stage to prevent Vickers putting it in. Sure enough, back at sea, *Reso* was heavy aft and had to trim with the after tanks nearly empty. We protested in vain; so, back "on crew" before sailing for DASO, I ordered that the ninety tons should be taken out by ship's staff, and forbade the aforesaid constructor to come on board until Dick Husk and his men had finished. Not for the first time in this programme it was brought home to me that it is most unwise to prove yourself right and the establishment wrong. Safer the other way round.

Back however to the Sea Trials, which took place in and off the Clyde. They were intense, trying and tiring. I remember signalling "She handles like a lady" early on in the Trials and we never had cause to depart from that opinion. Some of the systems were recalcitrant, but happily not those of ship control. Four hours dived at full power (in uncomfortably shallow water to save passage time) proved "George" (the auto-pilot), kept impeccable depth, even though he had earlier had moments of uncertainty. Nevertheless, I sat behind the planesmen throughout the four hours and sweated. For the Trials the Port crew had the ship, but we fed in Starboard crew officers and men to give them experience and ours a rest. As Vickers' "Master" I remained in command throughout, of (until *Vanguard* put to sea) the biggest submarine ever to fly the red ensign.

We were the subject of intense interest from the "Malin Head AGI", the Soviet intelligence gathering trawler GS40. On at least one occasion he tried to put me off my course, and I have a wonderful length of cine-film which shows him closing on a near-parallel course on my port bow, perhaps 100 yards away. Through that gap appears HMS *Malcolm*, escort, driven with the utmost panache by Lieutenant Commander Kelly Lowe (now sadly dead). GS40 got the point - namely that we were only a few miles from home, whereas he was a thousand or more from his base and repair facilities, and our forward hydroplanes stuck out like Boadicea's chariot scythes.

Sea Trials completed - some were postponed to meet the tidal constraint - we returned to Barrow. I had spoken to the Barrow Pilot before sailing from Faslane and stressed that he could not, as was the practice with merchant ships, "land" the submarine on the wood-sheathed piles at the entrance to the lock so as to swing her into position to enter. But that is exactly what he tried to do and, having only the authority of a temporary merchant ship master, I had to relieve him of the conn, retrieve his mistake if possible, and get *Reso* into the lock without touching, all in not much more time than it takes to write this, with no room to use a tug, and with the last of the flood under my stern. I berthed *Reso* in the dock, shaking, and went to meet my "owner", Vickers Managing Director Len Redshaw, as he came aboard in the lock. I am not sure if he realised how near we had come to a bump. If he did, he said nothing. Anyway he welcomed us back.

As far as the rest of the world was concerned, however, we might have been a minesweeper returning to harbour from a day's exercises. The reader will see later why I use this simile. No one said anything, good or bad, by signal or otherwise except for Commander Tony Boyall, Polaris Staff Officer to the Commander-in-Chief Western Fleet. Tony, bless him, rang up and congratulated us on the successful completion of the Sea Trials. If it was because he realised that there had been, otherwise, a deafening silence, then I am the more grateful to him for a gesture typical of the man.

Back in Barrow the Port crew turned over to the Starboard and went on leave, and the submarine was back in the hands of the builders. If there were major defects to remedy I do not remember them. In due course, in October, *Resolution* was commissioned and the white ensign hoisted, Commander Ken Frewer was in command, with his Starboard crew, but I also read my Commissioning Warrant in what I have always felt was a rather stilted ceremony. Ken sailed a day or so later for Faslane, where he berthed after the submarine had been formally accepted into Her Majesty's Navy. The Port crew and all the families of both crews, packed their bags, their children, their welfare organisation and their independent little world, and left Barrow for Helensburgh and Rhu, there to be among the first occupants of the newly built (and in some cases uncompleted) married quarters.

Ken continued with trials and work-up while we, the Port crew, went to look for our offices in the Clyde Submarine Base at Faslane. Offices? Four, one for each submarine, each with a couple of desks. To be fair to Faslane and the system, temporary office space was found for most of the 140 odd officers and men, while urgent action was put in hand to build an office block on the roof of the Naval Technical Department. The omission may be explained by the fact that the US

Navy sent its off crews away from the parent tenders (depot ships) whereas we had always intended to use the off crew in support of the on crew when the submarine was in harbour, and train in the Base when she was at sea. There being nothing to copy, the RN had failed to perceive the need for off crew space in the Base.

December 1967 saw the Port crew "on" again for a safety work-up before departing to the USA for DASO. "Work-up" really meant "self work-up" since we knew more about the submarine and how to run her than any work-up team - or thought we did. Nevertheless such a team was detailed off, including an officer fresh from command of a diesel submarine. Dick Husk took exception to this and arranged the work-up programme so that successive incidents took place at the opposite ends of the submarine, in quick succession and "on the watch". By the end of what must have been a very brief period - a week perhaps - the officer in question, later Flag Officer Submarines, a Vice-Admiral and a Knight, was completely exhausted, while there was a wicked gleam in the eye of my First Lieutenant, who had incidentally satisfied himself that the crew knew what they were doing

We also underwent an inspection, during which I had the thrill of throwing 8500 tons of deterrent submarine around the water like an attack submarine, in the course of a dummy attack. For the last time I may add. Captain Gordon Tait, who conducted the inspection, appeared to enjoy the experience as much as I did. Anyway we were declared "safe", just in time for the Christmas stand-off.

And so to DASO. The plan was to make a leisurely passage over New Year 1967-68 to the vicinity of the Azores, for some deep water trials of our underwater detection equipment (sonar) thence to Charleston, South Carolina to load five "DASO" missiles (two for each crew and one spare) and on to Cape Kennedy. It did not quite work out like that, but first a digression - our piper.

I had written to the Commanding Officer of the Scots Greys, Lieutenant Colonel (now Field Marshal Sir) John Stanier, with whom I had shared a thoroughly irresponsible and enjoyable Joint Services Staff Course in 1961, and asked if I could borrow a piper for the trip to the USA. Lance Corporal Cairns joined us before we left Faslane and endeared himself to the entire ship's company by donning full ceremonial uniform and piping his way from the tiller flat aft to the tube space forward at midnight on New Year's Eve, as we ran dived to the Azores. His kit was the subject of constant delight; to sit on the bridge with a rifle as shark guard during "hands to bathe" off the Azores, he appeared in (I think!) Royal Stuart tartan trews, which he later wore while keeping watch on the hydroplanes. He practised his pipes regularly, sometimes in my cabin (after all it was my fault that he was there), sometimes in the fore-ends, but no-one seemed to mind. Either they were polite, or all liked pipe music - both equally unlikely - or else the configuration of a submarine served to muffle the noise. Once at Cape Kennedy, he was the darling of all the local hostesses - "Oh, and please bring your piper", and in demand in all the bars and other places of entertainment. He behaved impeccably, never had to pay for a drink; and was undoubtedly better known than the submarine herself. His presence on board prompted a whimsical Parliamentary Question, and an equally whimsical answer from the then Under Secretary for the Navy. I shall return to him later.

We had not completed our trials off the Azores when, with a long face, my Electrical Officer reported a defective alternator. We had three of these beasts, which produced the alternating current to meet all the electrical demands in this big ship. The defective one was the hardest to get at, being outboard of one of its sisters in an auxiliary machine space. So we hoped to be able to leave it. But then the inner one failed, and I had to report two out of three defective and my intention to return, on the surface, to Faslane. The defect, common to both alternators, was certainly beyond our capability to make good. Thankfully it did not happen to the third alternator. By the time we got back to Faslane, my engineers had the inner alternator, weighing over a ton, slung ready to be hoisted out of the submarine, and the outer one unbolted, ready to move.

Faslane swung into action: we lay alongside counting the lost days and hours, and enduring a westerly hurricane (blowing us onto our berth fortunately) which gusted to an unbelievable 177mph and blew the roof off the RN Polaris School and several married quarters. It also blew away a lighter that had been secured alongside us. The lighter was recovered but we never discovered where the lighterman got to.

We were repaired, tested and sailed, direct for Charleston, running at 19 knots, with only one short period every 24 hours when we slowed down and came to periscope depth to fix our position and receive signal traffic. Our passive detection capability was negligible at this speed so I abandoned all attempts at concealment and transmitted on our very powerful active sonar while running deep and fast. A beacon maybe, but also a warning to other submarines, friendly or otherwise to keep clear. Later, as Captain of the Polaris Squadron, I was criticised by Flag Officer Submarines for telling one of my captains to do the same on another fast trans-Atlantic passage. So maybe I was wrong.

En route we had a "scram", that is the reactor was shut down by its own protection system because of a possible fault. I recall no fault, but as we "free-wheeled" and worked to bring the reactor back to power, at the same time preparing to run the diesels if we had to, all non-essential electrical equipment, including ventilation, was shut down. A Chief Petty Officer on watch in the engine room passed out in the temperature of 120^0, and getting him up and out of the engine room added to our problems. However both he and the reactor recovered and on we went.

We were welcomed to Charleston by the US Navy's Submarine Squadron 18, receiving "Permission to Join", and went straight to a berth at the Naval Weapons Station which embraced the Polaris Missile Facility Atlantic (POMFLANT) to load our missiles. The Captain of the Station was John Renfro, an old friend from Washington days, and my wife and I went back and stayed with them after DASO.

Missiles safely embarked we sailed down to Cape Kennedy for the DASO. Demonstration and Shake Down Operation is really back to front. You were "shaking down" your missile system and personnel and "demonstrating" that you were fit to take sixteen strategic nuclear missiles on patrol. It took about a month and was very intensive, each day starting at about 0600, slipping at 0730, spending all day "in the hover", that is stopped in neutral trim at 90 feet, for drill after drill, and returning alongside between 1600 and 1800. A 100 foot mast, embarked at Port Canaveral and secured to lugs welded to the back of the submarine's bridge fin, enabled communications with escorting ships (including the American destroyer *Fred T Berry* and the British destroyer *Aisne*) and the Range Control ashore, and in due course, telemetric monitoring and control of the missile when fired.

DASO was perhaps the most testing period of all: for the first time we were on parade before the US Navy, in the form of the deeply experienced DASO team, SP205. More than eighty American crews would have successfully completed DASO before us. The team helped us of course - that was what we were all there for - but they gave us no special treatment, and plenty of criticism. We made a little history out of a minor mishap. Anticipating the need for ample stocks of duty free liquor for this three month round trip, the cavernous space of one of the missile tubes was used to store wardroom wines and spirits and ship's company beer. Somehow, a bottle got broken during a day in harbour and the appropriate alarm bell rang, followed by the deadpan voice of my Assistant Polaris Systems officer broadcasting "Brandy in tube alarm".

Anyway we kept to the schedule and on 15 February 1968, at 1115 Eastern Standard Time, 15 milliseconds late after a five year programme, I gave permission to fire and up popped the first Polaris missile to have Royal Navy painted on the side, arcing away into the clear blue sky, to deliver the dummy warheads "in the pickle barrel" a thousand or more miles down the range. Rear Admiral Levering Smith USN, the Director, Special Projects, pronounced the shot successful; Rufus Mackenzie was so excited that he congratulated the wrong crew (hastily corrected); before they and the three other admirals aboard (two British and one American) joined the Wardroom in a modest celebration. Then *Resolution* surfaced and returned to harbour to the strains of the "Black Bear" from the piper and with the broom, signifying a clean sweep, lashed to a periscope for all to see. My wife, amongst others, watched the show from HMS *Aisne*. A colour photograph of it hangs in the Submarine Museum at Gosport.

We spent a day or so turning over to the Starboard crew before taking some well earned leave in America. Lance Corporal Cairns, Scots Greys, put on a request to "see the Captain, on a personal matter". He wanted to go home, instead of staying, as had been planned, for the Starboard crew DASO. Fearing some unhappy revelation, I asked why. "Ah'm Porrt Crew Surr". What could I say? So back he went with our gratitude and good wishes - and was picked up by the Provost Marshal in London, somewhat the worse for wear. Colonel Stanier signalled me, asking for a performance reference. I was happy to reply in glowing terms and Cairns was let off with a warning. Later, when visiting the Scots Greys in Germany, on some ceremonial occasion, Cairns was paraded before me. "Commander, your piper; what do you wish him to play?" What else could I ask for but the "Black Bear" and the Greys, bless them, tolerated this infantry march in my honour.

This little tale has a darker side. Cairns was expressing what was sadly apparent to him - the disharmony between the two crews. Individually we were long time friends; collectively we just did not get on, and I am ashamed to say that we, the Captains, were not innocent of this discord. I believe and hope that it did not extend to the crews of the other three submarines.

The Starboard crew plunged into DASO with just as much enthu-siasm. An unhappy incident early on marred what would otherwise have been a smooth progression to an equally successful shot. Somehow the *Fred T Berry* was in collision with the Telemetry (T&E) mast attached to *Resolution*. The US Navy immediately blamed the *Berry*; somehow, and to our horrified disbelief, the Royal Navy tended to blame *Resolution* - blind, at 90 feet, with the mast clearly marking her position.

That apart, his DASO successfully behind him, and with the mast lugs removed from the bridge fin (the cachet of the DASO qualified SSBN) Ken brought *Resolution* back to Faslane for "Post Shakedown Availability" - a long maintenance period - before turning her over to me again for load-out and deployment. It is easy to write that, but there seemed to be an awful lot to do, and both crews were hard at it right up until we sailed for the first patrol, with leave taking second place behind the all-demanding schedule.

Somehow we seemed to be out of step with our masters. Captain Ken Vause, the first Polaris Squadron Commander (SM10), now sadly dead, valiantly ran protection of us two COs and our crews at a time when the Navy , including the Submarine Command, certainly seemed to doubt us, and at times to be disappointed in, or even disapprove of us.

Before we sailed on patrol the Commander-in-Chief, Western Fleet visited the submarine. He "cleared lower deck" and told my assembled ship's company that as far as he was concerned we were just another ship in the fleet - "no different to one of the minesweepers". Perhaps he meant well; perhaps consciously or unconsciously he was expressing the Fleet's view. The comments of my ship's company, who had dedicated themselves for the past three years or more to our state of readiness, could be described as mutinous. Thank heavens, they saved them until after he had gone.

The foregoing observations can be dismissed as over-sensitivity on our part and irrelevant to the Polaris story, but it is my recollection that, while many of the members of the Polaris Executive, from the highest down, were honoured, the only awards among the crews, by the time I left *Resolution* in 1969, were an MBE to my Marine Engineer Officer for documentation he produced in the early building days at Barrow, and a BEM to my Coxswain, which took account of his time as coxswain of *Dreadnought.*

Anyway, we duly "loaded out" - embarked 16 missiles with nuclear warheads, at Coulport, and on 14 June 1968 sailed for the first patrol, passing RMS Queen *Elizabeth II* inbound in the Firth of Clyde. I wondered what interest, if any, we aroused.

I will not go into detail about the patrol. Even now, security constrains me to a degree. It was not boring; even on patrol we were learning, gaining experience, recording. For most of the patrol our carbon dioxide absorption plants - "scrubbers" - did not work and we came up to periscope depth each night to "ventilate", renewing the atmosphere in the submarine through the periscopic inlet and exhaust masts. It was glassy calm for most of the patrol with clear skies, and I sat in the Control Room for the hour or so that it took each night, with both periscopes manned, glumly contemplating our chances of detection.

For the entire patrol, signals from the Loran C Chain, the primary navigational aid then available to us (satellite navigation came later) were not transmitted and we relied for navigational updates on "bottom contouring" - literally reading the map of the ocean bed. When analysed at the end of the patrol, our records showed that we had stayed "in spec" - in other words within the accuracy required for strategic missile delivery. Very reassuring for the future, since bottom contouring relies on no outside signal system.

Towards the end of the patrol we heard the news of the uprising in Czechoslovakia and, being the deterrent, wondered if our first patrol would be extended. We had emergency provisions on board, and could certainly have extended from 56 to 90 days (far short of later record patrols), but happily it was not to be so. But this brought forward two little problems. Firstly, so conditioned had my crew become to the well ordered daily routine (structured with some care by my officers) and the bland, but cheerful "Familygrams" each crew member was allowed to receive weekly, that the return to real life, little Willie's measles, the broken washing machine, the cost of repairing the car, was viewed with some apprehension. Secondly, for a 56 day patrol, that well-known submariner, Captain Bertie Pizey of the RN Film Corporation, had come up with sixty cracking good films (some even pre-release), so we had to fit in four extra films shows in each of the Messes.

And so we returned safely to the Clyde, but not before, on surfacing, we had ditched over the side untold empty cardboard boxes, the detritus of 56 days' meals for 150 hungry submariners, less of course the scraps and tins which were ground or crushed respectively and discharged dived on patrol. Pollution and the ecology were not headline news in those days. Nevertheless we re-learned about packaging control the hard way.

On the third, my second, patrol, three memories will suffice. It was winter, and consequently rough. Even though we increased our patrol depth by doubling the length of the "floating wire" aerial, the fact that the optimum course to receive signals on it was beam to sea meant that we rolled steadily, slowly and maddeningly, 11-12 degrees each side. The soup slopped out of your plate; if your berth was athwartships (mine was) you slid up and down, up and down; tempers frayed. In spite of this Christmas was celebrated with carols, a choir, a sermon (3 minutes) from me and a congregation of over half the ship's company (one third of course being on watch).

I have always found my obligation, when in command, to conduct a Christian service on Sunday both uplifting and humbling, but never more than on these patrols. I always included a "Prayer for Polaris" which I had written. The rest of it can be read on the wall of St John's Chapel in Faslane, but the final passage bears repetition:

"Give us the will, but never the wish, to obey the order to fire. But O Lord, if it be thy will, grant that that order may never need to be given." We can give humble thanks that our prayers were answered.

The third memory? Oh yes - on New Year's Eve, news came through of my selection for promotion to Captain. A great relief, as I had only one more shot to go.

Six years had come and gone since Nassau. We had put the show on the road. We believed in what we were doing (only three of my crew ever questioned it), deterring a credible, recognisable threat. Now, 30 years later, along come our successors with Trident. I wish them well.

Chapter 35

A Crew Member's Story
Arthur Escreet

My introduction to submarines began in 1965. I was, then, on Leading Electrical Mechanics (LEM) Qualifying Course at HMS *Collingwood*. One lunchtime my Divisional Officer called me to his office and informed me that fifteen Leading Hands had been selected for the Polaris programme. I was one of those Leading Hands. He then showed me a DCI, which stated that you would spend twice as much time ashore than at sea. Needless to say I decided that this was for me and volunteered. On completion of Leading Hands' course I was drafted to HMS *Dolphin* for my Part One submarine training. Welcome to the submarine world.

Part One training, although biased towards diesel boats, was an interesting course. The six weeks I spent there included the Submarine Escape Training Tank (SETT). I stood at the top of the tank and looked down 100 feet, wondering how I will escape from such a depth. However, with the training being of such a high standard, it was a piece of cake and an exciting experience. With Part One training completed, I was sent to Faslane and the Polaris Training School for Polaris weapon training. On completion of training I then travelled to Barrow-in-Furness, with my 'oppo' Dave Curtis (Port crew) to join *Resolution* (Starboard) at the Vickers Shipbuilding Group. *Resolution* was within approximately nine months of being ready for sea trials. My duty station was the Missile Control Centre (MCC). The MCC was fully equipped and computer and missile system testing was in progress.

Finally *Resolution* was ready for sea trials. The Port crew sailed her over and the Starboard crew was sent to Faslane. Starboard crew (junior rates) were the first to move into the new accommodation blocks and they were very comfortable for the era of the Base. The evening in the Junior Rates bar was often completed by the lads going back to the accommodation blocks walking in a line with one hand on your mate's shoulder in front. The song of *Hi-Ho*, from Snow White and the Seven Dwarfs, then echoes around the Base.

At this time *Resolution* was obviously big news, being the first of Britain's four nuclear deterrent submarines. Newspaper reporters and film crews often visited the submarine before she was to leave on her first patrol. Eventually the film "Polaris a Promise" was made.

The next stage of the work-up was the Polaris missile firings in Florida, USA. The Port crew sailed the boat over and the Starboard crew flew out from Prestwick Airport. Florida proved to be a fantastic place and the Americans certainly know how to do things in style. The hospitality shown to both crews was second to none and I will always have fond memories of the Yanks.

The Port crew fired the first of Britain's Polaris missiles and the Starboard crew witnessed this firing from the deck of an American frigate. It was a great sight as the missile left the water and majestically rose into the sky. The crew changeover then took place and the Starboard crew fired the second missile. My operational station for the firing was as Missile Trolley operator in the Missile Compartment. It was a strange sensation to feel the submarine shudder as the missile was ejected from its tube. Shortly after, *Resolution* sailed back to Faslane and eventually was ready for her first patrol. This was to be carried out by Port crew. The patrol was for eight weeks into waters unknown to the majority of the crew; the Starboard crew ran the second patrol.

Life on board during the patrol was, at many times, tedious and boring. The highlights were when weekly Familygrams were sent down from the Wireless Office. This was the only time you received news from home and, even though limited to forty words, was a comfort. My duties in the MCC consisted of fifteen minutes of computer checks each day. Scrubbing out during the Dog Watches helped to break this monotony, although this was a chore. Hobbies were allowed on patrol, but had to be verified. This was because some hobbies contained toxic fumes and fibres which could be damaging to the oxygen cleaning systems. I took a paint-by-numbers kit. Eight weeks at sea was ample time to complete it.

The routine of the patrol was broken up with Weapon System Readiness Tests (WSRT) when the missiles were given a simulated launch.

The eight weeks on patrol passed through various stages. For the first two weeks the crew settled down, having just left loved ones at home and not at this stage missing them. The second two weeks became a matter of going on watch, coming off watch and perhaps watching one of the 56 movies which we carried on board. The fifth and sixth weeks saw some of the crew becoming a bit bored and petty niggling took place. Midway through the patrol a "Sod's Opera" was put on. Items of ladies underwear were produced, making one wonder what sort of people you were at sea with. However, it was an enlightening opera and relieved some of the boredom.

By the seventh week morale began to improve as we realised that home was not far away. The eighth week saw the onset of "Channel fever" and thoughts of an evening in female company. And then back alongside the wall and "homers". It was amusing to see many of the crew return onboard the following morning with eyes in four watches.

It was during the off-crew period when I passed my preliminary examination for Petty Officer. When my B13 arrived I was Captain's requestman for promotion. The Captain, Commander Ken Frewer, considered that, at the age of 23, I was a bit young to be a Petty Officer. Although I was promoted he recommended that I attend the Petty Officer's Leadership Course at *Royal Arthur*, This I duly did and was taught many rudiments of being a leader, which even to this day I have found useful.

I eventually left *Resolution* and was drafted to *Collingwood* to complete my Petty Officer's course. From there I was drafted to the Polaris Training School as the Administrative Petty Officer. During my time at the School Drafty informed me that I had obtained qualifying marks for Mechanicians' Course and, if I was prepared to sign on for 22 years, I would be allowed to take the course. This I duly did.

Two years later saw me successfully complete the course and I was asked if I would like to return for further training in the Polaris section or be retrained in Sonar. I chose Sonar and was sent on 2001 and Miscellaneous Sonar courses. On completion of these courses I was drafted back to *Resolution* (Starboard) as a sonar maintainer.

Resolution (Starboard) was under the command of a Captain whom I considered to be an excellent seaman officer, but who was such a disciplinarian that the ship's company were constantly afraid of making a mistake. This led to a crew with a very low morale. This period of my time in *Resolution* was not a happy one and, being new to sonar, presented a very difficult experience. However the plus side was that I worked with a terrific team of forward electrical staff. My boss was Lt Hill and the other sonar maintainer was CREA Frank Weaver. Frank and I worked well as a team and we became good 'oppos'. My watchkeeping station was the Navigation Plot, in the Control Room. This was interesting because it involved navigating to and from the Naval Base at Faslane and, when dived, plotting the course and speed of sonar contacts. Working in the Control Room also gave enormous insight into the general operation of the submarine.

By the time we left for the next patrol I had settled down into my new job. All my sonar sets (I had 16 in all) were maintained and ready for sea. The peace and quiet did not last long. All the sonar sets were fully operational for 24 hours and after two weeks at sea problems began arising. One set in particular gave constant problems and, in one period of the patrol, I went 40 hours without sleep, attempting to fault-find the problems. I was eventually ordered to my bunk to get some sleep, only to be woken up two hours later because the recorder had broken again and the Captain wanted it repaired immediately. During the patrol, however, I did have time to study for my Chief Petty Officer exams, which I sat after the patrol and passed. Because I was constantly being called to the Sound Room the patrol passed quite quickly. I gained a tremendous amount of experience during this patrol.

Eventually the Captain was relieved by Commander Ross, the finest Captain I have ever served under. The morale of the crew was terrific and when my draft cycle was coming to an end, I requested to remain on board. Drafty, however, wanted to send new trainees to sea and my request was denied.

And so my final days as a member of *Resolution* (Starboard) crew drew to an end. I have omitted many incidents, both happy and not so happy. However, I will always be proud to say I served in submarines, and particularly *Resolution* (Starboard).

Chapter 36

A Coxswain's Story

I joined HMS *Resolution* (Starboard crew) on 4 January 1967 straight from submarine training class. Supposedly we were hand-picked from the best of the submarine trainees, other qualified submariners and a number of general-service chappies. As it turned out I think everybody got rid of their riffraff to the Polaris boats but we were soon moulded into two highly trained and motivated crews.

Our time standing-by *Resolution* building passed quite quickly. The local girls were friendly and a lot of marriages took place both during and after the Barrow period.

The Port crew did the contractors' trials and we did the acceptance trials. Port did the first patrol and I remember her coming back with her families on the jetty at Coulport. All smiles on both sides. All this has now stopped - no families on the jetty, just a quick crew change and away.

We did the second patrol of about eight weeks and settled into a routine of "on" and "off" crews with a very acceptable month's maintenance from time to time.

However, various engineering problems caused upsets to the routine, requiring extended patrols of fifteen weeks or more for the others. This was not good for morale which was much improved when normality returned.

When the Polaris boats first commissioned there were some who looked on themselves as part of an elite group rather than normal submariners. A spell in other classes of submarines could bring a change of this tune.

In the early days Polaris crews were a deal older than they are today and they and their families were better able to handle the separation. Today I think many of the younger wives are less experienced and resent the absence of their husbands.

With the increasing age of the Polaris boats there were longer hours of maintenance required. This and the provision of armed sentries in harbour added to the burden.

On board accommodation stayed much the same over the years, the Senior Rates annex being a blessing. Shoreside things have improved in leaps and bounds. Senior Rates have always had single cabins but now when the lads go to sea they no longer have to share their cabins with the other crew.

I am glad to think I joined way back in 1967 as a junior rate and now I am a coxswain. There are a few others left from the first commission but times have changed, the system, the crews and certainly the workload, but morale remains high and discipline overall is good.

At sea things have come on tenfold. We now have videos, loads of films and a vast amount of keep-fit gear like bikes, rowing machines, weights etc. Having done my time in an SSN (Fleet nuclear submarine) the noise level in a Polaris boat leaves me speechless. I don't suppose I shall ever change that - keeping the troops happy is the main concern of the command.

Domestic matters - drink is frowned upon and I think its days at sea are numbered. Familygrams are well received but do cause problems. A lot of people have them on the same day every week and if they don't arrive on time they start to worry and are a pain to live with.

Since the beginning we have had our ship's magazine, a useful expression of chaps' feelings. We do find the officers more approachable these days and are able to discuss moans about the service.

Food has always been good but we struggle, as in all things, to stay in budget. Somehow the PO Cook always stays in the black!

I feel sorry for a lot of the young lads - no jollies, no foreign commissions. They don't seem to mind nor do a lot of Senior Rates with very little foreign service. It is a different navy. Experience is gained on the spot and work-up staff know much more than they did thirty years ago. As a result they put us through our paces much more than they did in the past.

Our nearby town of Helensburgh still relies a lot on the base for its economy, a fact which causes occasional spasms of local friction. It was ever thus. Rothesay relied heavily on the cash from submariners ever since World War Two and complained nevertheless of their activities. "Shift the submarines" they said and when *Maidstone* and her squadron did shift to Faslane there were many lamentations ashore. On the whole, though, relations are pretty good with the locals at Faslane.

As I look out of my cabin window the Base looks like Stalag 13 - barbed wire fences, police with dogs, search-light towers and police patrol boats. The tensions are not what they were but there always seems to be somebody wanting to get at us. We just think that we have been part of the force which kept the peace for thirty years.

Epilogue

Ceremony to Mark the De-Commissioning of HMS *Repulse* and the end of the Polaris Programme 28 August 1996

Speech by the Rt Hon John Major MP

We are here today to pay tribute to the work of the Polaris Force.

The debt we owe to them, I believe, is very large. For the last 28 years this Force has mounted continuous patrols that have been vital to ensure this country's peace and security and, because of these patrols, any possible aggressor throughout those 28 years has known that to attack the UK would provoke a terrible response.

In particular today, we are here to pay tribute to the last of the four Polaris submarines, HMS *Repulse*, which returned from her 60th and final deployment in May.

But not only *Repulse*, of course. I pay tribute today to the other three boats and their three crews in her Class, the *Resolution* herself, *Renown* and *Revenge*. Each in their own way has made her own unique and invaluable contribution to the remarkable record of maintaining a Polaris submarine at sea, our deterrent at sea, on deterrent patrol, undetected by friend or foe, every minute, of every day, of every year, from 1968 until May of this year.

To those of you who have served aboard any of these submarines, past and present, I offer you the thanks not just of those others of us here but of people throughout the country.

The years of the Polaris Force have seen some dramatic changes in our world. In 1968, when *Resolution* began her first patrol, East West tension was running very high. The Soviet Union had invaded Czechoslovakia and the Vietnam War still raged. And yet, in 1994, I was able to sign an accord with President Yeltsin agreeing no longer to target our nuclear forces at each other's territory. Today, the West enjoys a co-operative relationship with Russia unthinkable even ten years ago.

But throughout those turbulent years, the Polaris force has always been there, always ready, always prepared, always the ultimate guarantee of this country's security. As I said the debt is very great.

No tribute to those of you in the Force, whatever your contribution might have been, would be complete without a special mention of the contribution of your families at home. They, as well as you, have borne the continual strain of enforced separation. They have had to maintain the family while you were away on duty. None of the achievements of the Polaris fleet would have been possible without their forbearance and their understanding. To them, too, I offer a very special thank you, and I am glad that so many are here today. I would like to thank as well all those who maintained the submarine and its deterrent away from the boat itself, whether at the Base here, in Coulport supporting the weapons system, on the tugs moving these massive submarines in and out of port, at the headquarters in Northwood, or in the design and support organisations further afield. Each of you has played your part.

Throughout the Polaris programme, we have enjoyed very close co-operation with the United States. This cooperation is continuing with Trident. Our two navies have a very special trust and understanding. I am delighted that so many representatives of the United States Strategic Systems Programme are here with us today, together with officers and crew of the USS *West Virginia*.

There is naturally a tinge of sadness today. But it is the ending of a chapter today. There is no need to be sad about a job well done. As Trident takes over from Polaris and Chevaline, so the *Vanguard* Class takes on the torch from *Resolution* and her sisters.

In a few moments I shall unveil this plaque marking the proud achievements of the Polaris Force. And, as I unveil it here, so at the entrance to this facility just a little way away, a small stone monument is also being unveiled. This monument is to serve as a quiet and dignified reminder of the unique contribution to peace and security by these submarines and by the men who served in them.

Let me say a final word about our nuclear deterrent. I have no doubt that we are right to maintain a minimum credible strategic nuclear deterrent for the United Kingdom. We will continue to do so for as long as our security needs require to do so. It would be folly for us not to do so, even though circumstances have changed. The world remains an uncertain and dangerous place.

Vanguard and *Victorious* are already fully operational, and meeting all our expectations. I look forward to seeing them joined, in 1998, by *Vigilant* and, around the turn of the century, by *Vengeance*. Together these four submarines will carry the UK's strategic and sub-strategic deterrent well into the 21st century.

Our deterrent, as part of the Atlantic Alliance, has helped to prevent war in the past. It will help to do so in the future. That is what it is for. All those concerned, many of whom are present today, can take great pride in that. I wish you well for the future.

Index
Index by Lieutenant Commander M Forder BA.

The index covers the Dedication, Introduction, Text and Epilogue, but not illustrations. Wherever possible titles and ranks refer to the ultimate achievement at retirement.

docks, floating 61, 70, 80, 177, 182, 183
Dolphin, HMS (submarine base) 51, 187, 188, 232, 251
Dossor, Rear Admiral F, Polaris Project Office 49, 146
Douglas-Home, Sir Alec, Prime Minister (later Baron Home of the Hirsel) 108
Dounreay Nuclear Establishment 31, 57, 100, 125
Draper, Dr C Stark, MIT 23
Dreadnought, HMS (SSN) 16, 50, 82, 119, 172, 214
    operation 111, 198, 223
    propulsion 31, 42, 57, 117
Dreadnought Project 13, 31, 42, 56, 155, 230
Dunlop, Captain K J, Technical Assistant 56, 76, 167-74, 223
Dymoke, Rear Admiral L D 56

East, Captain J D, Deputy Superintendent Clyde 215, 217, 218
Electric Boat Company, Groton 59, 153, 158
    procurement 121-2, 126, 140, 160
    training 112, 131
Elizabeth, H M the Queen Mother 154, 179, 200, 212, 240
Elliott Space and Weapon Automation Ltd 131
Ellis, Captain H M, Manning and Training 56, 76, 223-7
Elvy, Commander F J, Weapons Engineer 136
EMI (Electric & Musical Industries Limited) 131
Escreet, Chief Petty Officer Electrician Arthur 251-4
Ethan Allen, USS (SSBN) 17, 24, 118, 224
Evans, Commander D L P, Technical Directorate 161, 225
Evans, Commander P V, Weapons Engineer 136, 163
Everitt, Bill, Armament Supply Department 209
Ewing, Vice Admiral Sir Alistair, Naval Secretary 28

Fairley, A, Senior Surveyor of Lands 169, 174
familygrams 233, 249, 252, 256
Faslane Naval Base
    building 83, 153, 169-71
    operating 175-94, 214-18, 219-20, 243-4, 245, 256
    selection 62, 80, 86
Fieldhouse, Lady Margaret 232-5
Fieldhouse, Admiral of the Fleet Sir John 213, 215, 232-5
Fitzer, Herbert C, Esq. 43, 56, 159-64
Fletcher, Derek, Vickers engineer RNPS 163
Fort Langley, RFA (armament stores vessel) 208, 212
Fred T Berry, USS (destroyer) 246, 248
French SSBNs 82
Frewen, Admiral Sir John, Vice Chief of Naval Staff 105
Frewer, Commander K D 239, 243, 248, 253
Fuller, Constructor Commander Geoffrey H 44